Date Due

The Practice of Psychotherapy with Children

The Practice of Psychotherapy with Children

MAX HAMMER, Ph.D.
Lecturer, Graduate School
University of Maine

ARTHUR M. KAPLAN
Professor and Head of the Department of Psychology
University of Maine

1967: THE DORSEY PRESS

Homewood, Illinois

© THE DORSEY PRESS 1967

First Printing, July, 1967

Library of Congress Catalog Card No. 67–21007

Printed in the United States of America

for

Barry, Alex, and Estelle,

and Caren and Mitchell,

Our Children to Whom We

Dedicate This Book

Preface

THE PURPOSE of this book is to provide the practicing psychotherapist, the student of psychotherapy, and those in other allied professions and occupations—such as educators, physicians, and clergymen who are concerned with the psychological well-being of children—with a comprehensive text by which they might better understand, manage, or treat emotional disturbance in children and thereby help them to actualize the abilities and growth potential inherent in these children.

This volume is not intended to serve as an introductory text in the areas of child psychotherapy or child psychopathology although it would contribute much as a supplementary source for such introductory courses. It is intended, rather, to serve as a reference for the child psychotherapist so that he can utilize the wisdom of the many years of experience of outstanding clinicians as a guide in working with specific problems in therapy and specific children's disorders.

Each contributor discusses the problems he expects to encounter in working therapeutically with a specific children's disorder and what means he has found most effective in treating and managing the child with such a disorder. In addition, each contributor discusses the particular theoretical considerations inherent in the disorder. For optimal utilization of this volume, it is therefore necessary that the reader be grounded in the fundamentals of therapeutic practice with children as well as the basics in child psychopathology and personality theory.

One can write about child psychotherapy from many theoretical and systematic points of view; however, this volume is not intended to serve as a survey of existing systems of child psychotherapy. Such an attempt would require several volumes, especially if one wished to concern oneself with a variety of problem areas and disorders. While we recognize the value of other theoretical systems such as operant conditioning, self theory, and Existentialism, etc., we have chosen to focus primarily upon one, namely, the psychoanalytic system. We hope that in this way we can insure better continuity and facilitate more effective communication. At the same time, we have encouraged the contributors also to include other approaches whenever they have found them to be helpful. The suggestions made by each contributor should in no way be interpreted as the only way such problems can be resolved. Rather, it is the way one outstanding clinician tends to deal with the particular problem.

As editors, we were very pleased to have been able to secure as contributors practicing child psychotherapists of very high calibre and stature, and for this reason have limited our task as editors primarily to one of maximizing clarity rather than insisting upon any particular content. Therefore, at the risk, in some instances, of discrepancy in points of view between contributors, or overlap in other instances, we have given extensive latitude to each contributor to elaborate upon the various techniques and experiences that each has found to be particularly significant and meaningful in his therapeutic work with children. We feel that the slight repetition that accrues as a function of some overlap in theory and technique can be an advantage rather than a handicap, in that it will serve as a good opportunity to better facilitate the learning and comprehension of the various dynamics and techniques discussed. Also we feel that while each chapter contributes to the total presentation of the book, it should contain sufficient theory, dynamics, and methodology to be read and understood as an independent and complete unit for those who wish to use this work as a reference book.

The first chapter introduces the reader to a number of theoretical considerations, the understanding of which is necessary for conducting psychotherapy with children. Included are such topics as The Goals in Psychoanalytically Oriented Psychotherapy with Children; Where and How Therapy Is To Take Place; The Setting for Play Therapy; Providing Treatment for Parents; Utilization of Individual or Group Therapy with Children; and the Personality and Motivation of the Child Psychotherapist. The second chapter considers an area often omitted in books dealing with disturbed children but one which is presently gaining in significance, namely, Learning Disorders in Children. Those employed in, or having contact with, educational institutions should particularly find this chapter helpful. The next three chapters deal with the most commonly encountered neurotic disorders in children—Phobic and Anxiety States, The Obsessive-Compulsive Child, and Hysteria. These chapters are followed by a consideration of psychotherapy of children with Psychosomatic Disorders and a chapter dealing with Conduct and Acting-Out Disorders. The next two chapters deal with the psychotic child. We have asked two outstanding writers who have made original theoretical contributions to present their respective points of view. In these two chapters are reflected the essence of the literature in the area of the psychotic child. It is our feeling that no one contribution could adequately reflect the many diverse approaches to the treatment and management of the psychotic child, thus we have decided to include two chapters dealing with this topic. The last chapter deals with the various problems one is likely to encounter in Psychotherapy with Adolescents.

Helping disturbed children offers an opportunity for much more than just personal gratification to the therapist. Our children today are serving as our lifeline to the future. What we can help them become today will insure the kind of world we will have tomorrow. We hope that this book contributes in some way toward that better tomorrow.

> There is only one child
> And his name is all children.
> CARL SANDBURG

We would like to express our appreciation to the contributors for their very fine cooperation and their commitment to the purposes of this volume. We wish also to thank the editors for Dorsey Press, Howard F. Hunt and Donald W. Taylor, for their many helpful suggestions. Our appreciation is also extended to Mrs. Marion Bouchard for typing the many drafts and final manuscript. We are especially indebted to our wives for their continuous support and understanding, without which this volume would have remained a topic of conservation instead of coming to fruition.

MAX HAMMER
ARTHUR M. KAPLAN

List of Contributors

Loretta Cass, Ph.D., Chief Psychologist, William Greenleaf Eliot Division of Child Psychiatry, Washington University, Saint Louis, Missouri

Austin M. Des Lauriers, Ph.D., Chief, Psychology Department, Michael Reese Hospital and Medical Center, Chicago, Illinois

Max Hammer, Ph.D., Lecturer, Department of Psychology, University of Maine, Orono, Maine

Lucie Jessner, M.D., Professor of Psychiatry, Georgetown University Hospital, Washington, D.C.

Alex H. Kaplan, M.D., Maryland Medical Building, 4652 Maryland Avenue, Saint Louis, Missouri

Arthur M. Kaplan, Ph.D., Chairman, Department of Psychology, University of Maine, Orono, Maine

Dr. Irving Kaufman, Newtonville, Massachusetts

Peter Knowlton, M.D., Bryn Mawr Medical Building, Bryn Mawr, Pennsylvania

Hyman S. Lippman, M.D., Director, Amherst H. Wilder Foundation, Child Guidance Clinic, Saint Paul, Minnesota

James T. Proctor, M.D., Medical and Training Director, Children's Medical Center, Tulsa, Oklahoma

Richard M. Silberstein, M.D., Director, Staten Island Mental Health Society, Staten Island, New York

Table of Contents

Max Hammer and
Arthur M. Kaplan

Theoretical Considerations in the Practice of Psychotherapy with Children

THE GOALS IN PSYCHOANALYTICALLY ORIENTED PSYCHOTHERAPY WITH CHILDREN

It GOES, almost without saying, that for every emotionally disturbed child the therapist will need to set up goals specific for the child; but it is also meaningful to talk about therapeutic goals which can be appropriate for almost all emotionally disturbed children.

Probably all systems or schools of psychotherapy would agree that the one basic and general goal for all children is emotional growth and maturity. How one defines maturity may be somewhat different for each theoretical system. We will take one such system—the psychoanalytic—and discuss, essentially from this point of view, the various components of maturity and growth, as well as some of the factors that can facilitate the emergence and growth of these components.

Psychosexual Maturity

Freud equated the psychosexual stages of development with the various libidinous zones of the body(2).* He would define maturity as the

---

* Boldface numbers refer to References listed at the end of each chapter.

progressive moving of the libido through the oral, anal, and phallic areas with the eventual achievement of genital sexuality. Freud would say that the achievement of mature or genital sexuality is not possible when the organism has fixated some of its libidinous energy at one of the earlier libidinous zones. He speaks of oral fixation, anal fixation, and phallic fixation and suggests that these "infantalisms" remain within the person and prevent him from achieving adult sexual maturity. Thus one of the primary goals of psychotherapy with children with such fixations is to help them desexualize these various components of their body so that they may progress toward the achievement of adult genital sexuality. One such device is the utilization of sublimation. Sublimations may be defined as nonbodily activities and substitutes for bodily eroticisms.

The child with a strong oral fixation who is not able to adequately sublimate the oral drive will continue to seek his satisfaction via direct oral gratification rather than through some substitutive activity which is more socially acceptable. For example, the child who still seeks food as the prime source of his gratification will, in all likelihood, encounter reading difficulties in school, for he is not willing or able to replace the swallowing of food with the "swallowing" of words. He refuses to let himself be "fed" in any way other than by food.

The individual with strong anal sadistic components who is not sublimating properly is likely to be acting-out destructively upon members of his environment. He will be unable to make a suitable adjustment because he is depreciated by society. The individual who can sublimate his sadistic drives—for example, by prizefighting—is not only accepted by his environment but is usually held in esteem for his "killer-instinct." Helping a child to sublimate his anal eroticisms can not only help the child in his growth but can also contribute toward the beauty and culture of the world. The energies that go into maintaining the anal fixation can, via sublimation, be directed toward artistic creations in such fields as painting, sculpture, and architecture. The child's latent creative potentialities can grow along with his emotional and sexual maturity.

The child with fixations at the phallic level may suffer difficulties in school due to his inability to compete or to handle his concerns around exhibitionism. The child fearful of competing will purposely, although it may not be conscious, do more poorly than the other children in his class. The child who has unconscious yearnings to exhibit himself will, in all likelihood, become panicked when he has to assume the limelight in class activities.

Thus, the provision of ample opportunity to sublimate is one important way to help the child grow and achieve greater maturity.

Relinquishing the Pleasure Principle for the Reality Principle

Another way Freud defined maturity was in terms of the reality principle taking precedence over the pleasure principle. Of course, this is only
a relative matter because no one can or should become all reality principle.
All work and no play would truly make Jack a very rigid fellow. In
essence, Freud defined the pleasure principle as that yearning for immediate gratification which is so truly characteristic of very young
children. He defined reality principle, essentially, as the capacity to
postpone immediate gratification for later gratifications in the face of
reality factors which make immediate gratification detrimental to the
organism.

Essentially, the child is helped to accept the reality principle via both
his ego-syntonic identification with the therapist, and the desire to please
this person who represents the reality world and the reality principle to
him. In order to be like the therapist he will perform as the therapist
performs. The therapist, demonstrating his mature ego to the child by
means of his own frustration tolerance and ability to accede to reality
demands without temper outbursts or undue hardship, provides the child
with the model of maturity which the therapist would like the child to
identify with and emulate. We see an example of the operation of the
reality principle when the child relinquishes his feces at the time and
place designated by his mother. Here the child is giving up the immediate
pleasure of retaining his feces for the more ultimate pleasure of having his
mother's love and approval. In the same way, the emotionally disturbed
child will relinquish his need for immediate pleasure in order to emulate
and please the therapist and consequently receive approval from him. By
doing so the child's ego grows and matures.

Another aspect of the reality principle is the child's capacity for reality
testing, that is, his capacity to accept whatever confronts him without
needing to avoid or distort.

One way to promote the child's reality-testing capacity is via the use of
clear limits. It is unfortunate but true that many therapists equate therapy
with permissiveness and are under the mistaken notion that because the
child has suffered deprivations, what he therefore needs from the therapist is unlimited indulgence. If this were done it would only serve to keep
the child regressed and would not facilitate the maturity or growth of the
ego. Nothing meaningful therapeutically can take place without realistic
limits. Limits define the boundaries of the relationship between therapist
and child and tie it to reality. Permitting a child to do whatever he

"wants" to do is unrealistic, for it does not represent what he will meet in the real world. Reality is such that this kind of behavior is just not tolerated. Essentially, we recognize a child's need for help because in some way he is out of step with his reality world. To be effective, the therapy hour must not be so divorced from everyday life situations that there can be no generalization or carry-over into the child's world outside the office or playroom. In addition, one is never sure that the child really wants what he says he wants. He may just be testing to determine if the therapist can be manipulated, or whether the therapist can be a strong enough person to resist the manipulation and thereby provide him with a sense of security. We must relate ourselves, always, to what the child is "saying" he needs rather than what he is verbalizing he wants when these seem in conflict.

Limits are also important because it will frighten the child terribly if you do not make it abundantly clear that you intend to protect him and yourself against any destructive impulses he may have. The therapist also contributes to the arousing of unnecessary guilt when he permits the child to do things that the child knows full well are not tolerated in society. Without clear limits, the therapist provides an atmosphere which is threatening to the child because lack of structure does not help the child to know what to expect from his immediate environment. Thus the therapist will be contributing toward the arousal of undue anxiety in the child.

Limits are particularly necessary for those children who do not have the sufficient controls from within to contain their own behavior. By setting consistent limits with the child, the therapist is thereby providing him with external controls until he can eventually establish controls from within. This helps the child feel secure and helps his weak ego to grow. If the therapist does not set clear and consistent limits for this kind of child, it is likely that he will provoke the therapist to do so anyway with possible deleterious effects resulting. For example, it is not too unusual for such a child to place his feet out of a second-story window and then turn to the therapist to see what he will do about it. No child can hope to function adequately in society without sufficient control of his impulses, and this control can never be achieved without being confronted with limits from the therapist.

More specifically, the limits to be discussed below are seen as essential in all therapeutic interactions with children. Additional limits may be set by the therapist based upon some rationale related to the child's problems.

Limits Are Important. One essential limit is that the child is not permitted to physically abuse the therapist or the therapist's clothing. This is important, since the therapist in pain can no longer be an effective therapist. Also, the child suffers extreme guilt when he hurts another human being, especially one who has tried to be good to him and to help him. Most of all, the unrestrained child has learned that the therapist is powerless to defend both the child and himself against what has, at least now, become his (the child's) frightening, aggressive impulses. Thus, a corollary is that the child must also not be permitted to do anything that will or might injure himself or his own clothing.

Another limit that should be established is that expensive or irreplaceable objects should not be permitted to be destroyed by the child. But a child might appropriately break inexpensive objects, especially when this act has therapeutic value. For example, if the child is overly inhibited in the expression of certain affects, he can be encouraged rather than discouraged in breaking such things as balloons so that he can learn to master his fear related to the expression of his destructive impulses.

Another limit which is quite important is the time limit. The child must be informed that there is such a limit and the therapist should be consistent in not permitting the child to extend this limit. If the child feels that by calling time on him the therapist is rejecting him, then this becomes grist for the therapeutic mill and needs to be dealt with accordingly. Some therapists find it helpful in the playroom to let the child know when there are only a few minutes left in the hour. This permits the child to prepare himself to leave and to finish up what he is doing without feeling overly frustrated and rejected. It also provides the therapist with a few minutes to deal with the child's feelings about the termination of the hour, should he have any such feelings. If the child refuses to leave and refuses to accept the explanation, then it may be necessary to pick him up and carry him out, but of course this needs to be done without anger or hostility toward the child.

Another important limit is to designate where the therapy is to take place. The child is usually not permitted to leave this room (except to go to the bathroom, or for water). It should be obvious that nothing therapeutic can be accomplished if the therapist is chasing the child around the block or through the hallways of the clinic. This should not be tolerated since it will probably disturb other workers in the building. More important, the therapist needs to communicate to the child that he cannot run away from the responsibility of facing his problems. If the child chooses to leave anyway, he should be permitted to do so, but this terminates the therapy hour and he is usually not permitted to return again that day.

Child Must Adjust to Reality.   In addition to limit-setting, the child's reality testing is enhanced by keeping in mind the general goal that it is important to help him recognize that he must adjust to his reality world rather than expecting it to adjust to him. The latter attitude would tend to perpetuate the infant's sense of omnipotence and thereby prevent him from maturing. It is important for not only the therapist, but the parent and the teacher as well, to recognize that the child should not be overly protected from reality regardless of how stressful he may interpret it to be. The child needs to learn to cope with various aspects of his world and he cannot learn to do so if he is overly shielded from these unpleasant realities. Learning to cope in this way is an important aspect in improving reality testing. For example, a mother who continuously tries to protect her child from aggressive bullies never permits the child to learn to adequately cope with aggressiveness. This applies to his own aggressiveness as well as that of others. Permitting the child to be gradually exposed to unpleasant realities and stresses serves to immunize him in the same way as does the building up of antibodies against a disease. This helps the child to later be able to better cope with stress, failure, and frustration without becoming overwhelmed.

Maturity of Object Choices

In psychoanalytic theory maturity is also frequently defined in terms of the maturity of the choice of love object. The progressive development of object choices proceeds from autoerotic to narcissistic, then to homosexual, and finally to heterosexual. Prior to the resolution of the oedipal conflict the child is typically autoerotic and narcissistic in his object choice. That is to say that early in infancy the infant derives extreme pleasure in the manipulation of his own body parts because of the highly libidinized investment in these body parts. Later in childhood the object of love for him is still himself, but it is not so heavily concentrated upon the stimulation of body parts. In narcissistic love the child is concerned with the maintenance of self esteem and so he seeks to be loved by others. The child wants to get something from the object without being concerned with having to return anything. Here, for the first time, an object becomes important to the child but only as a source for his own gratification. After the child has resolved the oedipal conflict he moves into latency, and in his relationship to peers we see the beginnings of the use of homosexual objects. These relationships are usually not sexual in nature but rather take the form of close associations like pals and buddies. This becomes heightened at the time of early adolescence, when gangs become extremely important to the child and even some sexual exploration among members of their sex is not uncommon. As the child moves on toward later adolescence and adulthood, his object choice becomes heterosexual in nature as he transfers his original tie from his mother to a member of the opposite sex.

Thus we find in many emotionally disturbed children that they have not progressed beyond the autoerotic stage and many adolescents have not progressed beyond the narcissistic stage. These children are therefore immature in terms of their object choice.

It then becomes clear that the essential goal for the therapist is to help this kind of immature child to redirect his cathexis away from himself and toward some external object, usually the therapist. Thus, by means of the establishment of a good relationship with the child and the use of transference feelings, the therapist can help the child learn to invest in a more mature love object and thereby continue the child on toward eventual mature heterosexual love objects.

Maturity as Defined by Greater Autonomy from Parents

The child is immature to the degree to which he still maintains his infantile attachment and dependency upon his mother. As in the metamorphosis of the butterfly, the child, too, must learn to grow his emotional wings and fly. If he remains tied to his mother, he cannot achieve the necessary differentiation to help him to feel he is autonomous and able to face life on his own.

Sometimes, as a necessary first step toward helping a child relinquish his infantile dependencies, the therapist must, by means of his relationship to the child, in a sense seduce the child away from his tie with his mother. The therapist can then, over time, gradually "wean" the child from his tie to the therapist. This process is facilitated by the therapist's continued warm encouragement of the child's capacity to make his own meaningful decisions, and the child soon comes to see himself as a separate "I." The child, by recognizing that he is doing his own thinking and making his own decisions and by doing for himself those things that interest him without the deliberate "helpful" intrusion of the therapist, comes progressively to feel himself a separate, distinct, and relatively unique "I."

Thus, the reader can see that the goals of psychotherapy with children are very much related to how one tends to define growth and maturity. Although some allusions were made here in regard to therapeutic procedures that could be ameliorative for immature children, more specifics will be offered in the sections to follow.

CONSIDERATIONS AS TO WHERE AND HOW THERAPY IS TO TAKE PLACE

In the field of psychotherapy with children there are a considerable number of debatable issues. One such issue—whether a child should be treated in a playroom or office—is related to the issue of whether play therapy is more effective than the exclusive use of verbal interaction.

The proponents of play will typically point out that for the child, play is a more natural mode of communication than are verbalizations. Early workers with children (among them, Melanie Klein [5]) recognized that play could serve as a substitute for the free associative process in arriving at the child's unconscious processes and basic conflicts. These workers typically point out that play provides the therapist with a microcosm of the child's world, and through it the therapist can learn how the child's behavior and attitudes contribute to the child's emotional difficulties. Others add that the child learns to master reality by playing. What the child has experienced passively in the past or what he anticipates in the future can all be dealt with through his active play. The tensions which have been established by passive experiences or which will be established by future events (for instance, a family move, surgery, and so forth) could overwhelm the child. But through his play the child can evoke these tensions in a minor degree so that he can learn to master them gradually.

Others who take an essentially negative view in regard to play therapy will typically point out that in order to be consistent with the general goal of greater maturity for the immature, emotionally disturbed child, the therapist needs to keep in mind that play is essentially pleasure principle in nature and is therefore more regressive and less mature than a therapy based upon a verbal interaction between therapist and child. Verbalizations represent the use of symbols (words being essentially symbols for reality), and the use of verbal symbols is a much more mature mode of functioning than is the manipulation of objects. They will typically point to the work of Piaget to support this. Piaget(6) has shown that maturation takes place progressively from operations with objects to operations with symbols representing objects and relationships. Goldstein(3) also talks about maturity in terms of moving from the concrete (e.g., objects or play) to the abstract (e.g., verbal symbols). They conclude, therefore, that maturity is related, in general, to the ability to express oneself in words rather than by physical actions.

It is our impression that both points of view are basically correct and that the essential question that needs to be asked is not whether play therapy is more effective than a more verbal form of therapy, but rather when is each most appropriate?

Play Therapy, or Verbal Forms of Therapy?

It should be obvious that for some children a strictly verbal form of therapy would not be appropriate. The child who is not verbal, either because he is psychotic, mute for psychogenic reasons, or so overly immature either developmentally or emotionally that he has not developed adequate speech, will likely be approachable only by means of the medium of play. There are those children, too, who can profit more from play therapy than verbal therapy because, in the balance between inhibitive and excitative forces, they are overly loaded on the inhibitive side. The child who is overly inhibited in terms of motoric or affective motility, or the child who is overly fantasy-ridden or withdrawn, will probably profit most from a playroom setting. Here, through the medium of play, the child can actively discharge some of his pent-up affects or impulses and find that it is safe to do so without incurring the wrath of adults. Motoric and affective discharge can also serve to drain some of the psychic energies which the child is directing into obsessive thought or fantasy. Because the child is blocked from discharge, these dammed-up energies are being redirected by the child into excessive fantasy. For example, the child who fantasies or daydreams too much in school needs to be allotted extra time for free play and recess in order to drain these energies, which would then permit him to be better able to concentrate upon his school work.

On the other side of the homeostatic scale is the child who is too excessive in his rate of discharge of excitation. This type of child, such as those that are impulse ridden, or acting-out disorders, or hyperkinetic due to brain damage, would probably do much better in a smaller setting such as an office. This kind of child needs a reduction in excitation and needs to learn to inhibit discharge, which is very difficult for him to accomplish because his ego is too weak to block the excessive drive for motility. This kind of child feels safer in a smaller office with less stimulation, for it provides the structure and controls on his impulses that he cannot provide for himself. A verbal form of therapy may be helpful in teaching the child to supplant behavior with words, thereby helping to build within him his own controls. The therapist needs to be cautious here because blocking the avenue of discharge too drastically or suddenly for some children could overwhelm them with anxiety. Where the child's anxiety level is already very high, it might be best to start him in a playroom reduced greatly in stimulation and gradually introduce him to smaller areas and more verbal interaction as time goes by and he begins to show a diminution in his level of anxiety.

A verbal form of therapy is also more appropriate than play therapy for those children who suffer from intense neurotic conflicts and possess sufficient verbal and intellectual capacities to deal verbally with their problems. There are also some children who are intellectually and socially very precocious and prefer "talking to the doctor rather than playing with toys like a child."

There are some therapists who, perhaps because of a shortage of space, attempt to conduct play therapy in their offices, but this is usually inappropriate because the child will either overly inhibit himself or feel very guilty should he spill paint on the rugs, get crayon marks on the walls, or damage some of the furniture.

Misconceptions Regarding Play Therapy

We would like at this point to say a few things more, related to some popular misconceptions in regard to play therapy. Some child therapists seem to feel that the essence of play therapy lies in the *playing* per se, since it affords an opportunity for permissiveness and catharsis, both of which are seen as therapeutic. It should be obvious, however, that if play alone were therapeutic, all we would need to do is advise the parents to get the child a good variety of toys and send him home to play. As stated earlier, play provides the therapist with a microcosm of the child's world which the therapist can then utilize to help the child to grow. In addition, with some children play makes possible the therapeutic relationship between therapist and child which is so necessary for the achievement of the goals discussed earlier in this chapter.

For example, it is not just the fact that the child has an opportunity to get angry and express it that is therapeutic. Rather, it is the fact that he can get angry in the presence of someone who not only accepts the anger, but understands why the child is angry and can communicate this to him.

The therapist can then offer him alternative ways of handling or reacting to the person he thinks is responsible for his angry feelings. The therapist can also use the anger to help the child with his reality testing by showing the child that perhaps he has become angry because of some misinterpretation he has made of the therapist or of the world in general. Without therapist intervention, play cannot be therapeutic and will remain just a reflection of the repetition compulsion, that is, an attempt to master inner conflicts by repeating them in various circumstances.

A child who has always needed to express his anger to his mother, for example, but has never felt the freedom to do so may, in his play, hit the punching bag, play with soldiers, throw darts at a clown's face or a target, or smash a female doll. However cathartic this form of play may be, it is not therapeutic in nature unless the repetition compulsion aspect is resolved. The therapist contributes toward the resolution of the repetition compulsion by helping the child bring to consciousness the nature of his feelings, thereby facilitating their integration. Play, being essentially primary process in nature, is like a dream; and, just like the repetitive dream or nightmare, although it may be cathartic in nature in the sense of leading to emotional expression, it does not free the individual from his distress, and so the dream continues to repeat itself. It is only when the dream is interpreted and the repressed affects integrated into the ego that the repetitive dream ceases. And so it is with play. If the therapist utilizes it to help the child integrate that which is rejected and repressed the child will grow. If this is not done, then the play will have little therapeutic value. Play alone is not sufficient to bring about therapeutic change. It is how it is *used* that makes play a tool which can lead to therapeutic change.

As mentioned earlier, for very severely disturbed children whose contact with reality is impaired and whose verbal capacity is limited, play can also be a valuable therapeutic catalyst. But here again it is not the play itself which is therapeutic, but the fact that play can serve as the device by which the therapist can help the child to make contact with his environment as well as help the therapist to establish affective contact with the child. Play can help to establish the beginnings of object-contacts and it is this which can be therapeutic.

Play, when it is not used appropriately, can even be deleterious to the child's growth because it may merely represent the repetition of regressive gratifications. All play can probably be traced back to the original play with the erotic polymorphous perverse body. Toys represent substitutions of our body parts, and playing with toys is essentially masturba-

tory in nature for it represents unconscious playing with our own eroti-
cized body. Therefore, in the emotionally disturbed child, play solely for
pleasure could foster regression and would therefore oppose the basic
goal of helping the child to accept the reality principle. Therapy must
help the child to give up illusory (body) satisfactions and seek pleasures
in harmony with reality.

THE SETTING FOR PLAY THERAPY

The selection of office or playroom materials and equipment should not
be based necessarily upon what one thinks the child will find amusing or
entertaining but should be consistent with, and facilitating of, the goals
that have been set up for therapy with children. We shall discuss a typical
well-equipped playroom which can serve as a model to be emulated or
altered depending upon the amount of space and finances available.

The Playroom

Ideally, the playroom should have the kind of walls and floors that are
easily washable and of a fairly durable material. The colors in the room
should be neither too bright and therefore overly stimulating, nor should
they be too dull or depressing in nature. If possible there should be a sink
and a toilet in the room, and these should be proportioned in size so as to
be comfortable for children to use. The same would be true for the table
and chairs in the room.

Brooms and mops and other necessary cleanup equipment should be
handy in the event that something breaks, and should be used as well to
clean up the room before the next child enters. It can be terribly upsetting
for a child to enter a room and find it messy, or with evidence of destruction in it.

If possible, there should be enough drawers in the room so that each
child can have a drawer of his own where he can place the projects with
which he is working and feel that these will not be disturbed by other
children. Drawer space is also valuable for the therapist's use, because
many times he will not want to expose certain materials that some
children could readily utilize for avoiding contact with the therapist;
other materials, such as pointed darts and guns, may be inappropriate for
children with very poor controls and are also better placed out of sight.
Toys should not be arranged in too neat and orderly a fashion, for this
could communicate to some children that the toys are little used and that

the therapist is overly concerned with cleanliness and orderliness. However, materials arranged in too much disarray could also be disturbing to some children, especially the child who tends to be overly inhibited or compulsive.

We have found it useful to select toys and materials consistent with the following goals: materials for diagnostic purposes; materials for building frustration tolerance; materials for children who need to be more expressive or aggressive; materials for improving a sense of adequacy and sexual identification; materials for promoting the therapeutic relationship; and materials for promoting sublimation. Although some materials can be used for several purposes, some examples of materials typically used for each purpose will be discussed.

Materials for Diagnosis

Playroom equipment and materials may be used for diagnostic purposes in the same way that the psychologist uses psychological tests. He utilizes some tests which are highly unstructured in nature, such as the Rorschach ink blot test which, because of its relative lack of structure, provides information relating to the deeper, unconscious layers of functioning. The somewhat more structured tests, such as the TAT and the even more structured sentence-completion test, provide the psychologist with information emanating from the more preconscious and conscious levels of functioning.

In terms of the structure of the personality, the unstructured tests and materials provide a picture of the "skeleton" of the personality somewhat like an X-ray does for the human body, whereas the more structured materials will elicit information which, in a sense, "puts the meat on the bones." For example, the unstructured materials may reveal that an anal fixation exists and that the child has intense anal sadistic impulses; and the more structured materials may help us to understand why these exist—for example, the mother's overcontrolling and castrating attitudes and behavior are what is principally contributing to the child's rage and destructive impulses.

Some examples of unstructured materials are as follows: easel and paints (tempera washes off easily) for both brush and finger painting; clay (plasticene is clay which has been treated to retain its softness and pliability indefinitely); crayons and paper; blocks for building and erecting; sand box; paste or glue; scissors; tape recorder and old typewriter (both excellent for eliciting insights into children who are frightened to communicate with the therapist directly but can do so indirectly by means of inanimate objects); and animals representing degrees of aggressiveness and passivity and various psychosexual stages of development. For example, alligators could represent and elicit concerns around oral sadism or castration anxiety. Castration anxiety is also seen reflected in the way some children will react to animals whose tails have obviously broken off. Snakes and horses may reflect other aspects of phallic problems.

Cows and bulls, hens and roosters, lions and tigers, bears and cats may all serve to yield clues as to the status of the oedipal conflict; they may also provide clues related to sexual identification and the content of the child's fantasy in regard to each parent. Animals such as mouse, rabbit, monkey, and other related small animals frequently yield clues in regard to the child's attitudes toward himself. Kitchen equipment and baby bottles may provide clues related to oral needs or deprivations; bounce-back punching bags, especially those that have a "good guy" and a "bad guy" on each side are particularly good for detecting aggressive trends and how the child deals with these, as are also guns of various types (dart, water, cap, and such).

Some materials which are somewhat less structured and therefore provide more specifics in regard to the child's interpersonal relationships with significant persons in his world are as follows: A doll family including grandma and grandpa dolls are very good, especially if they are pliable so that children may put them in any position or posture they choose; they should not be uniformed or so overly structured as to make it difficult for the child to use them in any way he may desire. Puppets, especially hand puppets, enable the child to put on skits and speak for all members of the family; again, these hand puppets should not be too structured or too specific in dress or expression. Animal as well as human puppets should be available for those children who would be too threatened by human figures. Many children find it much easier identifying with the animal world than with the human world—analagous to children preferring the CAT (Children's Apperception Test) to the TAT (Thematic Apperception Test). Materials with which a child can construct his own world, such as are found in Buhler's World Test, are also very helpful for diagnostic purposes. Items such as miniature cars, houses, fences, people, churches, streets, trees, and so forth are excellent for observing the kind of world the child would like to have for himself. For example, the very withdrawn child is likely to build a world with few objects, especially humans, probably surrounded by fences which enclose him and shut out the various elements in the world which threaten him. For girls, a doll house is especially good for observing their sexual role identification and how they see the home situation. Dolls for dressing and undressing are also good for sex role identification as well as for discovering the presence of sexual preoccupations.

Materials for Building Frustration Tolerance

Building frustration tolerance is one of the essential ingredients in developing greater ego-strength in the child. Jigsaw puzzles, graduated in difficulty, are an example of materials that can be helpful in building frustration tolerance. The child will seldom be able to complete such a puzzle in one session and therefore must learn to tolerate the frustration of an incomplete task. He must then wait until the next session before he can complete it. Also faced with frustration as he tries to find which pieces fit together and which do not, he does eventually gain a sense of adequacy and mastery when he is finally able to complete the frustrating task. Having these puzzles in graduated difficulties permits the child to choose one where he is likely to meet some eventual reward and prevents him from becoming hopelessly frustrated, which could be damaging. If there were just one puzzle and he could not successfully put it together, it could very easily reinforce his feelings of inadequacy. Such puzzles are also effective in teaching the child to master his world in an active, aggressive way especially therapeutic for those boys with a strong passive-receptive personality who typically attempt to gain security in their world by clinging, pleading helplessness, and placing themselves at the mercy of those they perceive as stronger.

The construction of model airplanes, cars, and the like can have a similar advantage in building frustration tolerance for many of the same reasons discussed above.

These kinds of materials would not be appropriate, however, for those children who already demonstrate some degree of compulsiveness, or who are typically those who tend to utilize intellectual defenses to block affective relating. These types of children will prefer the kinds of materials discussed here as a device for gaining emotional distance from the therapist. Children who are frightened of relating should not be encouraged in the avoidance of such a confrontation. It would be well to have such material out of sight.

Materials for Improving Sense of Adequacy and Sexual Identification

In addition to some of the materials discussed above, other materials which can facilitate an improvement in the child's sense of adequacy, for boys especially, are tool sets which they can use for constructing various things. This can enhance the boy's sense of adequacy and also help him to feel more masculinely identified. Competitive games such as Checkers or Monopoly can also serve the same function, and are especially good for those children who need to learn some control over impulses and who can perhaps learn to substitute more sedentary pursuits for impulsive acting-out. For girls, learning various arts and crafts can contribute toward a greater sense of mastery and adequacy, and female-identified materials such as toy stoves, pots, pans, and dishes can help her experiment with the feminine role. For those children who suffer from extreme feelings of inadequacy and will not attempt any of the above materials, even such a device as a flashlight which the child can learn to turn off and on can be of much value in helping the child achieve a greater sense of mastery

Materials for Children Who Need to Be More Expressive or Aggressive

Those children who are overly controlled or inhibited in the expression of their affects and impulses and those who are overly passive and re-strained in their motor expression can profit from such materials as those presented here. There are balloons, which children can blow up and break, and on which some children like to draw faces to be punctured with a dart. There are bounce-back punching bags toward which children can vent their hostilities without guilt because they can feel it is not really a person they are attacking. Toy soldiers, tanks, and trucks, as well as toy knives, guns, swords, and the like are also effective in eliciting pent-up aggressive drives. Various kinds of balls can be used for expressive running games. Darts and various kinds of dart boards, some with faces and others rather neutral, are useful for children who vary in the degree to which they can make manifest their hostility. Tools for sawing and hammering, pegboard and hammer sets, or drums and other similar noise-makers can also be effective for children who need to be more expressive.

Materials for Promoting the Therapeutic Relationship

Any materials which facilitate the interaction between therapist and child can be helpful in promoting the relationship between the two. Examples of these are games like checkers and cards, toy telephones, balls, and the like.

There are some therapists who deliberately intrude themselves into the child's activities and try to force a "relationship" to happen. For example, if the child is building a model airplane, they may insist upon helping the child with its construction. Such action can rob the child of the feeling of mastery that comes with accomplishing the task himself and could communicate to him that the therapist considers him inadequate in this task. It may make the child feel that the therapist has a strong need to be needed. This could serve to retard the relationship rather than enhance it. If the task is too difficult for the child he will soon come to recognize it himself, and be led to try something easier next time. This kind of experience, because it involves reality testing for the child, can be growth enhancing.

Materials for Promoting Sublimation

Sublimation is an essential ingredient of maturity; therefore, facilitating sublimation becomes an important aspect of psychotherapy with children. Examples of some materials which can be used for the sublimation of oral needs are cooking utensils; books to read, which help the child substitute the swallowing of words for the swallowing of food; and toy musical instruments, such as trumpet, clarinet, and fife. Materials which typically serve for the sublimation of anal drives are clay, finger paints, sandbox, parts for model building, chemistry sets, punching bags, and tools.

Materials which may be useful for sublimating phallic drives are various games, for the sublimation of phallic competitiveness; dolls for dressing and undressing, to sublimate phallic sexual curiosity; or a tape recorder which, if the child can pretend it is a radio microphone, can help in the sublimation of possible phallic exhibitionism.

CONSIDERATIONS IN REGARD TO PROVIDING TREATMENT FOR PARENTS

Workers in the field of child therapy are quite divided in regard to which family members should be treated when a child is manifesting emotional difficulties. Some insist it is necessary to see the entire family together and to treat them as a unit; others feel it is sufficient to treat just the mother and child, to bring about significant change; still others are insistent that the child alone needs to be treated, and that changes in the child will usually bring about changes in the other significant family members; finally, there is a small minority who feel that treating the parent(s) instead of the child is most meaningful and expeditious, and that this is sufficient to bring about change and growth in the child.

It is our contention that each of the above may be appropriate, depending upon the particular circumstances involved. It is likely that no one rigid approach will be appropriate for all circumstances, and that some rationale or set of criteria needs to be established to help the therapist decide which approach may be best.

When Should Parents Be Treated?

It should be pointed out that the child neither grows in a vacuum, separated and isolated, nor does he become a mere precipitate of the forces that impinge upon him. The problems that occur in children stem for the most part from the conflict between the child and the forces in his environment. The causes of a behavior problem never exist just in the child, any more than they exist just in the parents. It has become common for many therapists to lay the blame for the child's difficulties at the feet of the parents. This is frequently unfair. Any parent who brings her child for treatment is expressng some concern for that child, even though other factors may also be involved. It is possible that the parents are motivated only by selfish reasons such as the fact that they are "giving up" on the child and want someone else to try; or they are frightened of what the child may do to them; or someone from the child's school has been bothering them and they want to "get these people off their back." However, it is rare when we find that a parent feels only hate for her child. If she did not care about the child, she probably would not feel anything toward him at all. It is likely that the child could receive love from these "hating" and rejecting parents were he able to fit into the home situation more harmoniously.

We have found it very difficult to effect this harmony without the involvement of the parents as well as the child in the treatment process, because the gains achieved with the child can be very easily offset by parents who are not sufficiently aware of the child's conflicts and struggles. We have found it essential to involve at least one parent, usually the mother, in the treatment process. We usually include the mother because she has been closer to the child and has had the strongest influence on him for most of his life. This is especially true for the prepubertal child for whom the environmental factors must be considered an integral part of the treatment process. The adolescent is not nearly as dependent on the parents as a source of esteem and security. He can turn toward peer groups and heterosexual relationships for his security and esteem.

The therapist needs to have some contact with the parents even if it is not on a regular basis. He needs to be able to find out the latest developments at home in order to be clear if the child's reactions and anxiety in therapy are a function of environmental factors or intrapsychic factors. It is also necessary that he have contact with the parents so as to be able to help them help the child. As new insights arise in therapy the therapist will want to communicate some of these in the form of recommendations to the parents. Involving the parents also helps them to feel that they are a part of the treatment team and that they are contributing to the growth of the child, which tends to elicit optimal motivation from them.

There are some situations in which it is clear that the parents are not emotionally disturbed, and apparently their psychodynamics are not negatively influencing the child's personality development. There are instances in which a child's emotional upsets are not due essentially to problems in the parent-child relationship but rather stem from some trauma inflicted upon the child from outside the home. For example, the child may have been sexually molested, or he may have been hospitalized and surgically operated upon because of a severe physical injury. Each of these could trigger an intense phobic reaction which in all likelihood is treatable without the parents themselves being involved in their own psychotherapy. This is also true for those parents who suffer some anxiety because they are unsure of themselves in their role as parents. We find that as soon as the child begins to make some growth and the problems subside, the parents' anxiety also subsides. We have found this frequently in young parents who are raising their first child and are basically emotionally healthy people. They usually make relatively good parents as they mature and demonstrate much more confidence with the ensuing children.

Guidance Rather Than Therapy

In circumstances similar to the three discussed above we would tend to treat the mother and father as parents and not patients. They would be offered guidance rather than psychotherapy. In guidance, the focus is placed upon the child rather than the psychodynamics of the parent. In guidance, the therapist may help the parent gain a better understanding of normal child development, for some parents tend to apply adult criteria to child behavior and therefore their expectations of the child may be unrealistic. They may need to know that "silliness" or "clumsiness" may be characteristic and normal for a particular age level, rather than a sign of abnormality as the parents have feared. Parents frequently need to understand that trying to force a child to mature before he is ready only makes him preserve his childishness and immaturities. He may act more maturely, but he will likely always long to gratify these childish or dependent trends which he feels he was forced to relinquish. This results in his remaining immature emotionally.

Guidance may also deal with helping the parents to better understand the child's particular needs and experiences and how these may relate to his current problems or behavior. For example, the therapist may explain to the parents how the birth of a new child in the home is contributing toward the older child's regressive behavior.

Guidance may also focus upon the parent-child relationship, but the emphasis will be placed primarily upon helping the parents to deal with the child's behavior in various circumstances, rather than upon the underlying motivations of the parent-child relationship. For example, the parent with relatively good ego-strength just needs to be shown that putting too much pressure on the child has contributed to the child's school difficulties; once informed of this the parent can easily change. It is not always necessary to deal with why the parent has needed to pressure the child or why she tends to overvalue school work. If she is a fairly healthy parent, a change in her attitude may be sufficient to permit changes to take place in the child.

Parents Who Need Psychotherapy

Psychotherapy—in contrast to guidance, as we are using these terms—places the focus on the parent's own psychodynamics, and may deal with the parent's past experiences in order to help her see how these may relate to her current attitudes and problems. Psychotherapy, rather than focusing on the child, places the major focus upon the parent's neurotic disabilities. It is therefore essentially concerned with personality change, whereas guidance makes no attempt at altering the parent's personality, but rather is more concerned with imparting information that will help the parents deal more effectively with the child.

The diagnostic process becomes, then, a very important tool in the determination of who in the family is to be offered treatment, and what form that treatment is to take. An extensive interview with the parents and/or the use of psychological tests are invaluable as diagnostic aids. If the parent is judged to be severely neurotic, or if it becomes clear that the psychodynamics of the parent and the child are in some way interrelated, then it becomes necessary to treat the parent as a patient and offer her psychotherapy rather than guidance. For example, we may discover that the child, by means of his destructive acting-out behavior, has been living out one of the parent's repressed needs to act-out in this way. This parent is unconsciously receiving some vicarious gratification from the child's acting-out and really does not want the child to change. The child, in order to gain love and acceptance from this parent, has intuitively recognized that this is how he needs to behave if he is to please the parent. The parent usually communicated his need for the child to act this way when the child first started acting aggressively by saying, in the presence of the child, such things as, "I'm really proud of my boy, he told his teacher where to get off. Nobody scares him. He's a real boy." Other parents can communicate the same thing by what they do *not* do or say. This parent will typically tell the teacher or therapist, "I've told my boy not to get into trouble but he just won't listen. There's nothing more I can do."

Another typical example of where it is necessary to offer psychotherapy to the parent is when the mother really cannot tolerate her child's outgrowing his need for her. She usually has an intense need to be needed which she feels must be met if she is to feel worthwhile as a person. She is afraid that the therapist will prove to be a better "mother" to the child than she has been and fears losing the child's love and devotion. She will therefore do whatever she can to guarantee that her child does not really change. Other parents with similar dynamics are resistant to the child's changing because they fear that such a change will prove they have been the primary cause of the problem. She feels guilty about the child's problems and needs to show that if she could not help the child, no one can. She is also afraid that the child's growth will be a confirmation that it has been her influence which caused the child to have problems. She therefore will consciously or unconsciously undermine the child's treatment. She may consistently bring him late for his appointments, or she may prematurely remove him from therapy, insisting that he is "all cured." These parents will communicate to the child in some subtle way that if he changes, he runs the risk of losing their love. Without involving this kind of parent in treatment, very little can be accomplished with the child.

Still another very typical example of a parent who needs to be offered psychotherapy is the parent who is using the child as the object of her sadistic impulses and really prefers the child to be bad so she can justify her criticism and rage toward him. This kind of parent really does not want the child to change, because if she lost the object for her sadistic impulses she is likely to turn them in on herself in a destructive, masochistic way.

If the child is very mistrustful of the parent, then different therapists for mother and child are preferable, otherwise the child will likely be too fearful of confiding in the therapist. In most cases it is preferable for the same therapist to see both the parent and the child. It is much easier to coordinate the therapy that way, and it is also easier for the therapist to observe how the changes in one effect the changes in the other.

The therapist tries, essentially, to mobilize the inherent strengths in the family to assist and support the child. Sometimes it is necessary to offer therapy to the mother to achieve this. Other times the father in the home, with some guidance, could become a source of strength to both mother and child. It has been frequently observed that as the father becomes better able to meet mother's needs, she becomes better able to relinquish the use of her child for this purpose. Grandparents may also be used in this regard, especially where the parents are overly immature and narcissistic and are essentially unprepared at the present time to serve as the strong parents the child needs. The school should also be considered a vital part of the therapeutic team, and helping the school to understand the child can go a long way toward the eventual amelioration of the child's problems. Most children spend more time in school than they do with their parents, so that making school a rewarding and supportive place for the child can have much positive therapeutic effect.

Group or Individual Therapy?

Where it has been decided that the parent or parents need to be offered some kind of therapy, then the therapist must decide if group or individual therapy would be most appropriate and growth facilitating for the particular parent being considered. Most often the groups will be composed of mothers of emotionally disturbed children; however, in many instances a group composed of both the mother and father of the disturbed child may be most profitable. Group therapy has been found to be particularly effective with the following types of parents:

1. Mothers who feel "starved" in regard to social relationships. They feel unfulfilled as persons and see the role of housewife and mother as too restricting. They therefore harbor a great deal of resentment toward the child whom they blame for their predicament. Many of these mothers also tend to use the child as a compensatory object for their frustrations and become overly involved in their child's life. The group experience offers them, in addition to helpful insights, an opportunity to gratify some of their unmet social needs. They gain new friends and expand their world socially. As a consequence they come to be able to relinquish their overinvestment in the child.

2. Those parents who, because of overly strict religious upbringing, rationalize their overcritical and controlling discipline of their children in terms of moral righteousness. These parents are sometimes so rigid in their attitudes that individual treatment is frequently ineffective. Only when they hear that other parents in the group do not do the same things they do, or when their attitudes are challenged by other parents, do they consider making any changes.

3. Some parents, because of the rejection of their own dependency needs, will tend to see individual therapy as the placing of themselves in a very dependent role which greatly threatens them. As a consequence they generally tend to resist committing themselves to treatment because to ask for help means to them that they are acknowledging their helpless dependency. In group therapy, even if they choose not to actively participate in the group, they can still derive a great deal of benefit just from listening to the other parents discuss their similar problems. Observing that other parents are not reticent at exposing their vulnerabilities will usually eventually lead to the resistant parent also doing the same.

4. Some mothers, who are having trouble with their daughters because of their own earlier unresolved feelings toward a younger female sibling, can utilize the group as the stimulus for the reenactment of this transference. In this instance the group members "become the siblings," the therapist is "seen as the parent," and the mother can be readily helped to see that her reactions to the group members are similar to her reactions toward her daughter.

5. The group is particularly good for those mothers who, for one reason or another, suffer from much guilt in regard to their child's emotional problems. When they observe that others in the group have had the same or similar negative feelings toward their children that she has had, it tends to relieve much of her guilt. She does not feel as bad, knowing that she is not the only mother who has had "terrible" feelings toward her child.

6. For those prepsychotic persons who do not have the ego strength to effectively utilize individual therapy the group is a better alternative, and the support that the group can offer is frequently quite therapeutic.

A husband and wife group is frequently most effective in the following circumstances:

1. When the balance in the husband-wife relationship is extremely precarious, individual treatment for only one spouse could bring such changes in their attitudes and relationship to each other as to cause the possible collapse of the marriage.

2. Even though the marriage may not be in any immediate crisis of dissolution, there are some marriages in which the communication between husband and wife has broken down so badly that neither spouse can serve as a supportive agent for the other or for the children. In many instances the child has manipulated both parents and has played one parent against the other. In other instances there is deep resentment between the parents because they are competing with each other for the child's attention and affection in order to prove that they are the one who is the more worthy of love.

3. When husband and wife are in conflict over child-rearing and both are rigid in the stands they take. Here the overt conflict may be the manifestation of a more basic conflict between the two. For example, Mr. and Mrs. Jones are in conflict over how to best raise their 5-year-old son, Jeff. Mrs. Jones believes that it is best to protect, cuddle, and be readily available to Jeff. Mr. Jones, on the other hand, feels that his wife is making a baby out of Jeff. The basic conflict which goes unrecognized is Mrs. Jones's need to have someone around who can show dependency on her, and Mr. Jones's refusal to play and accept this role.

4. At other times one parent may be realistic in her approach to the child but is being undermined by the other parent who is overidentified with the child and reliving something of his own childhood through the child.

Optimally the group should be constructed in such a way that it will be fairly homogenous in terms of intelligence, and in terms of the nature of the problem in the child. Such homogeneity facilitates communication between the members and guarantees the greatest degree of benefit for those who, though less verbal, still can profit from hearing others discuss their problems. Possibly its greatest benefit stems from the likelihood that discovering that others have had similar experiences and feelings enhances the reduction of guilt and the increase of insight.

In some instances it may be more profitable to treat the parent without the child. At times the parent will use the child as a way of gaining entrance into therapy herself. She may not be able to ask for help for herself but can do so only in this way. At other times it is very clear that the child is not severely disturbed and that it is the parent, because of her emotional disturbance who needs to be treated, with the recognition that when the parent has worked out her problems the conflict with the child will likely end.

CONSIDERATIONS IN REGARD TO THE UTILIZATION OF INDIVIDUAL OR GROUP THERAPY WITH CHILDREN

Psychotherapy with children may take many forms. With prepubertal children, therapy typically takes one of the following forms: (*a*) individual therapy with the emphasis on the verbal interaction between child and therapist; (b) individual therapy with the emphasis on play rather than verbal interaction, although there will likely also be some of the latter; (c) activity group therapy with children which is essentially group play therapy. For those in early adolescence, individual therapy may either be focused on the verbal or play process, but group therapy is usually exclusively verbal in nature. For those in late adolescence, both individual and group therapy is usually of verbal rather than play nature.

In general, we would say that children with intense intrapsychic problems need individual treatment, whereas group therapy is considered best for those children who need and have missed good social experiences. In view of the fact that activity group therapy is a relatively new approach to the treatment of children, we would like to describe it. Slavson(7) and others have described in much detail the operation of this approach but we shall describe it only briefly here.

Activity Group Therapy

In activity group therapy the atmosphere is a permissive one. The children are permitted to use the materials and equipment in almost any way they wish. Some therapists like to serve food treats during these sessions in order to reduce anxiety as well as to build a group experience in an enjoyable activity. As the group progresses, many therapists then prefer to let the children take the responsibility of preparing the food. The children may act destructively or constructively, they may withdraw into themselves or enter into relationships with fellow members. They may work or be idle, do their homework, read comics, play or fight. They may eat with the group or in isolation. Outside visits to such places as bowling alleys or restaurants may also be utilized.

Typical of what usually happens is that the fearful child attaches himself to another withdrawn child so that they become a mutually supportive unit. They work and share things together. As they become more secure they tend to choose more outgoing members of the group as friends, until a stage in growth is reached when they no longer need support from others.

In the activity group, aggressive children may find their therapeutic support in a negative fashion. Either other equally aggressive children challenge them, thus making some compromise behavior necessary, or they are nurtured by the more normally behaving children who thereby serve as neutralizing agents. It is advantageous to have one or two relatively normally behaving children in the group, for their influence tends to accelerate the improvement of all the other members of the group.

The overly narcissistic child, the bully, the child who has been pampered and overprotected, and the manipulative child all meet, in the group, impediments to their excessive demands. For example, the bully may find that the group will not tolerate his attacking the weaker members and may forcefully demonstrate this to him. All these children benefit from improved reality testing as a function of the limits set for them by their little society, the other members of the group. These children gradually learn, sometimes by means of painful experience, to become aware of, and sensitive to, the rights and needs of others.

Children Who Best Profit from Activity Group Therapy

Children who generally profit best from activity group therapy are those who have behavior disorders but who are not excessive in their hostility or destructiveness, those with character disorders, and those who are mildly neurotic. Children who suffer from a severe neurotic condition usually cannot be reached this way. The child who has pervasive anxiety, phobias, intense guilt feelings, or conflicts cannot have his symptoms eliminated by this kind of treatment. In fact, the intensely anxious child may become even more frightened as a result of his own or other children's aggressions.

However, the mildly neurotic child may find great release in the permissive environment of the group where he can act out his repressed hostility and aggressions in creative work, play, mischief, or hilarity. Because his behavior does not call forth retaliation, punishment, or disapproval, pent-up emotions find appropriate discharge. The overly inhibited child, especially by observing others act up without punishment, feels the freedom to do so himself. This helps to reduce guilt feelings for hidden impulses of hate and destruction, or feelings of being bad and worthless.

Activity group therapy is also helpful for those children who, because they are so fearful of close relating, are blocked so strongly in this regard that they are unable to establish even a minimal relationship in individual treatment and are unable to communicate their problems. Such uncommunicative children need a less threatening situation than individual therapy offers. They require relationships of less emotional intensity such as those that are found in groups where relationships can be established at one's own pace on a basis of empathy and support.

Activity group therapy is also frequently successful with children whose behavior is basically a reaction to rejection, lack of love, over-protection, a stigma related either to physical or mental handicaps, feelings of inferiority or worthlessness, defeats in sibling rivalry, and the like.

Groups supply substitute relations and compensatory gratifications. Children who are confused concerning their sexual role identification and who, perhaps, have built up destructive fantasies about masculinity can profit greatly from activity group therapy. There are many boys who, because of a tyrannical father or because of forced submission to mothers and sisters, come to fear their own masculinity, which they equate with aggressiveness. They become afraid of expressing even normal aggressiveness, are unable to participate in the ordinary activities and games of boys, and react by excessive submissiveness and withdrawal. Many of these children live in a state of anxiety which if left unattended would likely develop into a neurosis. Such children profit greatly from the free interrelationships in activity group therapy.

Activity Group Therapy Not Always Helpful

Generally speaking, it is felt that activity group therapy deals largely with the correction of character malformations and reactive behavior disorders. It does not deal effectively with psychotics, sociopathic personalities, habitual delinquents, children who suffer from intense neuroses, or those who are excessively withdrawn. The permissiveness of activity group therapy is helpful to children whose character formations are not so deeply entrenched as to be inaccessible by corrective experiences, substitute gratifications, and permissive group relations. It cannot treat children who lack a minimal capacity to relate themselves to people or to bring themselves under control in favorable circumstances.

The essential requirement for membership in a group is a yearning in the child, at whatever level, to be with others, to be accepted by them, to be part of a group. This hunger for social experience may be seen as the counterpart to transference in individual therapy and is an extension of the more infantile love cravings of the child. The highly narcissistic or sociopathic child who exploits, for his own ends, the nonauthoritarian and nonrepressive environment is obviously unsuitable for the group. Thus, social hunger must be accompanied by a capacity to give up, in return for group acceptance, some of the self-indulgences, exploitative attitudes toward people, power drives, and infantile self-love. It is possible to accept children who, despite aggressive behavior, have the capacity to bring themselves under control, can become aware of their acts, and curb themselves in return for recognition and acceptance by others. If group acceptance means enough to a child he will learn to curb himself. Therefore it is helpful, before accepting a child into the group, to review the child's history to see if he has ever established a warm relationship with some person—a parent, nurse, grandparent, sibling, teacher, or other. A child who has not experienced, sometime in his life, such a sustaining relationship is not likely to attach much significance to group acceptance.

In selecting children for an activity group it is essential to include children of various psychological syndromes so they may complement each other or serve in other ways as supports. Including in the group children with a variety of problems offers the children an opportunity to balance each other and makes it possible for the child to make identifications with persons different from himself.

For adolescent groups, however, such diversification is not helpful. There is a need for a common element among them so they may understand and profit from the content and meaning of the discussions. If we place together people who are psychologically too diverse, there is little interpersonal therapy possible. Members of the group must have similar problems in order to make group discussion effective. A group experience is especially good for most adolescents because this is a time in their lives when they are typically involved with peer and heterosexual relationships. It is helpful, for example, for them to hear from others in the group that they too have sexual impulses and fantasies. They learn that these are common and normal and also learn how better to deal with them. They need to learn something of social behavior at this time in their lives and the group greatly facilitates this.

Group treatment can, according to therapeutic needs, be supplementary to individual treatment or exclusive of such treatment. Group therapy is never to be considered a substitute for individual treatment. Rather it should be recommended only when there is an appropriate rationale based upon the specific needs of the child.

CONSIDERATIONS IN REGARD TO THE PERSONALITY OF THE THERAPIST

For many years, researchers and writers in the field of psychotherapy have concentrated their efforts toward the development of psychotherapeutic systems and techniques with the apparent hope that one "right" technique would be discovered which could ameliorate the psychopathology of all patients. More recently, the literature has reflected the fact that researchers have begun to recognize that the personality of the therapist might be an equally, if not more, important variable in the determination of therapeutic success.

We will make no attempt to survey the literature in regard to the research in this area, for that is outside the scope of this book. However, in an attempt to better understand the variable of the personality of the therapist we will present first some observations, made over the years in our role as therapy supervisors, of the psychodynamics that are representative of child therapists. It is our feeling that insufficient attention has been focused upon this area. Then we shall proceed to discuss those personality characteristics we feel are essential in making for an effective therapist with children.

It is important first to point out that one's choosing to become a child psychotherapist is *never* accidental. A lifetime of experiences have influenced such a decision, whether the therapist-to-be is consciously aware of these or not. It is probably safe to say that everyone, to some degree, has experienced anxieties, frustrations, and deprivations at various times in his life. These early experiences will play a significant part in shaping the therapist in terms of the affective biases that he will hold and bring into the therapy situation. These experiences and biases are not likely to be offset by the fact that the student has learned his personality theory well and has "mastered" the therapeutic techniques that are presented to him in various academic courses.

Support for this can be readily noted in the research dealing with cognitive dissonance. Festinger(1) and others have found, essentially, that one experiences tension, discomfort, or anxiety, when confronted with knowledge that is contrary to what one has previously learned to believe, feel, or experience. When this occurs, suitable ways must be found to maintain the beliefs held heretofore. For example, people smoke for various reasons. Through a series of facts in various media they may learn that smoking is detrimental to one's health. For some, the facts will be sufficient justification to curtail their smoking. Many others, however, cannot react in this way. They need to continue smoking, since smoking represents something more, at least psychologically, than holding and puffing a cigarette. They can continue to smoke by distorting the facts or avoiding being confronted by them. Some remain in a bind in that they recognize their helplessness in coping effectively with the facts and changing their behavior accordingly.

Just as one smoker cannot change his need for smoking due to psychological reasons, so too it is unlikely that our student will be able to alter his needs and behavior on the basis solely of the facts presented to him. It is not uncommon for a prospective child therapist to become overly involved with his child patient as a function of his particular psychological needs. He may become angry with the child even though he recognizes from what he has been taught that this is inappropriate. He, too, is helpless in the face of his own dynamics.

He would maintain, essentially, that the student chooses the field of child psychotherapy in an attempt, probably unconscious, to fulfill himself; to have gratified all those needs long unmet. We do not mean to imply a value judgment here in regard to how the student is attempting to meet his needs nor whether he is doing so in a healthy or neurotic manner. Our intent is only to bring these psychodynamics to the attention of the therapist or student so he may judge for himself whether these needs are operating within him and, if so, to what degree they may be interfering with the efficacy of the therapy process.

Motivations for Choosing Child Psychotherapy as a Career

We make no pretense at exhaustively covering all of the possible motivations for choosing the field of psychotherapy as a career. We shall, instead, consider those we have found to be most salient and frequent.

Unconscious Compensation. Many choose psychotherapy with children as a career because they unconsciously are seeking to gratify and compensate for their own infantile fixations, frustrations, and deprivations. They envision an opportunity to regress in a socially acceptable manner by working psychotherapeutically with children. Similar to the father who buys electric trains for his son and ends up playing with them himself, the child therapist has an opportunity, by means of his play or contacts with the child, to gratify himself, either directly or vicariously. Thus the therapist with strong oral needs may make sure that his child patient has plenty of goodies to eat and may even share in this with the child; and the therapist with strong anal components enjoys and encourages the child's playing with paints, clay, and the like. The therapist with unresolved phallic impulses such as, perhaps, being previously frustrated in his competitive drives can now, with the child, compete and win easily.

There are other therapists who have a need to regress because in their childhood they felt that they were made to grow up and assume adult behavior and responsibilities too quickly. As a consequence they feel that they have been robbed of their childhood and so unconsciously still cling to it. They envision that in their career as a therapist with children they will have a chance to regain what they felt was originally forcefully taken from them.

Need to Love and Be Loved. For other therapists we find that the basic motivation is a need to be needed or loved. Usually they are trying to compensate for unconscious feelings of worthlessness precipitated by the fact that they were not valued by their parents. As a consequence they have come to see themselves as valueless and unlovable. They recognize intuitively that by being nice to emotionally disturbed children they will receive in return affection from these children, which the therapist can then use as confirmation for the fact that he really is lovable after all. To help a child grow and mature also provides many therapists with the satisfying feeling that they are needed and useful, and therefore not as worthless as they originally felt they were. We find that for some therapists there is the added gratification of gaining a sense of immortality which comes from their feeling that through their influence on the child a part of them will live on in the child. This is especially true for those who can see no prospect of ever having any children of their own or of having children of a specific sex with whom they can identify.

Some therapists identify with these deprived children and then attempt to provide them with the kind of affection, nurture, gratification, and the like that the therapist missed in his own childhood. They thus become their "own idealized parent." We have frequently seen this as the basic psychodynamic in some cases of homosexuality(4) in which the love for the younger person of the same sex is really a love for himself as a child. At the same time, he is simultaneously providing to himself the supply of missed gratification by being the good and nurturing parent that one never had as a child. It should be noted that these relationships are often asexual in nature. The giving and receiving of love and affection per se is the *raison d'être* for the relationship. There are some therapists with unconscious pedophilic tendencies and the psychodynamics here are quite similar.

For other therapists their most frustrated need has been finding some one they could love. They have enormous needs for physical intimacy which they feel can be expressed safely only with children. When they themselves were children they, in all likelihood, tried to love their parents but received rejection in return for their love. This hurt them severely and caused them to erect a barrier against ever getting close and loving someone. Their reasoning is that if one loves or admits needing someone, one is vunerable to getting hurt. They come to feel that disturbed children are a relatively safe object for this pent-up need to love, for these children are not likely to reject them because they themselves have a great need to be loved. Many therapists are also frightened at the prospect of loving adults because of latent homosexual fears in loving adult members of the same sex, or fear of loss of control of sexual impulses in loving members of the opposite sex. Thus, children for them become a safer love object.

Inwardly, many of these therapists have come to doubt their capacity for loving because they have not felt free to express their love for so long a period of time. They desperately need to have someone respond to their loving in order to prove that their capacity for love is real. Children serve as the best object for this need because of their great need to be loved.

Fear of Adults.   There are some therapists who still see themselves in some ways as children, and there are others who for some other reason are frightened of relating to adults. For example, because of their own unresolved castration anxiety, they are frightened of adults and can feel comfortable only with children who do not represent as great a threat in this regard. Many of these therapists are allied with children against the adult world and frequently, as a part of their countertransference, will attempt to punish the parents of the child with whom they are working in an attempt to retaliate against their own parents.

Related to this type of therapist is the one who prefers to work with children rather than adults because he rejects his own feelings of helpless dependency and yearns to be on the dominant side of a relationship. As a child, this kind of therapist has longed to reverse the vulnerability he has felt as a consequence of being intimidated by very powerful and controlling parents. He has said to himself, in essence, "When I grow up I'm going to make sure that I'm on top. No one will ever dominate me again." Because he can more readily feel superior to children, he chooses to work with them.

Guilt.   We have also observed that for many child therapists one of the primary reasons which leads them to choose this as a career is the need to undo some guilt, real or fantasied, in regard to their own child or their own sibling. Some feel guilty because their own children have not turned out well and they are seeking another chance. They want to undo the wrongs they feel they have done, or they just need to feel they really do have the capacity to be loving to a child. In other instances, the undoing of guilt relates to one of their own siblings; for example, "I was nasty to my baby brother and he died. In order to feel relieved of my guilt I must make up for this somehow, perhaps by giving my love to some child who is severely deprived." For other therapists, just the reverse is true. Wanting to give "love" to children is just a reaction formation concealing their real hostility toward children, and especially a younger sibling. Very often, the hostility was never expressed in the past when it might have been appropriate to do so. The risk of attacking the preferred child at home was too great and represented potential rejection by the parents. Usually these dynamics are quite unconscious. The therapist will rationalize his punitive behavior toward his child patient in terms of the importance of setting strict limits, or he may not at all recognize how his remarks or behavior are hurting the child. Under these circumstances, the child can become the therapist's whipping boy.

In a great many therapists, regardless of whether they are male or female, we have found an unconscious need to play the role of the nurturing mother. When it occurs in males the basic dynamic is usually that they have identified very strongly with their own mothers and are unconsciously very envious of the female's capacity to give birth and create. For some reason, these males are relatively blocked in the utilization of artistic areas for the sublimation of this creative urge. The unconscious fantasy is that when the new healthy child emerges out of the formerly disturbed child, the therapist feels much like a mother who has just given birth.

The above discussion of the various motivations for choosing child psychotherapy as a career should not be interpreted as implying that there are no healthy and mature reasons for making such a choice. It should be readily apparent that many may choose to become psychotherapists with children as a consequence of resolving and sublimating their conflicts and as such their choice would represent a nonneurotic decision.

Essential Personality Characteristics for the Therapist with Children

In view of the fact that in the psychotherapy interaction with children we have persons at two different levels of maturity—that is, one is a child and one is an adult—there is almost bound to be some problem in communication between the two.

Ability to Communicate. The differences between a child and adult are more than just chronological years. The adult tends to find that the use of words, concepts, and logic are his most natural mode of communication. For the child that is not so. The child tends to be much less verbal and much more primitive in his thought processes. The younger the child, the more pronounced will be this mode of communication.

In Freudian terms we would say that the adult is more secondary-process oriented, whereas the child is more primary-process oriented. It then becomes very clear that if the adult therapist is too divorced from his own primary-process operation he will find communication with, and comprehension of, the child's world to be very difficult. Many therapists, because of their need to defend against certain of their own repressed impulses and affects, will be very much on guard against, and will greatly fear the return of, any repressed material. This need to divorce themselves from their own unconscious or primary-process operation will guarantee a very low tolerance for such material in their own functioning and in that of the child. The therapist cannot hope to understand his child patient with awareness which impinge only on his cognitive self. Greatly cut off from his own unconscious, he cannot possibly then be sensitive to cues emanating from the child at that level. The best he will be able to do is know *about* the child, but he will not know the child through more immediate experience. Where this guarded intolerance for primary-process material exists, the only solution, in our estimation, is a personal psychotherapeutic experience for the therapist. Otherwise this material will probably never become available to him and his capacity to be sensitive to his child patient will be greatly limited.

Where the therapist is so guarded against his unconscious, there will also be discrepancies between what he values and is trying to achieve at an unconscious level, and that which exists at the conscious level. This division can eventuate in his being inconsistent in his encounters with the child. It is then possible that, like the schizophrenogenic parent, he will be communicating to the child conflicting messages which are likely to make the child more confused and disturbed. Without being internally and externally consistent, the therapist will be unable to serve as a source of security to the child. For example, a therapist on the one hand may try to communicate to the child an attitude of tolerance and acceptance of the child's hostility. The therapist's need to defend against the expression of his own hostility will also communicate to the child that such acceptance and tolerance is not real. This confuses the child and is likely to result in his becoming more anxious.

Maturity. The child therapist also needs to have an ego-syntonic tolerance for his own dependency needs and immaturities. These needs exist in almost everyone to some degree. If they are repressed or are ego-dystonic, the therapist will not find it easy to accept the child's more normal dependency and immaturities. Without his awareness, he will likely try to coerce the child to outgrow these needs before the child is really ready to give them up or should give them up.

For the therapist to be comfortable with children and they with him, he should be relatively mature both sexually and emotionally. This real maturity enables him to regress or meet the child at the child's level, when this is necessary, without its being a severe blow to his adult self-image. The child needs to be able to identify with the therapist's mature ego so that he may eventually be able to relinquish the pleasure principle for the more mature reality principle. If the therapist himself is not mature, the child will not be able to effect this change.

If the therapist is confused in regard to his own identity or worth, he will find it very difficult to maintain a clear objective reality of his own. Without this, he will in all likelihood overreact to a child's negative or positive transference and see it instead as a real reaction to himself rather than, perhaps, what he represents to the child. For example, if the therapist has repressed much of what is unacceptable in himself, he will unconsciously see himself as bad or no good. Therefore if, as a function of the negative transference, the child should get angry with the therapist, the latter will feel personally hurt and will be unable to detach himself and objectively recognize that perhaps this is how the child needs to react to adult authority or parental figures.

Empathy. In view of the fact, as mentioned earlier, that the young child is not primarily verbal, psychotherapy with children hinges to a great degree upon the relationship established between child and therapist. Thus, it is essential that the therapist be able to relate well. He must be naturally warm and not contrivedly so. It is our impression that cognitive knowledge of the therapy process is not sufficient for the practice of psychotherapy with children. The therapist's personality and natural faculties are equally, if not more, important. Success in therapy with children depends as much, if not more, on what the therapist *is* than on what he *does*. This holds true for parents as well, and is the reason why just giving advice to parents on how to react to their child in specific situations is rather meaningless. The warm parent does not have to be told how to be affectionate to the child, and the unaffectionate parent can not be told how to be affectionate. Affection is an affect and not a cognition and cannot be grasped or expressed cognitively. One cannot direct or teach another how to feel.

To discuss this natural faculty for therapy a bit more, we see it as being very similar to that possessed by those we call natural teachers. They have what we like to refer to as strong impact value. We see them as therapeutic personalities whether or not they are therapists by profession. Something nice happens to us when we are with them. They have a capacity to instill in others a feeling of comfort and security without really trying to achieve this as a deliberate goal. This person has an easy empathic capacity which is immediately sensed as genuine. He is comfortable with himself, and this self-acceptance and comfort readily communicates itself to the child, who intuitively recognizes that this person can genuinely accept him too. There is a warmth that emanates from this person—that glows and radiates from within. This transcends the therapist and "warms" the child. This therapist feels himself to be an authentic person rather than a role player or technician who really feels empty and confused. He has a clear objective reality, identity, and value system without being rigid. He knows who he is and what he wants. This clarity is communicated to the child and is translated into a feeling of security and protective strength upon which the child can lean and gain support should he need it. It provides the child with the security he has never experienced—a necessary security by which he can now take a chance and try new behaviors, experiment with new attitudes, experience new feelings, and so forth. In other words, this kind of experience provides the child with the climate conducive to change and growth.

It is our contention that the personality of this kind of therapist cannot readily be developed or brought about by deliberate conscious effort. It is often found in those who have received consistent and warm loving as a child along with some frustrations and hardships which have made negative experiences a reality, all of which later makes possible easy identification and genuine empathic capacity. This empathic therapist is someone who has experienced problems and conflicts but has worked them out and now is eager for all children to achieve the comfort and growth that he has experienced.

There are many therapists who, under the guise of maturity and objectivity, relate with children in a rather emotionally detached fashion. Children will intuitively recognize this as a defense against involvement and will usually bait the therapist, by continuous provocative behavior, into an expression of genuine feeling, usually hostility. Although to be too detached in one's relationship to the child is not conducive to therapeutic growth, neither is overidentification. In overidentification, the absence of some objective detachment will make it very difficult for the child to see himself as separate and distinct from the therapist and will militate against the process that helps the child mature and become less dependent and more autonomous. When the therapist becomes, himself, involved in the patient's emotions, he supports the infantile fixations instead of helping promote growth and maturity by fostering individuation and autonomy.

The therapist has to be able to be empathic in regard to the child's deprivations and suffering without he himself suffering or being overly affected. If he cannot, the child will become frightened because he will feel that he has caused the therapist to be unhappy, that he is very bad to have done so, and that he therefore must avoid ever expressing his discomfort to the therapist again. The child is also likely to feel that "this therapist is not strong enough to protect me—he cannot even protect himself from himself or me. I must protect him instead. I will tell him only nice things so he will not get upset." This places much too much responsibility on the child.

Detachment (what we mean is objective emotional separation—clear boundary distinctions) enables the therapist to be sensitive to what is going on within the child rather than to himself. Empathy therefore requires some degree of detachment.

The role of empathy should not be minimized in the process of psychotherapy with children, for we feel it is the basic ingredient in producing within the child a state of receptivity to what it is that we would like to accomplish with him. We feel that the importance of receptivity is all too often overlooked as a crucial aspect of the child's permitting himself to grow in any area. In school we find that regardless of how able a teacher may be, she will be ineffective in her teaching unless the child is receptive to learning. Many mothers have discovered the same thing in trying to toilet-train their children. If the child is not receptive to making the change from soiling in his pants to defecating in a potty, the mother is in for a very difficult time. We see the importance of receptivity even more clearly portrayed in the instance of the placebo effect. When the person is receptive to a change within himself this takes place, even if the "drug" that is offered to him is essentially sugar water. By the same token, we know that a drug may be ineffective with some persons because for some reason they are not receptive to it. For example, giving a laxative to a constipated child who refuses to defecate because of unconscious needs to defeat the mother he feels is trying to overpower him, will usually prove ineffective. Thus, we feel that without receptivity on the part of the child, no therapeutic change is possible, and without empathic communication between therapist and patient it is likely that there will be no receptivity. The therapist helps to achieve this state of receptivity in the child as a result of his capacity to relate warmly and genuinely to the child. It is our contention that this capacity for relationship is the personality characteristic probably most essential for becoming an effective psychotherapist with children.

REFERENCES

1. Festinger, L.   A theory of cognitive dissonance. New York: Harper & Row, 1957.
2. Freud, S.   The basic writings of Sigmund Freud. New York: Modern Library, 1938.
3. Goldstein, K.   Human nature in the light of psychopathology. Cambridge, Mass.: Harvard University Press, 1947.
4. Hammer, Max. Homosexuality in a women's reformatory. Corrective Psychiat. 1965, 11(3):168–69.
5. Klein, Melanie.   The psycho-analysis of children. London: Hogarth Press, 1932.
6. Piaget, J.   The origins of intelligence in children. New York: International Universities Press, 1952.
7. Slavson, S. R.   Child psychotherapy. New York: Columbia University Press, 1952.

2

Richard Silberstein

Treatment of
Learning Difficulties

LEARNING DISABILITY is one of the earliest, commonest, most sensitive indicators of psychiatric difficulty in children. A discussion of the entire diagnostic basis for disability in childhood learning would necessarily include the entire field of child psychiatry, so broad is this area, so varied and interrelated are the symptoms. Since the present discussion is limited to one chapter in a book, it would seem wise here to concentrate on those areas most commonly met and associated with learning difficulties in children, and to deal with the dynamics and treatment of those particular problems. Moreover, reading disability is representative of all learning difficulty, and an understanding of the normal processes of learning to read is essential, not only to the understanding of the treatment of that disability, but all learning difficulties.

DIFFICULTIES IN LEARNING TO READ

Learning to read draws upon all of the early libidinal drives of a child. It also includes the aggressive, competitive drive components. In the experience of taking in, of absorbing, reading encompasses the oral drive area. The qualities of curiosity, intellectuality, and "seeking-to-look" which are necessary to reading, are associated with the anal period of development. Further, the first reading experience incorporates the ambition and striving-for-prominence which represents the phallic period. Reading is also dependent upon effective sexual identifications that are associated with the oedipal period of the child's life. Reading itself is also a late ego function. It is associated with the ego defense of sublimation, and all of the processes that go into sublimation and conscience formation are necessary in order for reading to take place.

Critical Factors in Reading Skill

A variety of circumstances are crucial to learning to read. First, reading occurs as an expression of love or affection for the person who is teaching, and without a fondness or regard for the teacher, no person can learn from another person. Secondly, reading is one of many competitive drive outlets for a child. In the usual healthy classroom situation, reading skills are enhanced by competition among children as well as striving for greater teacher approval. Third, reading is an avenue for the satisfaction of curiosity. When you see a child beginning to learn to read, he is interested in knowing about the process itself. He is interested in discovering the nature of the contents of books. Reading is a way in which the average child can have his curiosity satisfied independently, without going to another person or an adult. We see this quite early in the normal child who looks through books to see pictures and is intrigued by them. Reading in children is also a satisfaction, then, of scoptophilic wishes, interest in peeking and seeing, in discovery. In particular it is a gratification of sexual curiosity (for example, the five- or six-year-old child who discovers an anatomy book and eagerly peers through the book to learn the difference between sexes). Reading also gratifies exhibitionistic wishes. The child in class will normally stand up to read. He will demonstrate to his teacher that he is capable of reading effectively and well, and will show off by means of this new skill.

Reading is also a normal technique of pleasing parents, since it gratifies the parents' interest and pleasure in the child's intellectual advancement. Skill in reading may also be a means of displacing, or equaling, the other siblings in the family. Older children are often stimulated to learn to read by their wish to do something the younger children cannot do. Or one sees young children very interested in progressing with their reading because they want to do as well as their older sibling. Reading also is a duty because it is a process which satisfies the superego or conscience. Therefore, there are children who force themselves to read because it gratifies the feeling of comfort which comes from following adult wishes or adult instruction. There are, then, a series of critical factors of internal psychology involved in the process of learning to read. Reading skill is sensitive to any upheaval or disturbance of these critical factors.

In addition to these factors, the general development of the child must be normal, and the premonitors of sublimation must be present. There are also a series of necessary interactions between internal and external factors which are prerequisites for learning. It is necessary for the average child to have a period of gratification at each level of development, at each phase of development. It is also necessary for that gratification to be frustrated to some degree in order for reading to take place. At the oral level, it is necessary for a child to have a normal feeding experience, a normal relationship with his mother, in order for him to have normal oral interests. It is also necessary that these oral activities be frustrated to some degree if the child is to be able to sublimate those interests and to turn them into another channel. It is necessary for a child to have some opportunity for expression of anal interest during the anal period, in order for him to utilize anal drives. It is equally necessary for these impulses to be partially frustrated in order to be turned into other directions. And so it goes.

In addition to these conditions of gratification, and later frustration related to sublimation, it is a requisite for the child to have parental permission to proceed with the development of a sublimation, and it is necessary for him to have an *opportunity* to learn a skill. And in the learning areas in which we are interested, it is also necessary for a child to have competent and adequate instruction plus the opportunities to read and to learn. Finally, there is a synthetic function involved in the reading process by means of which a child is able to take a symbol, reconvert that symbol into a picture, and then reconvert that picture into an output such as writing or speech. A complicated, organic, associative process is necessary for learning to take place, and an intact organic mechanism—that is, an intact cerebrum—is also a necessity. Now, we can divide the entire discussion of the treatment of learning difficulties into the organic versus the functional learning disability.

Organic Learning Difficulty

Fortunately, a great deal of time, energy, and interest has been devoted to a study of the organic basis for reading difficulty. Probably the best known of these studies was done in 1926 by Orton(3), who indicated that reading disability was related to right- and left-handedness, that is to cerebral dominance, and he described a difficulty called *strephosymbolia*. One can't discuss learning difficulties without discussing this. Strephosymbolia is mirror-reading. Strephosymbolia is also a part of the process of normal reading development. When beginners write their E's like this, 𝟥 , and their S's like this, ᴢ , you can read these correctly with the use of a mirror. Dr. Orton said this process of mirror-writing, or mirror-reading, called strephosymbolia, was related to cerebral dominance and showed itself also in right-to-left reading, rather than the usual left-to-right reading. These children also have trouble with p's, d's, b's, n's, (q,b,d,n) and so forth.

Some 11 years later, Arthur I. Gates(2) discovered that there was no relationship between cerebral dominance and strephosymbolia, and demonstrated this statistically. At present we feel that strephosymbolia is related to a disturbance in maturation of a *psychological* nature, and that it tends to respond to psychological treatment rather than to organic treatment. There are other related types of childhood learning difficulty which were once thought to be organic. For example, a child will read the word "was" as the word "saw," if he is reading from right to left rather than from left to right. This is a very common difficulty which, along with many related, allegedly organic, problems now seems to be psychological in its nature, and to be based upon two factors. One factor is disturbed early teaching, such as an attempt to switch a child from sight-reading technique to phonetic technique. The second is the disturbance in attention or concentration which is related to a vast number of difficulties, although not specific to any one. These seem, in general, to relate to the motivation of the child, and involve conflicts concerning the process of reading and learning itself.

In describing organic learning difficulty, it is enough to say that in all organic learning difficulties there is either some specific or some general area of cerebral cortical damage. We see learning difficulty in a variety of congenital, hereditary, and acquired neurological illnesses, and we find varieties of learning difficulties in every type of organic illness affecting the cortex, from epilepsy, to postencephalitis, to cerebral trauma. These illnesses can be acute or they can be chronic. While they are acute we do nothing with the associated learning disturbance, the associated aphasias, or other associated signs of neurological difficulty. When they are chronic, however, when the acute process has subsided, remedial instruction, efforts to motivate and reteach a youngster, can be an enormous help. These efforts assist the child in finding and developing undamaged, and previously unused, nerve pathways which can enable the child to speak, to learn to read, to learn to do arithmetic, and to learn acquired skills, even though he has lost these as a result of organic damage. All the basic factors essential to normal learning are also essential to the process of instructing a brain-damaged child in learning new skills, or learning the reacquisition of skills previously lost. The factors already discussed are as essential for the child with organic difficulty, in order for him to learn adequately, as they are for the undamaged child, the child who has had no organic difficulty. The person who is undertaking remedial reading, remedial arithmetic, or any instructional techniques with brain-damaged children, would do well to be acquainted with the treatment of the problems which interfere with normal learning processes in order that he may deal adequately with pathology resulting from brain damage.

Mental Retardation

There is a large category of learning difficulty relating to mental retardation. Mental retardation is a "catch-all" term encompassing a large number of diseases, some known and some unknown. It is classified according to degrees of intellectual deficiency, and is measured on standard tests. In contrast to the other organic causes of learning disability that we have discussed, mental retardation is diffuse rather than localized, and we always see I.Q. reduction in such children. Quite often mentally retarded children can be taught learning skills, depending on the severity of the brain damage, even if they cannot be taught the understanding that a better endowed child may acquire. I believe, in contrast to other authorities, that you can teach skills to children who possess much lower I.Q.'s than are presently thought teachable.[1] There are dozens and dozens of causes of mental retardation, as there are dozens and dozens of causes of specific brain damage. If there is an underlying organic disease present, the initial proper approach to the child's problem is, of course, to provide medical treatment. The special psychological treatment necessary for children who are mentally retarded usually includes placing them in a stimulating, but at the same time noncompetitive, environment. In so doing, you tend to reduce the effect of the I.Q. difference from normal children, which tends to discourage retarded children in normal classes in their attempt to satisfy their competitive urges. Placing these children in sheltered situations in special classes tends to enhance their ability to learn because they can satisfy the

---

[1] Retarded children are subject to the psychological trauma of institutionalization, disturbance in family pattern, and less refined teaching skills, all of which would cause severe learning disturbances in a child of normal intelligence.

normal competitive and aggressive drives associated with the normal development of learning skills, without having these crushed by undue or excessive competition.

Psychotherapy with organically damaged children, as well as retarded children, centers on (1) the elimination of secondary gain; (2) the investigation of defeatist tendencies resulting from past failures; (3) the investigation of fantasies concerning the cause and manifestation of physical limitations and the making conscious of these ideas through interpretation; and (4) an investigation of ideas relating to body image. These investigations are utilized to unearth pathological or restricting defenses so that a child may utilize his real abilities with a knowledge of his limitations. Psychotherapeutic assistance is often of great supportive value to organically damaged children.

Functional Learning Difficulty

Most learning difficulties, however, are functional. Psychotherapy is of greatest value in children with functional learning disability. Functional learning difficulties are also acute and chronic. Any psychological crisis or period of intense psychological distress in normal children usually results in temporary learning disability. Psychological first aid directed toward the cause of the distress is generally indicated. If the first aid is successful, and the source of the distress is not permanent, or if the stressful situation does not dovetail with the child's already existent problems, further intervention may not be necessary. If these conditions are not fulfilled, however, the learning problem becomes chronic, and extensive psychological intervention is often necessary.

The paradox of the treatment of chronic learning difficulties centers around society's anticipation of continued learning progress in a normal child. Not only must a child with a learning difficulty catch up to the learning plateau expected from him at the time treatment began, he must maintain current progress as well. The problems allowing a child to avoid promotion are so numerous and so involved that such a decision is made reluctantly and only after a thorough review of the numerous factors present in an individual situation.

TREATMENT OF DISTURBANCES IN EARLY OBJECT RELATIONSHIPS

Normal ego development is dependent upon adequate early environmental stimulation of an infant as well as the presence of a single consistent mothering person in the child's life. Any failure in these requirements, whether the failure is due to circumstances around the child or to accidents of "fate" such as prolonged physical illness of the child, results in one of a series of syndromes associated with learning disability. These syndromes require similar types of treatment and include institutionalism, hospitalism, anaclitic depression, as well as the residue of all severe early social deprivation. These are the disturbances in ability to relate to people often seen in children who have very early or very disturbed object relationships. Such children show classical findings when they are examined. They have a very spotty ability to learn so that they may have learned beyond their age in one particular area, and nothing at all in another area. Classically these children have difficulty in being able to mark the important temporal periods which are generally significant to the child raised under normal circumstance. To these children their ages, their birthdays, the seasons of the year, the times of day (particularly the ability to tell time), the months of the year, the months in which important holidays of our culture appear—such as Christmas, Thanksgiving, Fourth of July—are without significance. These symptoms indicate a disturbance in stimulation which occurred from outside, and are a sign of the difficulty in relating to people, and in people relating to them, that these children have experienced.

As is the case in child psychiatry in general, diagnosis is suggested by the history. These children are deceptive in diagnostic interviews, and we often do not understand the severity of their disturbances until after they are in psychotherapy. A youngster may be in psychological treatment, or in therapy, for some period of time before an understanding is gained of the etiology of the child's illness. When these children come to treatment they relate to the doctor very warmly, very affectionately, very easily in their first or second interview. It is almost as if they have to decide that they are in a position to win you over, or to woo you. As soon as they have decided (and this occurs in the first or second interview) that they have won you, you get nothing from them from that point on. The interviews then become sterile, barren, difficult to conduct, and hard to understand. The child tells you little about his own life because his real obligation is not to adult figures. The adult figures who, up to this point in his life, have been important to him, have deserted him. Also, if these children are institutionalized, they have little real control or knowledge of their own lives.

The important figures in the lives of these children are their peers. They are, by and large, peer-related children. In order to carry on psychotherapeutic treatment for the child with a learning difficulty in an institution, it is necessary that his peers have a favorable opinion of the therapist, just as it is important in the treatment of the child who is living in a normal family to have his family think well of you if you are to conduct your treatment satisfactorily.

In the treatment of children who have been very disturbed early in life, it is necessary first to be able to correct the immediate disturbances in his environment, to be able to stabilize his life so that it is not changing from day to day. The child cannot realistically anticipate a recurrence of the past difficulty he has experienced and, at the same time, feel confidence in those significant and important people in his current life. That is why a psychiatrist in an institution is often able to conduct more successful treatment if he lives on the grounds of the institution, especially if he relates well to the children in the group, if he has some way of inducing the children to want his friendship and good will, and if he has some skill with which he can win their admiration. Under these circumstances he may find it easier to conduct individual treatment of a child with a learning difficulty. This is a paradox, for under ordinary circumstances psychotherapists with children avoid real responsibility for discipline and the manipulation of day-to-day events in the lives of their patients. These responsibilities are purely parental, and a therapist's role becomes confused, both for the child and the therapist, under most circumstances, when this line is not drawn. This rule does not apply to institutionalized children. The therapist of an institutionalized child must be able to prove his *real* value to the child if the therapy is to be effective.

Children who have anaclitic depressions, or who suffer from institutionalism, and have early disturbances in object relations, are also said to do well in group therapy because these children gain motivation from the group. They are able to put into effect some of the normal strivings for group approval occurring in normal children under normal circumstances. In direct individual treatment of children suffering from anaclitic depression, or from institutionalism, one avoids a depth investigation, a depth interpretation, or a dynamic investigation of this youngster's life for a long time. It is best to wait until the child begins to introduce subjects. Most of these children feel that they are bad, guilty, evil people. If they were not bad, evil, or guilty, according to the way they think and according to the way they feel, God would not have treated them so badly. Therefore, these children are not children who will readily tell you their "aims," and it is a long time before you hear their thoughts. For the therapist to introduce the subject of their early life, or for the therapist to attempt in other ways to investigate the depth and dynamic nature of learning difficulties in these children tends to make these children threatened and resistant. They do not understand the nature of the investigation, and so they feel they are being accused. The prognosis in these children is good, for the long pull. Ultimately, most of these children are able to learn. Unfortunately, they are six or seven years behind their colleagues in learning, so generally they do not manage to get through our culture's usual type of schooling without early, specific help. In fact, without skillful, effective remedial assistance based upon a good relationship between therapist and child, in which the therapist uses his active interest and good relationship with the child to motivate the development of learning skills, those skills are long delayed and stunted when they do appear.

> *Example:*   Douglas T. was a fraternal twin in an orphanage. He was referred for psychotherapy because of violent tempers and "vicious" behavior. He suffered from a severe learning disturbance, his initial full-scale I.Q. was 68, with a wide discrepancy between his verbal and performance abilities. He loved his psychotherapeutic sessions, changed his behavior drastically, abandoned his impulsiveness, and became friendly and warm within a few months of starting treatment. His learning difficulty persisted, however. The institution maintained Douglas' treatment even though it was expensive because they feared a recurrence of his "viciousness." One day Douglas told his therapist, "You are so good and I am so bad, I don't deserve to see you." Sporadically, from then on, Douglas investigated his fantasies about his institutionalization. With this investigation he achieved confidence in his therapist. On a nonverbal level, he recognized his therapist's interest in learning skills, finally bringing his school work to his therapist for review. At the conclusion of therapy, Douglas had a full-scale I.Q. of 92.

There are many variations on the theme of the understimulated child and the child who suffered early maternal deprivation. The clinical problem seen in psychotherapy is similar in all of these children.

TREATMENT OF DISTURBANCE IN PHASE DEVELOPMENT

Disturbances in phase development often result in learning difficulties. Consequently, reading difficulties are seen at all levels in phase development. While treatment is directed toward limiting direct body satisfaction, and encouraging sublimation, specific techniques vary according to the fixation involved.

Disturbances at the Oral Level

We are often called upon to treat disturbances of phase development in which the child remains attached at an oral level. Because of this fixation, the child is gratifying his oral feeling directly, and his orality is of more importance to him than are other types of gratifications which are necessary to the development of learning. The child gratifies himself with his oral interest and does not develop adequate sublimated interest in learning. While there are many types of children who have this particular difficulty, the commonest is the obese child. This is the youngster who always has chewing gum in her mouth, who always has a bag of potato chips in her hand, and who is very much involved in the direct gratification of oral impulses in a way which interferes with the process of sublimation.

The old-time schoolteachers, you may recall, did not allow children to suck lollipops in class, did not allow children to chew gum in class, did not allow the direct expression of oral need in class, because the old-time schoolteacher said these things were a distraction, and interfered with the child's ability to concentrate on his learning. Then, or now, such activities pull away the child's energies in a way which interferes with the child's ability to learn. This is true of the child who is obese, and whose obesity is associated with learning difficulty. This is a disturbance in the oral phase development. In order for this type of disturbance to develop (eliminating those unusual cases based on hormonal difficulty), it is necessary for parental permission of the child's activity to have continued and not to have been withdrawn. In these children we often see disturbances in early feeding relationships between mother and child, followed by a continued gratification of the child's oral impulses by the parents and, in fact, a need on the part of the parents to see the child so gratified. The child is pleasing the parent by eating rather than by learning. If this is to be treated effectively, it is necessary that the joint satisfaction mother and child give each other, as it relates to food, be interfered with and broken.

The treatment of this type of learning disturbance always involves the active participation of the parent. Parental assistance is necessary in the treatment of most children, but is particularly needed here. The insight of the parent is as important as the insight of the child. It is not only necessary that the child's continued direct oral gratification be terminated; it is also necessary that the child be given positive motivation making it possible for him to secure gratification, affection, regard, and admiration from society, from parents, and from the therapist, as a result of learning activities rather than for being a nice baby "who ate up all the cereal." Two factors—(1) interference with the original primitive impulse (pregenital impulse) along with (2) the addition of positive motivations, both through parent counselling and through direct relationship between therapist and child—are necessary for the treatment of obese children.

Another related difficulty, with a similar etiology, is not so clear-cut, nor as specific, nor so easily investigated. We see a certain number of thumb-sucking children who are getting direct oral gratification from the use of their thumb, and who are just as happy to sit in class sucking their thumbs as they might be to learn from a book. They get their comfort and gratification from thumb-sucking rather than from learning. In those cases the etiology is similar to the obese child. The treatment is related. It is necessary to interfere with the activity, and then to supply positive motivation. The old-time schoolteachers knew this and said, "Stop sucking your thumb. Take your thumb out of your mouth." They said it interfered with learning, and it does. Nonetheless, these are children for whom both the food and the thumb-sucking are necessary for their psychological integrity. Parental interference with oral activities in these children either results in frightening psychopathology, or in defiance. Prolonged investigative psychotherapy resulting in insight seems preferable for these children, since insight often allows the child to abandon his orality in favor of defenses more favorable to the development of learning skills.

The old-time schoolteacher had another difficulty. There are a number of children in whom thumb-sucking is associated with regression. They were not thumb-suckers from birth. They fell back to thumb-sucking as an escape from, or an expression of, neurotic conflicts. These children do not respond well to a direct interference in their oral activities. They require investigative treatment to understand the sources or causes of their regression to thumb-sucking. In these cases, active intervention tends to do some damage to the relationship between the therapist and child. There are dozens of other types of difficulties in which the etiology is similar to obesity or thumb-sucking, and which are specific examples of a disturbance in oral phase development. It is necessary to be able to divide these cases into groups to determine the etiology before we can decide on treatment.

Disturbances at the Anal Level

There are a series of reading disturbances associated with disturbances in the anal phase or in the toilet-training period. There are children who have an opportunity to directly express aggressive drives, especially anal drives. In the first type you see the fairly common problem of a child whose mother has difficulty in disciplining him. These children may be hyperactive, yell out in class, may not be able to sit still, may get up and move around the room, and may walk across the room and touch other students. This young patient is very direct and candid in the playroom. He tells you what is wrong with your office and the way in which you handle your practice, decides you're either too old or too young or something else, feels compulsion in appropriating the play materials in the playroom, does not apologize if he breaks a toy which is attractive to him, may break a toy purposely.

These are children who are uncontrolled by their parents, and whose parents may derive pleasure and gratifiaction from the aggressive expressions of the child, particularly if the parents are in rebellion against their own memories of their own parents. They are, then, partially living out, through their child, the satisfactions they would enjoy were they young again. Anally fixated children are manageable psychotherapeutically only if you have the active cooperation of their parents, and only if their parents are aware of the opposing impulses within themselves which make it difficult to treat the child. It is often wisest to take the parents into a counselling relationship, or some type of discussion relationship with the therapist, for a period of time sufficient for the parent to gain insight into the nature of the parental role in the child's inability to be disciplined or controlled. This results in the most effective form of treatment, and quite often the youngster who suffers from disciplinary difficulty responds without any further direct treatment. If the mother is successful in indicating her disapproval of the way her child behaves, and curtails his active acting-out aggression, he can then settle down long enough to be able to learn. Remember that in the experience of normal reading and learning, it is necessary for gratification to take place, and also for frustration to take place. Without frustrating the child's direct aggressive drives or wishes, the youngster is not going to be able to sublimate, and is not going to be able to acquire adequate learning skills regardless of his native intelligence.

Similar to the disturbance in oral phase development we find a number of disturbances in which anal drives are directly expressed, such as children who are soiling, or children who are anal masturbators. This type of disturbance may have a vast number of etiologies. You may be dealing with a problem as complicated as that of a psychotic child, or as simple a problem as the child who is untrained. You may be dealing with a neurotic child. It is important to be able to distinguish the child who is untrained, or the child who has had inadequate limits set, from the child who is using soiling or direct anal expressions as an accompaniment to a more complicated type of intrapsychic difficulty. In these cases, an early period of exploratory treatment of the youngster, and a rather prolonged investigation of the history and parental attitudes, may contribute enough knowledge about the etiology of the soiling to enable the therapist to focus the treatment. By so doing, it is possible to shorten the period of treatment and make it more efficient and more effective.

Disturbances at the Phallic Level

We have a similar situation in children with disturbances in phallic phase development, and here we see children who directly express exhibitionistic and aggressive drives in such a way that they are not able to proceed with a learning experience. They are not interested in the learning experience itself, but only in demonstrating to their teacher how highly regarded they are. Quite often these children develop neurotic types of learning difficulties because they are so sensitive to the repression of exhibitionistic drives and are so easily discouraged when this drive is inhibited. A conversion of a phallic phase difficulty into a neurotic difficulty is often preferable because, in neurotic difficulties (as opposed to phase disturbances) children experience dissatisfaction with themselves and do not project their difficulty onto the world around them. Accordingly, they are more easily treated. Some parental restriction of bragging and boasting may be enough to produce the change. Quite often the teacher herself accomplishes this without any parental involvement, if she has a good enough relationship with the child.

Also, there is the enuretic child whose expression of anal and phallic drive is uncurtailed by the parents. That is, he is not toilet trained. He needs to be trained in order to assist him in acquiring the defense of sublimation. Children who are enuretic from birth (persistent enuretics) quite often recover from learning difficulties on the basis of training alone. The persistent enuretic must be distinguished from the regressed enuretic who may be neurotic, or may be showing enuresis as a sign of psychosis. In these children it is necessary to determine the type of illness. At the Staten Island Mental Health Center we have treated a number of persistent enuretics with only an electric training device. In a large number of these children this seems to be sufficient, not only to curtail the enuresis, but to avoid the development of any other types of symptoms. These children appear to learn better and, in fact, their learning appears to be enhanced following the curtailment of their enuresis. Earlier, while they were still enuretic, there tended to be a large number of learning difficulties among these children.

Difficulties in the Oedipal Phase

We also see learning disturbance resulting from difficulties in the oedipal phase. During the normal oedipal phase, children wish to please parents of the opposite sex and identify with parents of the same sex. Many variations of difficulty during this phase can occur. The commonest is the refusal of the child to learn, for fear of competing with the beloved parent of the same sex. Such youngsters must have an opportunity to discuss their fears, and the disguised ramifications of their fears, in psychotherapy. Unless such children are given the opportunity to compare their fears of competition with the true facts, their learning difficulties become chronic and spread to other aspects of their lives. Similarly, child guidance clinics commonly see some children who are sexually overstimulated and whose oedipal desires are gratified by parents of the opposite sex. The gratification is almost always an unconscious act on the parent's part. Interpretation to these parents, leading to more appropriate behavior on their part, is often sufficient to correct the situation. When parental overstimulation stops, acquisition of learning skills occurs quite readily in many such youngsters. As often as not, psychotherapy for these youngsters is unnecessary. This last type of child appears to be immature and pleasure seeking and seems not to enter the latency period. With the institution of controls, normal latency period behavior appears to occur spontaneously.

Other disturbances which occur during the oedipal period would include failure of identification, poor body image, and lack of contact with adult figures who have positive interest in learning. Curiously enough, learning is generally seen (unconsciously) as a masculine attribute. This is in spite of the fact that latency period boys tend to see girls as more compliant and better learners. Boys, therefore, whose fathers are threatened by learning processes, have difficulty in accepting learning, especially from female teachers. Similarly, boys who have developed passive identification are passive also in the learning process and cannot perform well academically. The youngster who compares himself with the parent of the same sex and finds himself lacking physically in this comparison, quite often feels insufficiently endowed intellectually to be able to learn. Girls also show learning difficulty as the result of feeling inferior in comparison to boys, whom they feel are better endowed than themselves. Finally, boys with marked castration fears confuse compliance with lack of masculinity and refuse to cooperate with instructors because they see compliance as a "sissified" process. This last is particularly exaggerated when schools utilize instructional materials that are insipid or that have been "detoxified" by the removal of aggressive material.[2]

Nonetheless, learning difficulties based on these important distortions of phase development are, by and large, responsive to psychotherapy alone. It is insufficient to counsel families concerning the etiology of this type of learning difficulty, although it is also helpful. Therapists generally see this type of problem early in their work with children. It is also necessary for the child to be aware of the nature of his resistance and to bring reality testing to bear on the problem. When these types of difficulties exist, children may be as aware as their therapist of the fantasy underlying the difficulty, but remain unable to modify their behavior because the experience which has contributed to the fantasy remains unconscious.

> *Example 1:* Robert T., a Jewish boy with deeply religious parents, was the second of five children. His religious feeling consisted largely of rebellion, while his four sisters were very compliant with his family's religious observance. Robert came to therapy knowing he would not study because this was a girl's job. He ignored his father's studious devotion to religious literature. In this behavior he concealed his secret wish to be a girl like his sisters, but warded off his fear of being like them by refusing to behave like them outwardly. In psychotherapy it was necessary for Robert to separate his longing to be like his sisters from his learning behavior, and to modify both processes.

---

[2] Some researcher should someday estimate the percentage of increase in reading difficulty which has resulted from the elimination of history from the public school curriculum in the first several grades.

Example 2:   David T. lost his mother when he was five years old. As many children do, he dealt with the pain of her loss by identifying with her. He was unable to study, even though he was very interested in learning, because he felt unconsciously, "Mothers are not students." It was necessary for David to be aware of, and later to modify, his identification. In this case, his therapist's obvious interest in academic matters proved to be helpful.

Example 3:   Mark L. had an alcoholic father and a promiscuous mother. Mark looked on his father's rages at night as evidence of disagreeable masculinity. When Mark became aware that his father's rages represented weakness rather than strength (along with other matters), he became able to compete in the classroom and to participate in group sports.

Quite often disturbances in learning relating to oedipal phase difficulty are the result of neurotic resolution to these problems, or regressions to more primitive phases. These types of difficulties will be discussed separately.

Failure of Latency Development

A large number of learning difficulties are associated with the failure of the development of latency. This type of child is a very pleasant, very outgoing, very affable, nonanxious, quite direct young fellow whose history indicates that he has been exposed to direct sexual gratification of one kind or another. The gratification may have come through lack of parental modesty, or the use of the child by the parent as a direct sexual object. These children receive direct sexual satisfaction which makes it unnecessary for them to learn to read.

Example 4:   A six-and-a-half-year-old young man was quite disinterested in school (even though he had started first grade at five and a half) because he had a mistress. He had a young neighbor girl, a year older than himself, whose house he visited every day after school. Her parents were away, and these children would play with each other sexually. This young man was much more interested in the gratification he got from the neighbor girl than he was in school. He would sit in school all day waiting for the last bell to ring, and out he would dash to the girl's house, and successfully circumvent the necessity for sublimation in his life. A similar situation existed in a whole group of school children who belonged to a "sex-club" of somewhat older children. A mother gave her daughter the key to the house, and the children went to this home. There they would have sexual gratification in the afternoon, and their ability to learn went down in the process. Their school work suffered. The principal made strong complaints about this state of affairs and the group was sent to the Mental Health Clinic. It was necessary in this instance, as it always is in this problem, to restrict the direct, sexual gratification the child is having in order for learning to take place. These children have a disturbance in the development of latency, and the treatment of these children consists of parental, or adult, curtailment of the direct types of sexual gratification.

Further, there must be provision of adequate, sublimated, civilized, substitute gratifications which are as satisfying to the youngster as direct gratification. Quite often the learning problem disappears with this simple treatment alone. Unfortunately, it is frequently necessary to do a good bit of work with a child before you have enough of the child's confidence to know about sexual events which contribute to learning difficulties. Therapists are often in a dilemma when such discoveries are made. Is it better to work the matter out with the child alone, or to enlist parental support? These decisions must be made individually.

The failure to enter latency is related to failure of superego development. Failure to enter latency is related to an inability to restrict the child from direct gratification and impulse, which is one of the aspects of superego development. There are two aspects of superego development. The first is the development of the punitive portion of the superego of the child. The second is the development of an ego ideal, or standard. In circumstances where an ideal is not set by the family of the child, or where there is insufficient meaningful contact with adults in a child's life, the child is unable to develop an incorporated standard of what is expected of him so that when he meets it he is pleased, and if he fails to meet it he is displeased. Here we also find the development of learning difficulties. This most often happens in children who live in very disturbed social situations. Parents are dead, divorced, or missing. We find it in children who are institutionalized. In these cases the treatment consists of either the therapist acting as an ego ideal for the youngster (in which case the therapist makes a commitment to stay with that youngster for a number of years), or some other person in the child's life makes a similar commitment to that youngster. This sometimes can be done by a counselor or social worker in an institution. It can be done in Child Guidance clinics by personnel who plan to remain in the clinic for a long period of time. It can also be done by private therapists. These children require relationship type therapy, not investigative type therapy, and it is necessary for the therapist to make a commitment that he will stay with this youngster for a long enough period of time to establish an enduring relationship.

Pubertal Problems

In all the difficulties discussed under disturbance in phase development thus far, the difficulties exist at the time the child enters school. There are, however, a certain number of learning disturbances which children develop after entering school. One of these is the disturbance in phase development associated with puberty. In these children, one finds that the youngster has learned well, up until the time he began to develop secondary sexual characteristics. At this time the child suddenly becomes withdrawn; his marks fail. He may show the same intellectual spark shown earlier in his life, but he remains in his room for long periods of time, troubled with conflicts surrounding masturbation. He is shy, particularly with adults and with children of the opposite sex at the same age. This may be transitory or this may be chronic. It is sometimes of importance not to interfere and not to treat, as in the case of the child in whom this has not gone on for very long. The usual parental encouragement to learn is sometimes sufficient. If this condition persists beyond the seventh grade, into the eighth and through the middle of the eighth grade, generally it is wise to institute some investigative psychotherapy to determine the cause. Pubertal problems always involve a terror of sexuality on the child's part because of reawakened oedipal phase problems. Regression to even earlier phase problems is most common and results in further difficulty. If we transpose earlier problems of phase development to an older child and treat them accordingly, pubertal learning difficulties can be understood quite readily. In the treatment of these children, however, it is necessary never to forget that they are older and larger, they can communicate more readily, and they are more independent and consequently more resistant to parental involvement or interference.

DISTURBANCES IN EARLY EDUCATION

Thus far under functional disturbance we have discussed chronic disturbances which occur at an early age and persist. The first of these is the disturbance in phase development. A second type of functional disturbance is reading disability associated with disturbances in early education. These are multiple, and the most important is a disorder in the child-teacher relationship.

Poor Teacher-Child Relationship

The child's first teacher is of great importance to the child's introduction to school and to his attitude toward school. If the first teacher develops a poor teacher-child relationship, dislikes him or herself, or has some personal characteristic with which the child cannot identify or to which the child develops a negative reaction, or if the child has a negative transference reaction to the teacher, the child cannot learn from her. It is necessary for a person to be able to like or love another person in order to be able to learn from him. Without this, no learning can take place. The extension of a poor relationship to a first teacher may spread to involve the child's entire personality. He may be unable to relate to subsequent teachers because of this. Quite often a change of school, plus psychotherapeutic investigation of the disturbance in his teacher-relationship (even a short psychotherapeutic investigation) is helpful in discovering and correcting the basis of this problem. Here, direct remedial assistance is quite often necessary, even mandatory.

Rarely, the disturbed early teaching experience is not related to the teacher, but sometimes is an act of "fate." At a special reading clinic operated by the Staten Island Mental Health Center, a series of children from a specific school, in a specific class, were seen, all of whom had reading difficulties. The study of these children revealed no particular personal intellectual deficiencies, nor any personal neurotic difficulties which would account for this large group of children who were having a most difficult experience in learning to read. Investigations of the school history indicated that this class had experienced a frequent, rapid change of teachers, some of whom were unpleasant or disagreeable. One teacher became pregnant, another teacher became sick, and these children did not remain with any one first- or second-grade teacher long enough to learn that teacher's technique or to develop an attachment. Further, this group of children went on into the third grade where they studied with a teacher who had unpleasant personal characteristics. The whole group of children were unable to learn to read because of confused and unhappy early teacher-child relationships. It is a significant comment on the

strength of children that about half of the children in this class managed
to learn anyhow.

Physical and Psychic Trauma

There are a certain number of children who suffer a series of prolonged physical illnesses during the course of their early learning experiences. They miss the critical period of introduction to learning under
pleasant circumstances which a child ordinarily anticipates, and which is
necessary for a comfortable early learning experience. Sometimes one sees
psychological regressions accompanying physical illness which are very
tempting to the child. They may be more tempting to him than the
learning experience itself, and so these children also develop a learning
difficulty in the third or fourth grade. This type of difficulty, if it is
prolonged, can occur at almost any age level. It occurs not only because
the child has missed material, but because the temptation, the pleasure,
of being regressed is greater than the pleasure of working productively in
class. These children sometimes require direct psychotherapeutic intervention. Sometimes they require special motivation in the form of remedial help. Most often this problem can be avoided by maintaining and
continuing their instruction through parental interest and through home
teaching, which continues the child's interest in his studies throughout his
illness. This child then goes back to class without feeling defeated,
hopeless, or inadequate. He often finds the learning situation in class
more attractive because he has been stimulated to learn through individual instruction. Prevention is the best form of treatment for this
difficulty.

A certain number of difficulties associated with varieties of psychic
trauma occur in conjunction with original attendance at school. An
illustration is the youngster who begins first grade without having gone to
kindergarten, or is in a new school neighborhood, a neighborhood in
which he had not been before. His colleagues in class have been friends
for a year previously in kindergarten, and some of them longer than that
because they had lived in the neighborhood and had known each other.
This child entered class as an outsider and was made the scapegoat the
first day of school. He tolerated this very poorly because he was too
immature to deal with it, and he then returned to the school situation
each day anticipating the recurrence of the bullying. He was unable to
learn because of the anxiety aroused in him that whole first year of his
schooling. He did so poorly that first year that he failed; he had a similar

experience the following year. This child required treatment to unearth the residue of the traumata. This situation was originally not a neurotic situation and could have been avoided by adult recognition and adult intervention.

Negative Motivation

A moderate number of children have learning disability because they have poor motivation. These are the children whose parents are actively disinterested in their learning experience. There are parents who don't care whether their children learn or not, who are not gratified by their children's learning successes, who are disinterested in their children's schooling, who indicate their disinterest by their attitude, and to whom it makes no difference whether that child learns or not. These are usually children from a poor social situation. Often they come from low economic families, although one sees this in high economic families also. These children have difficulty in learning because of failure of motivation. Sometimes it is necessary to treat the child in order to motivate the family, when family counselling is insufficient to arouse the parents' interest in the child's learning situation. A classic example is a parent whom we saw in the Special Reading Clinic. He said to his youngster, with pride, that he had only gone to the fourth grade in school. He thought it was unnecessary for his child to learn to read, to write, or to do arithmetic well. In his opinion, these things were not important in life. He suggested that if his child was really fond of his father, he would comply with his father's wishes and would avoid a learning situation.

A corollary to this type of disturbance in early education is the child who has a large number of responsibilities in his home, either because of sick or absent parents, or large numbers of siblings. He has such an excessive number of interests, activities, and duties which are non-academic and nonlearning in their nature that his energies, interests, and motivations are absorbed in these duties and interests rather than in school situations. A similar situation is seen when there is excessive turmoil in the home. The parents are actively battling, quarreling, and acting-out upon each other. The child is preoccupied with his status in life, his status in his own home, and with his future. He is not able to concentrate on refined matters such as learning.

One also sees a certain number of children who become negatively motivated because of the premature introduction of learning material which becomes overwhelming, discouraging, and unpleasant for the youngster. Some of these children are unsuccessful in mastering the material. They may continue to respond to instruction with defeatism, even though their poor example is long in the past. Other children master the prematurely introduced material, but have another type of difficulty. They are prone to rejecting learning in adolescence because the experience of learning reawakens infantile conflicts.

In some educational districts we see another type of reading disability associated with early education disturbance. These areas are in the process of revising their educational techniques and procedures. For example, a child who was taught sight-reading techniques, who was unsuccessful in learning to sight-read, and who was then switched to the phonetic style of learning to read without adequate instruction in phonetics, remained a poor speller and poor reader in the sixth grade. Sight-reading technique involves the learning of words by looking at them rather than by sounding them out. The child who is taught phonetics is taught the sound of vowels and consonants, the sound of syllables, and so is able to put words together by sounding them out. But the child taught sight-reading technique has to memorize words and depend upon memory rather than a rational basis for deciphering symbols. For the most part, sight readers have reduced vocabulary and also have difficulty with spelling. Some learn the phonetic method in later grades out of a personal interest. But when a child attempts to switch from one method to the other he becomes confused. He tends to pass over the individual letters, not recognizing their importance, and tends to mix up the appearance of letters. This is a disturbance in early teaching.

There appears to be a critical period of learning which is optimum. If the child goes beyond this period in learning a particular skill, he has missed the time of greatest physiological ability. While he can still learn, he never learns as well as he would have. It is unfortunate when children reach the age of 13 or 14 without being able to read. It is extremely difficult to assist these children to acquire reading and learning skills. Intensive relationship therapy, combined with techniques to enhance motivation and accompanied by intensive special education, is most likely to succeed.

Other learning disturbances come about through faulty techniques in instruction. The difficulties children encounter as a result of this confusion are manageable, but management must include a recognition of the child's faulty foundation. The psychological resistances associated with the child's original disappointment in learning may require psychotherapeutic intervention. In general, however, psychotherapy is of no value in these cases, unless there is evidence of other neurotic involvement on the part of the child. The best treatment for these difficulties is relearning, that is, remedial techniques. It is important in all of these education disturbances that the teacher or therapist who is working with the child be acceptable to the child, and especially that the personality of the teacher be compatible, and not threatening in any way, to the personality of the child.

We have discussed a series of situational as well as educational reasons for learning difficulties, and the treatment thereof. We have also discussed a series of phase development disturbances which contribute to learning difficulties. Character disturbances, psychoneuroses and psychoses, and their contribution to the creation of problems in the process of learning will now be discussed.

CHARACTER DISTURBANCES

Recently Lawrence Kubie said that people with emotional disturbances were divided into two classes: onion-eaters and garlic-eaters— those who are made uncomfortable themselves and those who make other people uncomfortable. The character neuroses could be comparable to the garlic-eaters. The character disturbances, then, have the same dynamics as the neuroses, and fit into roughly the same levels of development as the neuroses. That is, they can be seen as oral, anal, phallic, and oedipal levels of development. However, the character disturbances one sees clinically in children, as they contribute to learning difficulty, are divided into passive types and aggressive types of character disturbances. Quite often, it is very difficult to distinguish which is which in children, because one sees passive behavior as a defense against aggression, and one also sees passive behavior as a primary wish of the child. One often sees aggressive behavior as a defense against passive wishes, and, again, one sees aggressive behavior as a primary type of disturbance in youngsters. One sees children who have ego-syntonic behavioral patterns, in which the child's method of acting is rigid and inflexible, comparable to an obsessive character in an adult and where it is sometimes difficult to determine whether this is an illness or an aspect of growth and development. One also sees youngsters who tend to be provocative and self-destructive and whom we might call masochistic.

The Child in a Power Struggle

However, to discuss the contribution of character difficulties to learning disturbance in children requires discussion of specific syndrome types, and the most important syndrome type is the passive-aggressive youngster who is constantly in a power struggle. This is a child to whom it is more important to win than it is to accomplish realistic, purposeful achievements. The energy of the child is bound up in power struggles, and these have variable significance to the youngster. Occasionally these power struggles involve a wish to be the authority, to be the boss, on an oedipal basis. Occasionally the power struggle involves an exhibitionistic purpose. Occasionally the power struggle involves a sadistic purpose; occasionally it is a masochistic one in which the child has learned to secure pleasure from injury and requires some punishment in order to feel comfortable. Thus, one sees a whole variety of dynamics behind the child with learning difficulty related to passive-aggressive personality difficulties as manifested in power struggles. The treatment of youngsters like this is complicated, because the child sees the goal as a realistic one. He does not see his goal as unreasonable. He sees the world around him as pressing in on him, controlling him, and requiring him to do things which he feels are not to his liking and are neither suitable nor pleasurable to him. This battle becomes very much involved in his whole learning situation.

Children of such a nature are quite often brought up by parents who are either excessively fond of them, or who are so ambivalent that the parent cannot exercise strong controls without crossing one of his own ambitions for the child. This kind of youngster is a child whose behavior is characterized by sophistry and by intellectual arguments. In the nature of the child's behavior one can see the results of the parent's behavior toward the youngster, in which the parent has allowed the youngster to quarrel ad infinitum about such matters as justice or injustice, fairness or unfairness, what is proper and what is not. The most outrageous example of a child with this kind of difficulty, who has learning problems, is the child who complains at home about the nature of the material that the teacher gives him, about the nature of the subject assignments in school, or about the quality of the instruction he receives from his teacher. The parent tends to "buy" this kind of argument if it is a true power struggle of the type that we are discussing.

Some of these difficulties are internalized and some of these difficulties are still external. In latency children, one finds that these difficulties may still be external and still may be modifiable by counselling of the parents. In many of these difficulties, particularly of the later latency-period children, and in the adolescent in particular, these types of learning situations are fixed and difficult because sophistry is internalized. The use of power struggle and sophistry has spread through the child's personality like a cancer, and become tied up with all the rest of the youngster's difficulties.

Certain principles are involved in the treatment of this type of youngster. First, it is important not to become involved in disputation with this type of child. As soon as you become involved in disputation, you become involved in his usual technique of dealing with the world. It is necessary to be objective with this type of child, avoiding his sophistry. These children offend our moral sensibilities. Here is a little person who decides that he is capable of telling the teacher what it is all about, what is right and wrong, how to teach the course, what materials to buy, what is stimulating and what is unstimulating. To adults this tends to rankle. It makes us indignant, yet as soon as we get indignant we are lost. So it is important to listen to his affairs properly.

Second, it is important to talk with him about what is good for him or what is not good for him. In discussing the problems of such children one always asks, "What happens to you?" One attempts to deal with the reality of this type of child for a very long period of time. These children are in difficulty because of the ego-syntonic nature of their behavior. They must be made to feel uncomfortable because they, themselves, are basically satisfied with their approach to the world. To be helped they must first be made uncomfortable about their behavior, lest they become "stuck" with their characterological difficulty. One must deal with them, especially in the beginning of treatment, in terms of reality. These children tend to cut off their noses to spite their faces. In order to accomplish their power purpose they will give up realistic gains that they might otherwise have. For example, a youngster like this one in treatment currently would, in order to spite a teacher, flunk—literally flunk—an examination. This would make him feel that he was in control of the situation, that he was not being controlled by the situation, and that he was capable of mastering the teacher's aggression toward him. He would really not be aware that he was hurting himself in the process of doing this.

There are three phases to the technique of dealing with these children:

1. Making unrealistic behavior as ego-alien as one possibly can.
2. Ultimately, if we are successful in the first phase, encouraging the child to want to know "why." He, himself, will become concerned about the type of difficulty he is in, and will want help. He will even attempt to investigate himself.
3. Psychic realignment in which the child's unrealistic behavior becomes intolerable to him and he develops anxiety, which now drives him to examine the origin of anxiety.

This illness is always chronic and is seen at two major age levels: latency and again in adolescence. In the adolescent it is the more seriously disturbed youngsters who have this type of problem.

Example: A child came to treatment at the age of ten. His mother had died when he was five, his father had remarried. The boy was attempting to hold on to his real mother out of guilt, and his relationship with his father was threatened by his father's authority. The boy had an I.Q. of 140 and came from an Orthodox Jewish family who was distressed by the boy's refusal to employ his potential for learning, especially his refusal to study religious subjects. He rejected the study of Hebrew, the performance of any religious duties, and constantly complained that religious studies were unimportant compared to studies in English. He complained that his teachers were mainly interested in teaching him Hebrew and religion, and that they did an inadequate job of English instruction. Actually, he was also failing English, arithmetic, social studies, and other English subjects. He argued that his failure was because of the religious emphasis.

The boy was transferred to a public school, with permission of the therapist, while he was in treatment. This enhanced the therapeutic purpose since it was anticipated that he would have the same difficulties in public school. When he did actually fail in public school also, the boy became concerned about himself. He became aware that he was fighting for his father's love, but was, at the same time, warding off the tenderness his father wished to show him. The price of his father's love was religious observance. Religious observance, in turn, meant weakness, sequaciousness, and femininity to him. The price of his father's love also meant giving up the memory of his mother, along with his identification with his real mother, and accepting the new stepmother. To study Hebrew was passive, and to study English was aggressive. The result was that he could study neither one. It was a double dilemma because to identify with his mother was feminine, as was the study of Hebrew. To resist his father was masculine, as was the study of English.

Since the father in this situation was not willing to accept the child's defenses, this boy had to be carried in treatment from the age of 10 to 17. His problems characterize large numbers of character disturbances we see in children involved in power-struggle problems which block their ability to learn. One can see a whole variety of dynamic purposes that are expressed in this example of character difficulty. First, there is the challenge to the father that we see on an oedipal basis. Secondly, one can see the punishment for aggression. Third, one can see the unconscious homosexuality in the youngster (in treating children it is rather dangerous to interpret homosexuality in these terms, or to interpret it directly, as this tends to interfere with the child's psycho-sexual development). Fourth, one can see the identification with the dead mother that this child was warding off, and which he used to handle his grief about his mother's death. One can also see that his lack of success tends to relieve his challenge to his father and to make him feel that his guilt is expiated in regard to challenging his father. Finally, one sees the regression to passivity in which this child takes an excellent person, himself, and forces him backward to the position where his talents are not usable and where he has to be taken care of and supported. One can, of course, see all the secondary gratifications of having his family concerned about him—distressed about him, and about the state of his soul, and the state of his academic performance. All of the worry and concern and love that is poured into a wayward child is poured into this youngster who gets these feelings gratified as a secondary, not primary, matter. This is the epitome of one type of problem that we see as a characterological problem and is an example of the treatment of that type of problem.

The Passive-Dependent Child

Another type of problem that we see occasionally, which is much more difficult to deal with, is the passive child whom we sometimes call the passive-dependent child. These children are extremely reluctant to perform for themselves. They are children who want to have their learning done for them. They do not want to write out their assignments because it is too much work. They do not want to read an assignment; this is too difficult. It is always necessary for an adult to be alongside and to do for this type of child. Through a pose of helplessness this youngster succeeds in seducing the adults around him to do his work for him because he is pathetic, and helpless, and in difficulty.

These youngsters have the fascinating technique of playing dumb. They also have the technique of saying "I can't." When one sees a child with this kind of character difficulty, the child says "I just can't do it, I am helpless, I am incapable, I don't know how, show me how." When you or the parents attempt to show this youngster how to do it, the child fumbles and says, "I simply am unable to help myself." The technique of treatment here is to attempt to convert his activity into ego-alien behavior. It is much more difficult to do so with this type of child than it is with the first type. The nature of this type of child is that one quite often cannot tell if the child really has a constitutional inadequacy or not. These children also tend to be very frustrating. They tend to make you annoyed with them because of their posing. They seem to be playing dumb. Their expressions of "I can't" seem to be techniques or maneuvers. These characterological maneuvers may or may not have behind them unconscious purposes that can be understood by investigation. Sometimes we are successful in finding the dynamic sources of these techniques and sometimes we are not. Sometimes we examine the family circumstances of such a child and find very competitive, or very domineering parents. But the development of these techniques is understandable if the child has very overprotective parents. There are situations in which one cannot really find the dynamic source of this type of difficulty.

There are numerous variations of characterological difficulties that contribute to learning disturbance. These are so variable, however, that we could take several weeks to discuss that aspect of learning difficulty alone. The two examples above are major illustrations of the problems and treatment involved in learning disturbances related to characterological difficulty.

The Psychoneurotic Child

Psychoneuroses are, like character difficulties, solutions to conflict. In psychoneuroses, the conflict is always unconscious, internal, and quite often symbolically expressed in symptoms. The commonest type of neurotic problem that one sees in children as contributing to learning difficulty is the daydreaming child. This child is, for reasons unknown when initially working with him, fantasying a good part of his day or a good part of his studying career. He is using daydreaming as an escape from anxiety. Because he is escaping from anxiety in this way, he is quite often defective in learning or in reading. One sees this at two levels: (1) in latency, particularly in early latency; and (2) in adolescence. It is commoner in adolescents who are immediately going through the trials and tribulations of pubescence. The usual adolescent tends to withdraw, to try to work out problems through daydreaming. One almost always sees the seventh and eighth grader having learning difficulties on the basis of problems of adolescence. He withdraws and daydreams in an effort to work out problems and then comes back to live in the world again. This child is troublesome to teachers because the teacher sees that he is capable. He is a child who can perform very well and, in fact, the child does perform about every fourth day. Then the child will be with the teacher and will function effectively, but soon withdraws.

One tends not to treat the problem at all during pubescence. If it persists past pubescence, one places the child in investigative psycho-therapy in an attempt to understand and resolve the conflict that con-tributed to the symptom. This is also true in early latency. If a child in early latency is failing to learn because of daydreaming, or apparent daydreaming, the youngster should be brought into treatment.

One of the early great contributions to the understanding of learning difficulty was the contribution of Phyllis Blanchard(1), in which she demonstrated that the letters on the page, or the words that the child was reading, would stimulate fantasies in this type of youngster. Children with castration anxiety would see an open letter, such as "C" or "G," as having an open mouth. The letters created the fantasy of a monster of the biting or chewing variety. In Blanchard's original cases, two children, who spoke of letters biting them, were struggling to conceal and repress hostile wishes toward babysitters whom they wished to bite or eat up. Their reactions to the letters were, on the one hand, expressions of guilt and the need to be punished, and on the other hand, expressed wishes disguised by fear. This type of dualism—that is, expression of both pleasure and punishment—is characteristic of all neurotic difficulties.

There are other ways in which letters and words on a reading page can produce fantasy and unrealistic fears. These are equally effective in inter-fering with the child's reading and in causing blocking.

Example: A youngster would block on the word "roar." He would see the word "roar," and would add the first three letters to it to make it "horror," and would be reminded of a forbidden movie that he had seen. The movie had been highly exciting, highly stimulating, and at the same time forbidden by his parents. He had sneaked to the movie, and he would block at this point and be unable to proceed beyond this.

One also sees children, particularly in adolescence, who refuse to read because the material that they read is not yet sublimated satisfactorily for them. They find the material they read sexually stimulating, and they avoid the reading in order to avoid the sexual fantasy that accompanies this reading material. Quite often this type of youngster will read scientific material but will not read novels, for example. The opposite of this kind of child is the one with a character disturbance who does not read because he is hunting through the body of the book to find the sexual material which is all that is interesting to him. He is not interested in the rest of the material in the book. One sees the problems just discussed present, and the child is not at all aware that this happens. All he knows is that when he looks at a book, the letters become fuzzy, and the page attempts to disappear before his eyes. He tells you that he doesn't know what is happening to him, that the material goes away from him. One sees this in early latency occasionally. If you watch a beginning reader learning to read, he has difficulty in focusing on the page and quite often has to use a ruler, a card, or a pointer to enable him to hold his place. If the teacher or instructor gives the child an opportunity to avoid the use of the pointer to focus his concentration, the page tends to fuzz before the child's eyes, and then this also becomes confused with the general psychological problems he has. He may take advantage of this state of affairs to develop a conversion reaction in which he apparently is unable to read. The psychological problem is built on a physiological phase of maturation.

The difficulty of children who develop conversion reactions like this early in their reading career is that they tend to miss the critical period of learning. They tend to miss the period of development when they are most amenable to imprinting, and these children quite often move on into adolescence or preadolescence as nonreaders, and as nonreaders have a double problem. They have the problem of missing the critical period, and the problem of being unable to see what they are reading, or unable to interpret the symbols they are reading on the basis of its unconscious meaning to them, on the basis of the unconscious meaning of reading. If one sees children with this type of conversion reaction early, before one misses the critical periods, they are quite amenable to investigative therapy. If one sees children of this type late, at the age of 12, 13, or 14, they are exceedingly difficult to teach to read, and are most pathetic and unhappy children because they want desperately, consciously to be able to read. This type of child pulls on your heartstrings, and yet the critical period is lost. The investigation of the conversion reaction is helpful, but never as helpful as it might have been had you been able to reach this child at an earlier age. While these children are sometimes able to learn to read as a result of investigative therapy, their life is interfered with because they have gone too long as nonreaders and it takes them too long to catch up with their contemporaries. Treatment can rarely ever fully repair the damage that the neglect of treatment creates in this type of child.

One occasionally sees a psychoneurotic youngster who is phobic. Children with multiple phobias sometimes avoid learning in order to avoid the material which stimulates their phobias. It is interesting, however, that children with conversion reactions and children with phobias quite often do not develop learning disturbances at all. When a phobia is extreme, however, the phobic youngster avoids the learning situation. The treatment of this type of disturbance is classical. Children with obsessive neurosis may also have associated neurotic difficulties. These anxiety-bound children will take hours to do tasks other children can complete in a few minutes. In an effort to avoid imagined disapproval from teachers, these children end up in a state of psychic paralysis. They go through a ritualistic erasing and redoing. No reassurance will satisfy these children. Their learning failure is rarely based on a lack of knowledge; rather, it is based on an inability to demonstrate their knowledge for fear of imagined disapproval. In these youngsters it is necessary to investigate and discover the source of the child's anxiety. Often, one also discovers associated magical rituals which the youngster uses to relieve his anxiety.

Example: An eight-year-old boy stated he failed his arithmetic examination because he forgot to put his left shoe and sock on first when he dressed that morning. His teacher, however, reported that at the end of the allotted time, he had completed only half of his examination paper. The half he had completed, he had done correctly. Occasionally this ability to concentrate on details and minutiae produces scholars as well as failures.

Children who are depressed also tend to lose their learning abilities early in the course of their depression, along with the loss of appetite and their ability to sleep comfortably. Depressions can be acute or chronic. Whenever a child is involved in an acute situation which is painful to him, like everybody else he shows little interest in food, and he has some difficulty in sleeping, or sleeps too much. And he is unable to learn. One sees children quite often who are chronically depressed. They feel that they are wicked or bad, or have done wicked or bad things. These children also respond rather nicely to investigative therapy. It is the nature of these children to wish to please. These are children who feel more pain than does the usual youngster, and because they are feeling pain, and because they wish to please, they tend to respond very well to investigative therapy. One sees a quick response to their learning difficulty whether one fully relieves this type of youngster of the internal pain he feels or not. Relief of pain is another matter, and this is a more difficult problem than relieving learning difficulty alone.

Depressions are seen both in latency and adolescence. Latency depressions seem to have a more permanent effect on learning abilities. Latency depressions are more often associated with the child's fear of losing parental love or approval. Adolescent depressions are usually less chronic and associated with loss of a sweetheart, with homesickness or entering boarding school, or moves to a new area.

The Psychotic Child

Now it might be worthwhile for us to discuss psychoses, although the psychoses are more apparent than the psychoneuroses as a source of difficulty. Psychosis is a devastating disability which is seen as an acute or chronic loss of major ego functioning in responses to conflict. It is a variable type of illness wherein all graduations of symptomatology, extending from autism all the way to borderline difficulty, are seen. Psychosis is seen at all age levels, but the nature of psychosis tends to make psychotic children appear to be pseudodefective at times. Psychotic children, particularly in adolescence, may appear to act-out, and their acting-out may very well interfere with their ability to learn. The general approach to the treatment of the psychotic child with a learning difficulty is to do an inventory to determine what skills and assets the child retains, what skills and assets the child has lost as the result of his illness, and to what degree rapport or contact can be made between the therapist and the child suffering from a psychosis. Often the use of phenothiazine medications proves helpful in increasing such rapport. The child becomes more amenable to psychotherapy as a result of the use of phenothiazine medication, and may respond much more rapidly. It is also very important, in the treatment of children with psychoses, that the nature of the trying circumstances in their environment be dealt with through counselling and through case management. Occasionally one finds that these children respond more effectively in residential settings than they do in outpatient settings, although the modern approach is to deal with such youngsters on an outpatient basis.

Example: A little girl whose father had died when she was five years old was seen at the age of eight-and-a-half years. At that time she had a series of compulsions in which it was necessary for her to line up the hampers in the bathroom, line up the shoes in the bedroom, and line up her clothes in specific ways in order to "please the ghost king." She had no knowledge of what this fantasy meant. She did feel, however, that there was a "ghost king" who looked after her, who was pleased or displeased with her at various points in her life. Concern about this type of fantasy led to the suggestion that treatment be instituted. The family rejected the recommendation and the youngster was not seen again until she was 13. When she was 13 she was getting into great controversy with her teachers. Although she had always made excellent marks, her marks had begun to run downhill very rapidly. Her classmates told her parents that she had become "loose," that she was allowing boys to "neck" with her, and that she was pursuing boys, seeking affection from them in a rather bizarre way. When she was seen she was quite disassociated, quite incapable of speaking coherently, was assaultive toward her parents, and had undergone a severe ego-regression, the source of which was difficult to determine without knowing the background material. It was necessary to hospitalize her. She was dismissed from one hospital because she provoked her therapist. She was hospitalized in another institution where the institution was capable of placing effective external controls on her and was not threatened by her behavior. She was treated psychotherapeutically, and after a series of years responded slowly, with later recovery of lost learning functions. Later on she obtained excellent marks in the special schools she attended. She is now attending junior college, apparently with very excellent academic ability, but still some difficulty with personal relationships.

It should be noted that learning difficulties associated with psychosis demand treatment of the basic illness rather than of the learning difficulty itself. Unfortunately, psychotic children lose many learning years as a result of their illness. It is important to encourage such youngsters to continue with their education following recovery from their psychotic illness. This is essential if the loss of full ability is to be prevented.

Example: A brilliant 15-year-old boy developed an acute paranoid illness which required two years of hospitalization. The hospitalization was followed with outpatient electroshock therapy. His original therapist encouraged this young man to secure employment as an automobile mechanic. Psychotherapy was begun when the patient was 19 years old. It was continued throughout the patient's college and postgraduate career. As a result of psychotherapeutic care, the patient now posesses a Ph.D. degree and has produced many unique contributions to his field. While all psychoses do not respond so happily, much loss of human skill can be avoided by the therapeutic insistence on the use of undamaged skills in psychotic patients.

This chapter was begun with the statement that learning difficulty encompasses the whole field of child psychiatry. Consequently it has been necessary to review rather than to be comprehensive in the discussion of learning difficulty.

REFERENCES

1. BLANCHARD, P.   Psychogenic factors in some cases of reading disability. *Amer. J. Orthopsychiat.*, 1935, **5**:361–74.
2. GATES, A. I., and BOND, G. L.   Relation of handedness, eye-sighting and acuity dominance to reading. *J. educ. Psychol.*, 1936, **27**:450–56.
3. ORTON, S. T.   Specific reading disability—strephosymbolia. *J. Ameri. Med. Assn.*, 1928, **90**:1095–99.

3

H. S. Lippman

The Phobic Child and
Other Related Anxiety States

ANXIETY is the underlying problem in emotional conflict. Anxiety signifies danger. It is evidence that all is not well and that something is needed to protect the individual. If protection is not provided, discomfort and unease continue. If anxiety is severe and continuous and action is not taken to provide relief, serious—and even fatal—illness may result.

THE INFANT AND ANXIETY

The infant at birth suffers excruciatingly from anxiety caused by the rigors of labor and his sudden expulsion from the protective interior of the mother's body to the outside world. The sudden physiologic changes in his circulation and respiration produce what Freud termed the first traumatic situation, which he believed served as the prototype of all later severe anxiety situations.

The ego at birth is undeveloped. The steps in the development of the ego to the state in which it performs the vital function of integration and synthesis are described in detail by Sigmund Freud(12), Anna Freud (10), Waelder(23), Nunberg(20), Hartman(14), Benedek(1), and others. Because of the extreme immaturity of the ego in early life, the child's continued existence depends on care from others. This responsibility is eagerly accepted by the healthy, mature mother, who provides warmth, food, attention, love, comfort, and great patience—which we call mothering. She does what she can to lessen shock and discomfort and tries to recreate for the child the state of comparative well-being he experienced in the uterus. She relieves tension and anxiety, which continue to be great since so much of his early life is potentially dangerous. She is available to provide the repetitive care and conditioning which Benedek(1) calls "confidence," a feeling the infant introjects which creates a feeling of trust that all is well. There is no surer way of developing ego strength and no better means of lessening anxiety. In 1926, Freud(11) showed that anxiety was not the consequence of repression, as he had earlier believed, but was its motor force. Anxiety produces repression. Freud's study "The Problem of Anxiety" summarizes all the significant factors known about anxiety at that time, and should be read and reread to understand the development of anxiety(12).

Anxiety is a defense. It is important that the ego be able to recognize danger situations. The memory of early danger experiences makes the ego acutely aware of what is safe and unsafe. It learns which impulses are acceptable to the outside world and to the superego. Freud(12) emphasized that during the early years the ego is friendly to the instinctual drives seeking outlet. It is unfriendly only when it recognizes that the impulses if gratified will cause anxiety and suffering. The memory of early suffering from traumata is the best defense against recurrence. Much discomfort and pain cannot be prevented even with the best mothering. Visceral disfunctions, hunger that cannot be prevented, forced absence of the mother, physical illness—all are elements in life which must be tolerated. The ego must learn to master such anxiety.

Benedek describes in detail the development of separation anxiety. It begins with a mother who as a child is raised in an atmosphere devoid of acceptance and love. Her hostile relationship with her mother deprives her of the gratification of dependency needs indispensable for healthy development. In her marriage she seeks the dependency relationship for which she hungers, and if this is unsuccessful, she feels embittered and deprived. She is likely to reject pregnancy, and she cannot provide the mothering for her infant. She is denied the pleasure the healthy mother obtains from gratifying her child, with the usual result that the child suffers from discomfort and long spells of crying. The gratification of the child, according to Benedek, provides the mother a form of dependency gratification. When this is lacking, the mother fails to develop a feeling of confidence in her motherliness. In her desperate need for dependency she overindulges her infant, forcing her child into a passive dependency relationship filled with anxiety which is bound to be hostile because of the preponderance of hostility in the symbiotic tie(1).

Ferenczi, in a study of the unwelcome child, stated that

. . . children who are received in a harsh and disagreeable way, die easily and willingly. Either they use one of the many preferred organic possibilities for a quick exit, or if they escape this fate, they keep a streak of pessimism and of aversion to life. . . . The child has to be induced by means of a great expenditure of love, tenderness, and care to forgive the parents for having brought him into the world without any intention on his part; otherwise the destructive instincts begin to stir immediately(8).

We know from the studies of René Spitz(22) the severe consequences to development and life in the child deprived early of intensive maternal care. In the later life of the unwanted children Ferenczi(8) found frequent depression and an inability to tolerate frustration. Mild situations were enough to produce marked anxiety and a wish to die.

NEUROTIC ANXIETY IN CHILDREN

Freud(12) early differentiated objective fear from neurotic anxiety. Neurotic anxiety in contrast to fear could not be explained because its cause was unconscious. Freud(12) described three forms of neurotic anxiety. One is a generalized anxiety or apprehensiveness, often called expectant dread, or anxious expectation. The child grasps at any situation of potential danger, as a way of justifying anxiety he cannot explain or understand. Any reality situation is preferable to facing the unconscious thought or wish which, if expressed, would cause suffering to someone close to the child, or great guilt to the child. Clues to this form of neurotic anxiety may be provided in the child's dreams or play therapy sessions. Once exposed to discussion their dangerous character may be lessened. The child may learn that all people have hostile wishes at some time or other towards those they really love. This may be a father who in a moment of anger made remarks or threats which he had no intention of carrying out—which he could not carry out because of his deep love for his children and his great compassion. A brother whom the child says he hates, he also loves, as reflected in previous statements, and his brother loves him in spite of the fact that he, too, had hostile thoughts toward him (the patient). Just having the chance to talk about these thoughts may do much to break a vicious circle.

Another form of neurotic anxiety is an attack of anxiety or panic which may come on suddenly, and leave suddenly. This is seen in the hysterical child. It is my impression that this form of neurotic anxiety occurs less frequently in children than in adults.

The third is the mechanism of phobia, a circumscribed anxiety which attaches to objects and situations. The mechanism of phobia serves well to illustrate neurotic anxiety. Because phobias are closely related to conversion hysteria, Freud(12) felt it justifiable to align the two as anxiety hysteria. According to Freud, the phobic mechanism represents one attempt to resolve the conflict of ambivalence. The other means of accomplishing this is through reaction formation. In the case of Hans, Freud described how the child, faced with hostile feelings toward his father, whom he loved dearly, unconsciously projected his hostility onto a horse and through this inhibition was able to continue to love his father(12). This represents the use of phobia to deal with ambivalence. In reaction formation, on the other hand, the hostility to the parents is repressed, and the positive element of the ambivalence remains as excessive tenderness. Both of these methods inhibit the activity of the child. The phobia in Hans's case kept Hans off the street and limited his activity and opportunity to learn from reality experiences. Reaction formation utilizes important energy to keep dangerous material in repression—energy that is needed for dealing with life situations.

Castration Anxiety

Through the mechanisms of phobia and reaction formation the ego attempts to protect itself against castration anxiety. In a recent article (19) related to this subject were descriptions of two instances of castration anxiety induced by the recognition of absence of a penis in two young children.

Dr. Van DerHoop tells the following story. He was in Switzerland visiting friends whose five-year-old son had recently developed a phobia of a dog which playfully had jumped on him. The parents asked Dr. Van DerHoop to speak to their son about this, so he took a walk with the boy who, during the stroll, told the doctor that he very much feared that the dog in jumping on him would bite him. The doctor explained that little boys often found it pleasant to play with their penises, but felt that they were doing something wrong for which they might be punished. Perhaps something might happen to this organ. When the dog jumped on him he might have feared that something could happen to his penis—the dog might bite it off. Dr. Van DerHoop went on to explain that, in the first place, what the boy feared could not happen because the penis was firmly attached to his body, but what was more important, the dog loved him and he loved the dog, so the dog would not harm him. He might fear also that his parents might harm this organ, but his parents loved him and would not allow anything so bad as that to happen to him. The little boy, very attentive, walked along quietly, then turned to Dr. Van DerHoop and said, "You know, you are a very smart man."

A second instance dealt with a dream related by a 10-year-old boy who had been catheterized because of an inability to urinate for a brief period. He dreamed he was in the hospital and had several penises distributed across his abdomen. When urine failed to come out of one he tried another. He thus was able to avoid the trauma of another catheterization, which had been painful and very frightening(17).

On one occasion, Anna Freud was asked why it was that one rarely hears dreams from men in which the penis is recognized as absent. Castration appears symbolically as a severe gash, a broken limb, a lost eye or tooth. The child dreams he is dressed as a girl, or that he is a girl, but these are all indirect means of expressing castration. It was Anna Freud's opinion that the anxiety associated with castration is so intense that even in dreams it can only appear in symbolic form(10). Young children often refer to the fear that if the penis were lost they would die. "I would have to die because I couldn't wee-wee."

Freud(12) was convinced that the basic anxiety in the male suffering from neurotic illness was that of castration. This fear is closely aligned with the fear of death. I have discussed this subject somewhat at length because there are few references to this subject in the literature related to children.

Symptoms of agoraphobia and claustrophobia do not appear very often in child guidance clinic work. However, the writer has seen several adolescents with severe superegos who developed agoraphobia as a result of being sexually overstimulated.

Separation Anxiety

A common phobia in children is related to going to school. Because of the frequency with which separation anxiety is a part of this fear, it has been referred to by Adelaide Johnson(15) as separation anxiety rather than school phobia. There are many situations, however, in which the anxiety is not related to fear of being separated from the mother; fear of children on the way to school, fear of a certain teacher, a fear of failing in a subject may condition a child against going to school. Often one senses a fear of being sexually overstimulated by youngsters in the classroom, although the child is unaware of it. Most of the school phobias are severe enough to produce panic if one insists on school attendance. These are usually closely related to a hostile dependency tie to the mother. It is interesting to note that many more girls than boys suffer from school phobia, probably due to the mother's reaching out to her female child to find the dependency she longed for from her mother. The panic is so excessive in some cases that one is led to search for some extreme danger which may underlie the school phobia. It is believed that this is a fear of death related to the child's guilt for death wishes toward her mother. Such a child frequently mentions the fear that something terrible may happen to one or both parents. Back of this fear may well be the unconscious wish for their death. Being with or near the mother constantly reassures the child that her mother is alive.

Frequently the mother searches for a dependency outlet from her husband, but this is usually not available, since in many instances he also is neurotic, with great dependency needs and with little support to give the mother. The Judge Baker studies(24, 25) indicated that often the mother and father vie for a dependency relationship to their child.

Guilt which the mother suffers plays an important role in her inability to be firm with her child. The child recognizes her mother's weakness and exploits it to the point of being able to control her. The deep guilt of the child keeps him bound to the mother. These dynamic factors so often seen in cases of school phobia may be clear to the therapist. They are meaningless to the child and parents because of their unconscious nature, and cannot be interpreted to them.

As in other kinds of neurotic illness, the child who shows separation anxiety in his early years, who has repeated periods of absence from school, and then later develops the full-blown school phobia, is more severely regressed, more resistive to therapy, and requires a long period of treatment. School phobia that appears for the first time during adolescence is often very difficult to control and may be associated with severe regressive illness(4, 5). This does not mean that all adolescents with school phobia are difficult to treat—some of the best results achieved in clinics come from intensive individual psychotherapy with adolescent girls with school phobia.

Generalized Anxiety in the Child

One sees many children with multiple fears, difficult to explain. The child fears, among other things, the dark, being alone, animals, aggression competition, and new situations. Often one or both parents are similarly apprehensive and have nurtured fear in the child. The parents admit these fears, and yet they point out that only this child of their several children has such fears. Other parents exhibit generalized anxiety, and yet their child, or children, are relatively fearless. Freud(12) referred to generalized apprehensiveness as one of the forms of neurotic anxiety related to the inability of the ego to deal effectively with anxiety.

It is difficult to explain a tendency towards the development of anxiety which begins early in life, which is not related to the behavior or makeup of the parents, or the setting in which the child is reared. One must consider the possibility of constitutional factors in the child, in his instinctual drives or the capacity of the ego to integrate life experiences. Those who oppose this view feel that there is little evidence to support such a theory. There is little evidence, however, to prove that constitutional factors do not play a role. Studies involving the emotional relationships between the mother and infant early in life may throw light on the child's learning early to absorb fear and tension. One can take a crying infant from a tense, anxious mother, place him in the arms of a relaxed nurse, and the crying quickly lessens. Apparently the mother's pressure on the child, her trembling, or tone of voice are communicated to the child. It is reasonable to assume that repeated experiences of this kind might condition him. There is a possibility that a combination of constitutional and emotional factors in the mother help to determine the development of early generalized anxiety in the child. One should also include the undergoing of early traumatic experiences before the period of verbalization, which the child cannot recall, but which have conditioned him to anxiety and apprehension.

Often anxiety is masked, to become apparent only after the child's distrust has been lessened and he feels free to talk. The child may have been shamed early for being fearful, and may need to deny being afraid. Such anxiety may be revealed in play therapy with children, or through relating dreams which contain anxiety. Anxiety occurring in dreams is more acceptable to the child; after he relates the dreams it is often relatively easy to get him to discuss other anxieties and experiences in his waking life.

Occasionally a child will refer to vague, ill-defined feelings of discomfort or tension which cover an underlying depression. Frequently anxiety is masked by marked hyperactivity and restlessness. Anxiety should be suspected whenever a child is markedly irritable and shows a diminished interest in eating, play, and schoolwork. An alert mother or teacher will recognize pronounced changes in these activities. Such changes call for a complete physical examination to rule out organic illness, fatigue, and current experiences that produce tension. If these investigations fail to disclose reasons for the altered behavior, underlying neurotic anxiety should be searched for.

Anxiety is frequently masked by clowning(16). A timid child, teased because of his fearfulness, may find an outlet by actively bringing on laughter instead of enduring it passively. Although the clowning still provokes ridicule, it is tempered by some admiration. He has helped his tormentors to laugh. He has given them pleasure. Making them laugh has disarmed them, and they think less of wanting to beat him. Among tormentors are many who attack in order to alleviate their own anxiety, who may welcome the outlet of laughter and ridicule, preferring this to beating an anxious child—it is less guilt producing.

One should be especially mindful of underlying anxiety in the adolescent whose behavior shows sudden change. An increasing number of adolescents appear to be suffering from excessive tension and depression. The number of such youngsters attempting suicide appears to be on the increase in our community. Factors responsible for this increase are not well understood and require study.

It is well to keep in mind that anxiety may be a cover for organic illness, the ego's method of signaling that all is not well with the body. Freud(12) early cited a case of unexplained anxiety for which his psychoanalytic study could find no explanation. Physical examination revealed the existence of apical tuberculosis. Chronic sinus infection may be responsible for a feeling of depression which clears up when the infection is removed. Not long ago, a ten-year-old boy with marked anxiety, nausea, and dizziness was studied; he had been referred by his pediatrician because there was no evidence of brain tumor as suspected. The findings failed to substantiate factors in the home, school, or child that could cause such serious symptoms and progressive weakness. Further hospitalization was required; only four days before the boy died from a cerebellar malignant tumor did he develop choked discs and other symptoms of neurologic involvement.

Another relationship between anxiety and somatic symptoms is of interest. Freud(12) early showed how neurotic anxiety could be displaced onto somatic phenomena in conversion hysteria. The conversion symptom bound the anxiety. This early interrelationship was clearly demonstrated by Grinker(13), and others investigating war neuroses, in soldiers who suffered from severe forms of anxiety and terror for a period of time, then lost the anxiety manifestations which were replaced by somatic symptoms. An adolescent boy suffering from obsessional neurosis, also suffered from attacks of rheumatoid arthritis. One day he asked why it was that when he had severe arthritic pains, anxiety, which was generally severe, was not present. He added, "I guess the pain takes care of this." It was his way of saying the neurotic need to suffer was not necessary—his guilt was sufficiently punished.

The term acting-out behavior has its origin in psychoanalytic treatment in which the patient showed marked restlessness, anger, and moving about in preference to talking about thoughts and feelings—which could not be expressed because of underlying anxiety. Much of the aggression and combativeness in children is their method of expressing underlying anxiety and unhappiness. Often a child will be aggressive and pick fights during the day, and reveal a marked anxiety during the night when he suffers from night terrors.

An adolescent with school phobia revealed an overwhelming fear of tormenting, vicious boys in his neighborhood. He feared that on his way to school or at school he would be involved with these boys who stole, beat up other children, and provoked the teachers. He found little pleasure in these activities, but went along with them to keep the gang from attacking him. When finally his guilt made it impossible to use this defense, his real underlying anxiety broke out and he remained at home, afraid to leave. His major expressed fear was that he would meet some of the gang, who would get even with him for deserting them.

Anxiety and need for punishment are best seen in the neurotic delinquent, who has found a way of acting-out his neurotic conflict against others rather than against himself. As is true of all neurotic behavior, the attempt to resolve conflict miscarries and the delinquent, through his guilt, is apprehended and punished. Freud(11) introduced the concept of the individual who, through his unconscious sense of guilt, acted-out in delinquency because he unconsciously sought punishment. Many children are seen in child guidance clinic work who belong in this category, who are temporarily relieved by punishment which assuages guilt feeling and keeps the conflict from consciousness. The appearance of these conflicts in consciousness would cause intense anxiety. Individuals who are institutionalized, unable to find an outlet for these underlying conflicts, often are thrown into an acute panic state.

Anxiety about death is a neurotic symptom closely related to a death wish against another person or persons. In children the death wish is most often directed toward an unwelcome sibling with whom the child must share affection. Often it is an expression of envy against the rival in the oedipal triangle. This subject has already been referred to in the hostile dependency relationship between the child and the mother in school phobia.

Whatever the cause of anxiety, help is needed to assist the ego with a situation with which it cannot deal. Anxiety is the signal that the ego has lost the capacity to master the situation. Neurotic anxiety calls for special treatment, made available for the first time through the knowledge that has come from psychoanalysis. This leads us to the subject of therapy.

TREATMENT OF ANXIETY

Treatment of anxiety is a major objective in therapeutic work with children. Efforts are made to determine the causes of anxiety, its methods of expression and concealment. Study of the child includes individual interviews, psychological studies, and interviews with the parents and other members of the family old enough to contribute to the interview, and benefit from it. It is beneficial to have a complete psychological examination of children who manifest anxiety problems, whenever this is possible, to determine the child's capacity to perform and his current achievements; and to have projective tests for study of his personality. To the psychologist, working with the child for long periods of time provides clues to his work habits, feelings of failure, fear of failure, and need for perfection. These clues are important in discovering underlying anxiety. It is advantageous to have the child seen in group therapy also, and in many instances underlying anxiety which expresses itself best through this medium(16) can be observed. Reports from the school and social agencies supply information regarding anxiety in the child and in his family, providing data which often help to explain the anxiety. Many times reports from physicians and clergymen afford information not obtainable in other ways.

There has been an increasing trend to include all members of the family in therapeutic work with children. So many factors within the family play a role in the development of anxiety and conflict in the child that it is logical to explore these factors in the presence of the assembled family members. The child labeled as the problem feels less threatened to learn that his problem is often an expression of an emotional problem in the family. One may ask what it is possible to achieve through family therapy that we have been unable to achieve through individual and group therapy. One cannot help but be impressed by the ability of children and parents (with some exceptions) to learn to communicate frankly and openly in the family sessions and later on to some extent at home. Communication may help materially to lessen anxiety and tension in children who for the first time have learned that it is safe to express themselves.

Some parents refuse to speak frankly in the presence of their children. They are then invited to come in for joint interviews, or for individual interviews if this is what they prefer. Later in therapy they may be willing to discuss matters in the presence of their children. Any technique which makes it easier for family members to communicate with each other honestly and openly should be welcomed. Healthy communication lessens distortion and avoids messages that confuse rather than clarify. The clearer the messages can be, the less the need for guessing and misinterpretation. Generally speaking, communication is good in families in which the parents are emotionally mature. Even parents who are less mature, who are inhibited in expressing themselves because they have never learned that it was safe or good to do so, may learn quickly to communicate. Neurotic, deeply conflicted parents will probably not respond to invitations to communicate freely. They are too threatened by what may be revealed, and are too distrustful to make the attempt. One of the functions of individual therapy will be to get them to the stage where healthy communication is possible.

Objective Fears

Before discussing the treatment of neurotic anxiety, a word should be said about objective fears which can be troublesome and very disturbing to the child. Efforts should be made to lessen these fears. Dealing with reality situations that threaten the child may keep the fears from spreading or becoming chronic. Children vary in their sensitivity to emotional experiences. Sensitive children become fearful more easily; when this is recognized it is well to protect them from stories or movies that ordinarily produce fearful responses. Children who are ridiculed for showing fear may attempt to be overly courageous. This should be pointed out to them, with the explanation that their courageousness is based on their shame of having fears. A discussion of the reasons for their reality fears may help them to accept the fears and later to overcome them. Knowing that one must be careful in crossing the street, the parents can make a game of crossing the street carefully, looking both ways before starting across, then allowing the child to cross alone in the sight of the parents. It is well to provide packing boxes, boards, ladders, and barrels around the play space of the child which he may use for developing skills in co-ordination and in learning through caution. He can learn that taking unnecessary risks is neither smart nor wise.

The child who has developed fear of the dark or of heights may be unconditioned by games that are pleasant or rewards that give him pleasure. He will fear a dog less if he helps to begin to raise a dog as a puppy. Many reality fears lessen as he plays with other children who do not have fears. Parents who have a problem with generalized anxiety in themselves will have difficulty in lessening and preventing reality fears in their children. Selma Fraiberg(9) has an interesting discussion of fears and phobias in children, to which the reader is referred.

Anxiety that clears up quickly without an understanding of why it appeared may soon reappear, sometimes in another form. The concern of the parents who have sought help for him may satisfy the child that he is loved. Comforted by the knowledge that his problems are less severe than he had imagined, the child often loses his anxiety and no longer feels he needs help.

This development may lead the parents to believe that they have made an error in referring him. It is unfortunate if the parents fail to heed our warning and prematurely withdraw the child from treatment, thus deny-ing themselves an opportunity to get a clearer picture of the causes of the anxiety and other symptoms. The situation is different in those cases where there has been sufficient time for a careful study in which impor-tant clues have been discovered to help explain the anxiety and dis-comfort. Parents, content with this new knowledge, may want to discon-tinue help and try on their own. They will return for further help if their efforts fail to maintain good results. When the anxiety symptoms of one child clear up but are followed by symptoms in another child or in a parent, the family should be helped to see that treatment to promote emotional equilibrium in the whole family is necessary. Parents who object to the inconvenience of frequent trips to the clinic for treatment have not been sufficiently impressed with the need for therapy, or they lack a necessary emotional investment in the child. In those cases in which therapy is prolonged, it is well to review with the family at regular intervals what progress has been made and what more has to be done.

Treatment of anxiety or neurotic illness will depend largely on what can be tolerated by the child and by the family. It may stop shortly after the start if the family is threatened by the demands of therapy which they had not expected and are unwilling to accept. The required therapy should always be made clear before a treatment program begins. The parents may otherwise lack the force to demand that the child continue in therapy during the stages of resistance when he is threatened by the material revealed. Prolonged effort is required to help children suffering from severe anxiety who resist therapy because of a fear of revealing feelings. Their anxiety is related to the fact that what is hidden should remain hidden. The child who has repressed deep hostility in a rivalry conflict with his parents often lacks the courage to discuss subjects related to these conflicts. A few brief case presentations that follow will help to call attention to various factors in treatment.

Case 1: Gerald, a 10-year-old boy, for several weeks before referral had a need to report bad thoughts to his mother which unfortunately involved her. He told her that other mothers were prettier than she; he frequently wished that she would meet with an accident or illness; and at times he did not believe in God. This last was the severest blow to the mother who was a deeply religious woman. Gerald told her he often wished to see her naked, so that he could see the genital area of her body. At times he wished she were dead and in Hell. The mother, seriously threatened by this sudden behavior, told her priest about these symptoms, and he referred her to the clinic.

The parents were middle-aged, hard-working people with seven other children. The father, a quiet, passive man, ran a small business. The mother was a more volatile person, highly emotional, very much concerned—as we were also for a while—that Gerald was developing a psychosis. Interviews between the social worker and the psychiatrist dealt with sudden changes in Gerald's behavior, his loss of religious feeling, and his interest in sex. In spite of his symptoms he continued to play with his friends and to involve himself in sports. His interest in play and sports persisted throughout therapy.

Gerald had average intelligence and did passing work in school. Rorschach examination showed him to be preoccupied with destruction, fire, danger, and smoke. He felt that danger lurked everywhere. There was evidence in the Rorschach test of a rigid superego and considerable diffuse anxiety. Gerald was ill at ease in the interviews at first, but then relaxed and was able to speak frankly about the tormenting wishes that his mother were dead or crippled. He fantasied her breasts cut off and indicated a strong wish to see her naked and performing the sex act. After several weeks of therapy, he found it possible to keep some of the thoughts from his mother. He became aware that his mother was less seriously upset by hearing these thoughts than she had been. He assured the psychiatrist and his mother that he really did not wish these bad things would happen because he dearly loved his mother. He spoke about pregnancy and the birth process freely. He had known little or nothing about impregnation.

Interviews with the parents showed them to be rather rigid about sex, which they had never discussed with any of their children. They found it possible in time to discuss sexual matters with Gerald and with the other children. They were aware of Gerald's severe anxiety and assured him that these thoughts would leave him and the clinic would help him. They had long discussions about their religious views with the worker.

Gerald dreamed frequently and his dreams were discussed with him. He had a strong wish to find out why he had to have such bizarre thoughts. On one or two occasions he claimed to be improving faster than he was, and he admitted that therapy was difficult and at times threatening, but it was not difficult to have him continue with his interviews.

The attempt was made many times at regular intervals to elicit hostile feelings or underlying hatred of his mother. Generally I do not discuss underlying hostility with children as disturbed and confused as Gerald. My therapy was based on psychoanalytic concepts, it was not child analysis. If I had been seeing him in analysis several times a week, I would have reached the time when he could accept interpretations of unconscious material for which therapy prepared him. In Gerald's case, he seemed so eager to understand why he had such strange hostile wishes toward his mother that I decided to discuss conscious hostile thoughts he might have or had had toward his mother. If such discussion yielded material which confused him or contained distortions which could be easily clarified, I would discuss them with him.

Gerald was able to understand from interpretations that the hatred of his mother was very likely based on a wish and need to cover up a deep love which threatened him. There was nothing in the clinic material to suggest conscious castration anxiety. He was able to see that his marked anxiety and depression was based on guilt, and fear of punishment of his wishes. His belief that there was no God was due to a fear of punishment from God.

After six months it was increasingly apparent that Gerald wanted to discontinue his interviews. By this time his distressing thoughts had really lessened. When they appeared at infrequent intervals they no longer bothered him. The parents had not been able to accept the idea of prolonged therapy and showed an incapacity to involve themselves in underlying factors which contributed to

Gerald's illness. They reported that he was a vastly improved boy, happy and gay, and very different in all respects from what he had been earlier when he felt unhappy and fearful. When it became apparent that, despite our wishes, the parents were not interested in further therapy and were content with the progress achieved in seven months' time, the study was closed.

Case 2:   In contrast to this case is the one of Fred(18), which is reported elsewhere, an obsessionally neurotic nine-year-old boy with marked anxiety and fear of approaching insanity. He was a brilliant boy who had many problems of aggression in the home and at school. He could not tolerate anyone walking in front of him, because it stirred up the wish to push his face into the anal area of that person, and suck out his feces. Fred was very resistant to treatment at first, but within a few weeks became eager for help and came in regularly for interviews three times a week. His analysis lasted for a period of three years, during which time his parents were most cooperative in their weekly therapeutic interviews with the social worker. Fred was also included in group therapy which contributed significantly to his being able to relate himself to other children in the group and to the group worker. Group therapy was instituted early as a method of making the clinic an interesting place for him. In the beginning of therapy Fred was very resistant toward coming in for interviews. He was aware of his inability to make or retain friends in the neighborhood or at school. He enjoyed the activity of the group and the supervised contacts with other youngsters. He recognized that the group worker was fair, consistent, and firm with the children. She supplied a kind of control which he needed, but had never had. He remained in group therapy throughout his entire clinic treatment, and I considered this to be an important factor in his improvement. At the completion of his therapy most of his ritualistic behavior had disappeared, his anxiety was no longer present, and the aggression had lessened. His progress since that time and over a period of 12 years has been excellent in every respect.

Case 3:   James, another obsessionally neurotic boy, was seen briefly for a period of time when he was 11 years old. Within a few months his symptoms lessened and he saw no need for further treatment. His parents, in spite of continued urging that therapy be prolonged, were content with James's improvement. He remained free from compulsive symptoms until a year ago when he became markedly anxious, his compulsive symptoms became numerous and disturbing, and he was overwhelmed by anxiety. He is now in therapy, well aware of his need to remain in treatment until advised by me that therapy is no longer necessary.

One can see similar instances of discontinuing therapy in cases of school phobia after the child returns to school and is content to attend school. Several factors combine to explain this. The parents find it an effort to come to the clinic, to continue to pay a fee, to involve themselves in learning the role they have played. They and the child feel stigmatized by coming to a clinic, and feel that since their child is happy and things are going well in the home, there is little need to continue. Several youngsters insufficiently treated for school phobia have been seen, who later in life needed help for disturbing inhibitions and anxiety which had remained dormant for many years. A letter was received recently from a physician asking about therapy given a 10-year-old girl, now 40 years old, who had responded well to treatment lasting over a period of 10 months. Many therapists are aware that recurrence of emotional illness may be due to serious emotional crises in children and adults who have had very intensive therapy over a long period of time; however, this number could be materially lessened by prolonging the therapy of severely neurotic children whose behavior and symptomatology give clear evidence that further work is necessary to prevent later suffering. It is important that one discover means and ways of determining in which cases it is safe to use supportive measures that lessen anxiety in the child and those in which it is vital to uncover conflicts which are bound later to recur.

Supportive measures are helpful in making reality more acceptable. They are helpful for children with low self-esteem, who can respond to an explanation of their discomfort and unhappiness. In these discussions misunderstandings can be cleared up, and they may be able to recognize why they are oversensitive. The factors discussed in these interviews deal with reality situations which they can recall and which either they or their parents have talked about. Aichhorn once stated to me, "I always use simple forms of therapy first. When these do not result in improvement, I use other forms of therapy."

The uncovering of unconscious conflicts through insight therapy is required when anxiety, guilt, and disabling neurotic symptoms do not respond to other forms of therapy, such as dealing with the environment, supportive treatment, or the use of clarification. Unless insight therapy is used when needed, development is impeded with unfortunate consequences for later life adjustment. Until sufficient staff and time are available to meet more adequately the needs of children and families requiring psychotherapy, one will need to be content with present progress. A great deal more can be done now than 30 years ago. Vigorous action being contemplated at present may help materially to furnish the kind of treatment necessary.

Role of Parents Important

The role of the parents in the production of neurotic anxiety in children is an important one. This is well illustrated in school phobia. Here the anxiety of the parents produces the fear of separation in the child and maintains him in a state of fear. The child's anxiety in turn forces the parents to be overprotective, and the enslavement of the parents follows. Chronic exposure of the child to the anxiety-laden atmosphere in the home further inhibits growth toward independence(7). In many instances, nothing short of psychoanalytic therapy of the parents, and often of the child also, is required to uncover the unconscious conflicts that produce this pathology.

A follow-up study of the cases of school phobia studied at Judge Baker Guidance Center was reported in a paper by Dr. John Coolidge(6) at the Annual Orthopsychiatric Meeting in 1964. This study demonstrated that a high proportion of seriously disturbed children with school phobia, in spite of psychotherapy provided by competent staff for the child and his parents, continued several years later to manifest serious suffering. They remained inhibited, withdrawn, and emotionally conflicted. This is true of children with other forms of serious psychoneurotic illness, who do not respond to therapy. They continue to manifest neurotic suffering. I believe that such children and parents would stand a better chance of improving, and remaining well, if intensive psychoanalytic therapy could be provided for them.

Helping the child get back to school, so he can realize that it is safe, is a good procedure but it usually requires considerable effort to get the child and the parents to accept it. Parents with deep anxiety and guilt may fear that pressure will cause a complete mental break, and prefer that the child remain in the home until he indicates he is ready to return. The Judge Baker studies (24, 25) of school phobia indicate that intensive help in the school is sound. They found that when evidences of school phobia were located early, the illness could often be aborted. This demanded considerable effort and understanding on the part of the school personnel. In a project with a particular school, members of the

Judge Baker staff were able to deal intensively with the teaching staff. They pointed out to the teachers that they were not the reason for the anxiety but that the cause lay in factors within the child and the family. In this way they could offset the teacher's guilt and prevent undue severity or permissiveness to the child.

Many therapists have found that casework with the parents helps the mother to transfer her dependency relationship to the worker and away from the child. In the meantime, the therapist working with the child helps him to become more independent of the mother. This will happen if the child develops a working relationship to the therapist. The relationship soon becomes one of dependency, and relieves the mother of some of the discomfort of the child's excessive dependency. Some of the hostile elements in the child's dependency may be transferred to the therapist. Since the therapist is aware of the hostile components he can discuss the subject of hostile dependency with the child. In the more severe cases, the child becomes dependent on the therapist without lessening the dependency tie to his mother, especially if the mother cannot lessen her need to maintain the dependency relationship. The best results obtain when the mother or parents relate meaningfully to the caseworker and can respond to her therapy, while the child works well with his therapist. These cases of school phobia, in which therapy was maintained effectively with the parents and the child, were in the best emotional state when studied in the follow-up made by the Judge Baker staff, in the studies referred to above. Such treatment is helpful in returning the child to the school, but is more important for the future life relationship between the mother and child, and between the mother and her other children.

Adelaide Johnson(15) and her co-workers emphasized the need for separate therapists for the mother and child in cases of school phobia. Both should develop a transference neurosis so that unconscious hostility can be analyzed.

Because of the great dependency needs of the infant early in life, every effort must be made to neutralize quickly any unavoidable separation from the mother by replacing her with another person who can supply the child with mothering care. Such care cannot be provided easily and is probably best available in carefully selected foster homes. Bowlby(3) has made important contributions to our knowledge of the effect of early long separation of the infant from the mother. He made these studies in a hospital setting where, in spite of good care, young children who had enjoyed a strong positive tie to their mother reacted with great anxiety to her absence. Bowlby describes a rather definite pattern of behavior which he divides into three periods of varying length which merge into each other. There is first a period of "protest" during which the child is acutely distressed and agitated, and searches in every face for his longed-for mother. This may last from several hours to a week or more and is followed by a period of "despair." In this stage he is sadly agitated, cries monotonously, becomes withdrawn, makes few demands, and reflects a feeling of helplessness. Following this is a period of "detachment" during which he begins to notice people again and may appear to be sociable. When his mother comes to visit, his former attachment behavior is no longer present. He seems hardly to know her; there is a listless turning away. If he stays on in the hospital and has a series of nurses or care-takers, he rarely reacts to their leaving and behaves as if contacts with humans mean little to him. He tends to end up by refusing to risk attachment to anyone and becomes increasingly self-centered(2).

What Bowlby describes so eloquently is the development of nar-cissism. Anna Freud and others have stressed the danger of a long separation of mother and child. Anna Freud(2a), Max Schur(2b), and René Spitz(2c) disagree with Bowlby(2) who equates the suffering of the child with mourning that occurs in adults.

In child guidance work, countless examples of children are seen who have been deprived of their love objects early in life or in later childhood, and whose capacity to relate to others is therefore profoundly impaired. Many are so traumatized they cannot respond to foster home care unless a tremendous output of affection and care is available for long periods of time. Aichhorn* describes the narcissistic child as extremely hypersen-sitive, unable to tolerate tension or frustration because of a surcharge of libido invested in his ego. This subject has been discussed elsewhere, with description of the care and patience required to make it possible for a narcissistic child to develop the capacity of love for another human being. Dr. Stanley King(18), a gifted therapist and analyst, successfully treated several severely disturbed youngsters without resorting to interpretations of unconscious behavior. Dr. King accomplished this feat through accept-ing the child in his home and waiting over a long period for the child to be finally able to accept and trust him and his wife; only then was it possible for the child to express the anxiety and suffering he had endured before coming to live in the King home. Rapid improvement followed the child's ability to communicate his suffering.

---

* Unpublished–presented at a seminar in Vienna in 1930.

THE UNMET NEED FOR THERAPY

There is a great need—unmet at the present time—for dealing with the anxiety and suffering of severely deprived children who have a feeling of helplessness. They pass from one agency to another and from one institution to another. Many will probably never be able to respond to good care and therapy. Ways must be found for dealing with children and families who feel helpless. Their pleas for help cannot continue to be denied. There is sufficient evidence to show that emotional illness, suicide, and wanton destruction of life and property are intimately related to the feeling of helplessness.

It has been demonstrated that sufficient knowledge is available to deal effectively with severely deprived children, and one must be prepared to put these practices into effect. As soon as those in key positions accept the fact that it is crucial to help these children, this knowledge will be optimally utilized. The Family Centered Project(21) in St. Paul has demonstrated that disorganized families, torn by conflict, great unhappiness, and anxiety, can respond to patient, intelligent efforts from dedicated workers. Resistant and distrustful at first, conditioned to avoid social agencies because of unfortunate experiences in the past, they slowly recognized genuine feelings in the workers who sincerely wished to help them. At least half the families worked with in this manner ended up by developing strong dependency relationships to the workers and remained in casework therapy until they had been helped. Such a program has been called "aggressive casework practice." The aggression refers to the refusal of the caseworker to withdraw from the family until every effort had been made to involve them.

What has been described under therapy refers largely to the efforts of trained psychotherapists who work with children suffering from anxiety. The number of children who need help because of anxiety, depression and a feeling of helplessness is far greater than the number who can be served by trained therapists. Workers in every institution that houses deprived, retarded, delinquent, or psychotic children are aware of the great amount of suffering in these children from neurotic and reality fears, and feelings of tension, rejection, and neglect. They can be helped to recognize the indirect manifestations of anxiety in children. They are in a strategic position to offer comfort and acceptance to many children who have never experienced consistent acceptance. It is helpful if trained therapists encourage the untrained to make this contribution, since such help is often not attempted, through a fear it should be reserved for the trained staff. Untrained workers who start in this way may go on to take training if they discover they have a talent for working with troubled children.

What has been said about workers in children's institutions applies equally to workers in day care centers, clubs, playgrounds, and camps. Many of the principles learned in training for psychotherapy are very useful when applied to untrained workers who are in a position to help, are motivated to help, and who know their limitations.

An ever-present problem which trained psychotherapists have been unable to solve is that of finding time to provide the therapy required by seriously disturbed children who suffer from anxiety. Many of these children can benefit only from intensive psychoanalytic therapy. Without such therapy one can be quite certain that conflict and illness will persist. Parents are often unable to pay for such therapy, and the community is not ready to provide it. As a result, many workers have been discouraged from seeking training in child analysis.

REFERENCES

1. BENEDEK, THERESE.   Toward the biology of the depressive constellation. *J. Amer. Psychoanal. Assn.*, 1956, 4(3):389.

2. BOWLBY, J.   Grief and mourning in infancy and early childhood. *Psychoanalytic study of the child*, Vol. XV. New York: International Universities Press, 1960.
   2a. FREUD, ANNA: Discussion of Dr. Bowlby's paper, p. 53.
   2b. SCHUR, MAX: Discussion of Dr. Bowlby's paper, p. 63.
   2c. SPITZ, RENÉ: Discussion of Dr. Bowlby's paper, p. 85.

3. BOWLBY, J.   Separation anxiety. *Int. J. Psychoanal.*, 1960, **41**:89–113.

4. COOLIDGE, JOHN C., *et al.*   School phobia in adolescence—a manifestation of severe character disturbance. *Amer. J. Orthopsychiat.*, 1960, 30(3):599.

5. ————.   The residential treatment of children and adolescents with school phobia. *Amer. J. Orthopsychiat.*, 1964, 34(1):103.

6. ————, *et al.*   Ten year follow-up of sixty-six school phobic children. Paper presented at Annual Orthopsychiatric Meeting, 1964.

7. EISENBERG, LEON.   School phobia diagnosis, genesis and clinical management—*pediatric clinics of North America*. 1958, **5**:645.

8. FERENCZI, SANDOR.   The unwelcome child and his death instinct. *Int. J. Psychoanal.*, 1929, **10**:125.

9. FRAIBERG, SELMA.   *The magic years.* New York: Charles Scribner's Sons, 1959.

10. FREUD, ANNA. *The ego and the mechanisms of defense.* London: Hogarth Press, 1937.

11. FREUD, SIGMUND. Some character types met in psychoanalytic work. *Collected Papers,* Vol. IV. London: Hogarth Press, 1925.

12. FREUD, SIGMUND. *The problem of anxiety.* New York: Psychoanalytic Quarterly Press, 1936.

13. GRINKER, ROY and SPIEGEL, JOHN P. *Men under stress.* Philadelphia: McGraw-Hill Book Co., 1945.

14. HARTMANN, HEINZ; KRIS, ERNST; and LOWENSTEIN, RUDOLPH. Comments on the formation of psychic structure. *Psychoanalytic study of the child,* Vol. II. New York: International Universities Press, 1946.

15. JOHNSON, ADELAIDE; ESTES, HUBERT; and HAYLETT, CLARICE. Separation anxiety. *Amer. J. Psychother,* 1956, **10**:682.

16. KLEIN, EMANUEL. The reluctance to go to school. *Psychoanalytic study of the child,* Vol. 1. New York: International Universities Press, 1945.

17. LIPPMAN, HYMAN S. The use of dreams in psychiatric work with children. *Psychoanalytic study of the child,* Vol. I. New York: International Universities Press, 1945.

18. LIPPMAN, HYMAN S. *Treatment of the child in emotional conflict.* 2d ed.; New York: McGraw-Hill Book Co., 1962.

19. LIPPMAN, HYMAN S. Highlights, personal and educational, in the training and clinical experience of a child psychiatrist. *J. Amer. Acad. Child Psychiat.,* 1963, **2**(2):384–404.

20. NUNBERG, HERMAN. The synthetic function of the ego. *Int. J. Psychoanal.,* 1931, **12**:123.

21. OVERTON, ALICE, *et al.* Serving families who don't want help. *J. Soc. Casewk,* 1953, **34**(7):304.

22. SPITZ, RENÉ. Anaclitic depression. *Psychoanalytic Study of the Child,* Vol. II. New York: International Universities Press, 1946.

23. WAELDER, ROBERT. The problem of the genesis of psychical conflict in earliest infancy. *Int. J. Psychoanal.,* 1937, **18**:406.

24. WALDFOGEL, SAMUEL; COOLIDGE, JOHN C.; and HAHN, PAULINE. The development, meaning, and management of school phobia. *Amer. J. Orthopsychiat.,* 1957, **27**(4):754.

25. WALDFOGEL, SAMUEL; TESSMAN, ELLEN; and HAHN, PAULINE. A program of early intervention in school phobia. *Amer. J. Orthopsychiat.,* 1959, **29**(2):324.

Loretta Cass

Psychotherapy with the Obsessive-Compulsive Child

THE FAMILY OF DISORDERS in children dynamically encompassed by the term "obsessive-compulsive" is one of the more easily recognized and most consistently described as to etiology and course. The separate diagnoses within the group range from the very deviant, near-psychotic, or psychotic "obsessional child," through the obsessive-compulsive neurotic and those with character disorders bearing the obsessive-compulsive stamp, to the compulsive child functioning within nearly normal limits. All of these disorders and their close relatives show, in common, characteristics of the anal stage of psychosexual development and one or more of an interrelated set of defenses. The therapy of children with disorders within this group, however, varies widely as to mode and prognosis depending, among other factors, upon the age and time of onset of the illness, the pervasiveness of the disturbance in terms of the range and degree of ego functions involved and the availability of anxiety and affect for a therapeutic relationship.

THE OBSESSIVE-COMPULSIVE CHILD

The seriously disturbed obsessional or obsessive-compulsive child usually finds his way to a child guidance clinic or an in-patient treatment center. But the moderately disturbed obsessive-compulsive child is likely, in our culture, not only to go unnoticed at home and at school but, more frequently, to be highly valued as a "good child" who obeys rules and makes many of his own, who achieves well and causes little or no trouble through display of affect or aggression. The disturbance, when it is of moderate degree, is a culturally acceptable one which causes suffering only to its host and is, therefore, allowed to progress to more serious consequences in adolescence and adulthood. A degree of obsessive-compulsiveness is, moreover, the "natural" condition of latency and is often a welcome relief to parents after the turbulence of the oedipal age.

As is true in all but the most severe neuroses of childhood, the diagnosis and treatment of obsessive-compulsive neurosis is complicated by the fact that the personality is still in the process of development. The diagnostician must differentiate (1) those children who are displaying difficulties in psychosexual progress but who can be expected, because of adequate resources such as ego strength and capacity for coping with conflict, to overcome the temporary delay, from (2) those children who cannot be expected under the present circumstances to develop normally. Treatment of the former group may be undertaken to relieve childhood suffering but may not be indispensable for healthy adulthood. With treatment resources as limited as they are, this distinction becomes an important consideration.

Nature and Etiology of the Disorder

The relatedness among a variety of disorders which includes obsessional neuroses, compulsion neuroses, obsessive-compulsive neuroses, and compulsive character disorders is to be found in the common denominator between "obsession" and "compulsion." Fenichel defines compulsions as "obsessions that are still felt as impulses"(8, p. 269). Both compulsions and obsessions are "derivatives of warded-off impulses" which "betray their nature as derivatives by their exaggerated character, that is, by the disproportion of the accompanying emotions or by the rigidity with which they are adhered to"(8, p. 268). In the obsession, an intense idea represents the energy of some impulse or of another connected impulsive idea that has been warded off; in the compulsion, the original, instinctive impulse is evidenced in a compulsive urge to counteraction against it or in an urge to act in a manner disguised but more directly associated with the original impulse. In both cases, the observable phenomena—that is, symptoms or character traits—are condensations of both instinctual and anti-instinctual forces and represent a compromise by the ego. The ego "has to use its governing power according to a strange command of a more powerful agency contradicting its judgment. It is compelled to do or think, or to omit certain things; otherwise it feels menaced by terrible threats"(8, p. 268).

The "more powerful agency" to which Fenichel refers is the superego, and it is the appearance of the superego which fixes the time of onset of obsessive-compulsive neuroses. Most of these neuroses begin in the latency period at a time when, because of castration anxiety, parental rules and prohibitions against oedipal strivings are being internalized. When, however, the balance between oedipal impulses and anti-instinctual forces of the developing superego is uneven, the child, fearing the strength and consequences of the impulses, attempts to ward them off by regressing to the anal-sadistic stage. The anal-sadistic impulses then "grow at the expense of the original phallic Oedipus impulses; the genital Oedipus impulses decrease in strength as the anal-sadistic impulses increase." This observation prompted Freud to conclude that "the instinctual organization of the obsessive-compulsive neurotic even in the adult resembles that of the child in the anal-sadistic phase of development"(8, p. 274). It is in the fact of his regression from the phallic stage to the anal that the obsessive-compulsive differs from the hysteric. The hysteric has repressed his oedipal wishes but suffers from their influence in terms of symptoms and the constriction of ego functions.

The "choice" of regression as a defense in the obsessive-compulsive is thought to depend upon one or more of the following factors: (1) the outcome of the original anal-sadistic stage; (2) the strength of the phallic drives and of the threat opposed to their expression; (3) the strength of the ego. The attraction backward to the anal-sadistic stage may be due to constitutional factors, to unusual anal gratifications, to phallic frustrations which drive the child to seek earlier gratifications, or to the association of anal gratification with security gratification—for example, with approval for accepting the training procedures. The importance of cultural preference for anal-compulsive traits over phallic-aggressive traits should not be overlooked. Erikson describes the seriousness with which Western civilization takes its bowel training, proceeding on the assumption "that early and rigorous training not only keeps the home atmosphere nicer but is absolutely necessary for the development of orderliness and punctuality" (7, p. 77).

From the point of the regression on, the neurotic conflict takes on the characteristics of the anal stage and the predominant defenses are those typical of this stage. However, the residuals of the original phallic conflict are very often apparent in the symptoms of the compulsive disorder and the conflict per se often comes to light after the anal-sadistic conflicts are worked through in therapy.

Very often, in obsessional children, the content of the obsession is clearly phallic in meaning while its structure and mode of representation are clearly anal. For example, the phallic conflict may be preserved in a cathexis for cars, keys, or rockets while the repetitiousness, controlling-ness, stubborn retention, and sadistic use of these obsessions bear the stamp of the anality to which the child has regressed. Moreover, the excitement which a child displays over his obsessive object or compulsive ritual is often likened to that which is normally invested in the oedipal object. The obsession has become the "only love" of his life and the one area where constructive energy and curiosity are evidenced.

Fenichel raises the question as to whether a compulsive neurosis can arise as fixation at the original anal-sadistic stage rather than through regression from the oedipal stage. He points out that while cases of disturbance in the anal-sadistic stage do occur, the absence of typical compulsive symptoms in the syndrome would argue against their being classified with compulsive neuroses as such. Fenichel suggests, further, that "the compulsive character without symptoms represents an arrested evolution rather than a regression"(8, p. 531). In this compulsive character formation, the ego avoids the recurrent conflict between impulse and defense through adopting as part of itself an overall defensive structure—for example, a continuous attitude of reaction formation that is prepared to handle any breakthrough of hostility as soon as anxiety signals its imminence. The ego may be aware of this mode of adjustment and welcome it even though it severely restricts ego flexibility.

Symptoms and Behavior

In both hysteria and obsessive-compulsive neuroses, symptom formation originates as a defense against instinctual oedipal demands. In the obsessive-compulsive, however, there is, because of the regression, the defense against anal-sadistic strivings as well. The conflict is waged between these strivings and the newly formed superego. The more fully developed the child's superego is, the more the threat becomes one of danger from within, that is, the loss of self-respect and the fear of annihilation. Obsessive-compulsive children often experience fear of dying.

Example: Eight-year-old Laurie was brought to the clinic after a two-months' struggle with sleeplessness. Each night she tried to go to sleep in her own bed but usually lay awake, plagued by thoughts of death, ghosts, and skeletons. If she did drop off to sleep, these macabre visitors invaded her dreams and she would awaken, terrified. She could not be comforted until she was allowed to sleep with one of her parents.

This problem was especially hard for Laurie's very bright and sophisticated parents to accept. "Why couldn't their highly intelligent girl see how ridiculous her fears were and talk herself out of being afraid?" Laurie had had little difficulty solving most other problems she encountered.

Diagnostic study found Laurie to be an obsessive-compulsive child whose drive for perfectionism was matched by deep-seated hostility toward parents who expected much and gave little. Her neurosis had been of long standing but had, up to now, been represented only in tight defenses of a kind welcomed by her parents. Her present state of upset seemed to coincide with her awareness that her mother was pregnant. Laurie expected further loss of her short supply of parental affection, was extremely angry over this expectation, but could not risk expression of her anger. Guilt over it led her to fear that she would die and, in a child's mind, going to sleep is something like dying. In Laurie's case, her projective test stories showed direct association between the two events.

The compulsive act or compulsive thought (obsession) is both a substitute for the warded-off impulse and a stand against it. It has both the symbolic meaning of defense and of gratification. In some symptoms, the instinctual aspect is more prominent; in other symptoms, or, at other times within the same type of symptom, the defensive, anti-instinctual aspect is more prominent; still other compulsive symptoms clearly represent the struggle between instinct and defense.

In children, compulsive acts are often first noticed as rituals connected with eating, toileting, dressing, or going to bed. Initially, these rituals are simply repetitive but, to the child, indispensable accompaniments to routines and are undertaken to stave off the fear associated with the warded-off impulse. For example, the ritual at bedtime may serve to overcome the fear that going to sleep engenders in those children, such as Laurie, for whom going to sleep may be equated with the death they expect for hostile wishes; or, the ritual of touching each bathroom fixture may serve to reinforce superego prohibitions against touching the genitals. With progress of the illness, however, the rituals take over so much of the motor repertoire that ego functions of all kinds are curtailed. In one such child, a touching-smelling-counting compulsion had finally made school attendance impossible. The environment which will not lend itself to the execution of his compulsive rituals becomes unbearable to the child.

In other compulsive acts, the superego aspects are more prominent. "Washing" to overcome dirty thoughts, especially those about masturbation, is a frequent symptom-defense. Here the symptom is in the nature of undoing the intended act. In other types of "undoing," the symptom consists of two activities, one of which is the opposite of the other. For example, the child may need to erase nearly everything he writes when writing has taken on the meaning of some forbidden impulse, such as aggression. The doing-undoing sequence may gain momentum until almost all of the child's motor output is caught up in this circular self-defeating system. Compulsive children in religious families often find in the rituals of religion counteraction against the unacceptable impulse, or self-punishment for it. With the progress of illness, the symptoms may lose their superego characteristics and display more of the returning impulse. One lifelong obsessive-compulsive girl began, in adolescence, to torture herself and her family by her insistence on exact compliance to a host of religious rituals which had long since been discarded even by their church. Although her parents constantly pointed out to her the hostility involved in her ritualistic demands upon them, she could avoid acceptance or responsibility for it under guise of the dictates of her conscience.

In obsessions, the warded-off impulse is represented, directly or indirectly, in an idea that is rigidly clung to and about which the ego has awareness but little control. Frequently, the obsessive thought replaces the impulsive urge in a rather direct manner without the original affect. An obsessive child's Thematic Apperception Test stories may be a repetitious account of acted-out revenge without the expected fear or remorse. In one very seriously disturbed, obsessional four-year-old boy, thoughts about trains, their different types, differential details, distinctive qualities, their functions and dysfunctions occupied the whole of his thinking day and kept him awake at night. The trains represented, for this child, rather direct expression of sexual-aggressive impulses which he both feared and coveted. They were, at once, the symbol of incestuous gratification and the feared omen of his annihilation. In a later breakdown of ideas into action, he was nearly killed one day when he found it impossible to resist the urge to throw himself in front of a train. In almost all compulsions, the "idea" aspect is represented as a "command from within" to act. Children can often describe these ideas in graphic detail frequently anthropomorphizing the inner voice to resemble the internalized parent.

Some obsessions represent the anti-instinctual forces more clearly than the instinctual aspects. This is especially noted in reaction formations where attitudes directly opposed to the bothersome anal-erotic and anal-sadistic ones are cultivated. Instead of hostile and sadistic thoughts, the child thinks "nice" things about everyone; instead of the wish for rebellion, cooperation is the rule; kindness and a relentless search after justice replace cruelty and injustice. In the mild or moderate stages of the illness, the child is usually described by the school as an exceptionally "nice child," especially when the defenses are so secure that the opposing impulse or idea does not break through.

In addition to compulsive undoing and reaction formation, the obsessive-compulsive syndrome is also characterized by intellectualization and other forms of isolation. Ideas are separated from their traumatic emotional impact in various ways. The wish for expression of forbidden impulses may, for example, become a mere "thought," bereft of its action potential. The child may play a game with words, numbers, or letters connected to the conflictual ideas but disconnected from the affect originally present. One compulsive boy reeled off one self-concept for each letter of his own name in a casual, nonanxious manner even though the content was highly depreciating and bespoke the abject rejection he had experienced.

As long as the intellectualization is not too extreme and can utilize subject matter appropriate to school work rather than tangential, peculiar content, its defensive character may go unrecognized. These children are described as careful, bright, hard-working students and the teacher only wishes she had thirty of them instead of one or two in her class. It is only when the constriction inherent in the strictly intellectual approach becomes apparent or when the defense fails and, much to the surprise of the teacher, the impulse counterpart breaks through in temper, rebellion, or sexuality that the child's illness forces attention.

Of course, the more severe forms of obsessional disorders are not mistaken for socialization and conformity. The behavior of the extremely obsessional child is so unusual that he is classed among the "pseudo-neurotic psychotic" or "borderline" children described by Ekstein and others(6, 14, 22). Here the obsession encompasses most or all of the ego functions and may take on a bizarre form. One bright four-year-old boy could think of nothing but keys and would go to any length to get keys, hide them in the most unexpected places (e.g., a cake of soap), and use them at the most inappropriate times, for instance, the middle of the night. This child did not respond to out-patient psychotherapy and, eight years later, was in a psychiatric hospital where he was substituting one symptom for another while his general ego functioning had deteriorated to a "dull normal" level. These severe obsessions usually begin very early in life and often appear with the birth of a sibling or with another unbearable competition, such as the remarriage of the mother. M. Wulff (23) points out that, even at one year of age, the child develops a concept of "belonging to me" which corresponds to an anal cathexis of objects. Jealousy is commonly the affective component of this early development and is demonstrated in violent rage and sadistic outbreaks. Obsessions may then appear and represent symbolically the devastating impulse. Occurring as it does when the ego is still much too immature to handle the anxiety, the resulting disorder is much closer in nature to psychosis than to neurosis. Ego development is severely retarded except, in most cases, in the one area of the cathected obsessional thinking.

Even in regard to these severe ego involvements, the question arises of why the illness takes the form of obsession. As early as 1913, Freud had offered the interesting hypothesis that, in certain children, there may be "a premature advance of ego development ahead of libido development" and that this advancement "contributes to the obsessional disposition" (22, p. 131). Melanie Klein, disagreeing with Freud's insistence that superego development takes place to resolve the oedipus complex, claims that the superego forms much earlier to combat pregenital strivings and that objects introjected during the oral-sadistic phase constitute the superego. In this formulation, obsessional disorders are traced, as they are in Freud's theory, to a conflict between id and superego, but a superego which is not dependent for its existence upon oedipal conflict. Rather, the obsessions represent reactions of an infantile superego to the young child's anxiety stemming from the suppression of oral and anal aggression(22, p. 174). Certainly, the pervasive ego-enveloping anxiety of the very young obsessional child lends credence to the primitive oral-anal character of its genesis.

Prognosis for Recovery

Prognosis, with therapy, of children suffering from obsessive-compulsive disorders can be expected to vary widely depending upon (1) the age of the child and the time of onset of the illness; (2) the pervasiveness of the disturbance in terms of the breadth and degree to which ego functions are involved; (3) the presence of usable anxiety to motivate change; (4) the availability of affect for the therapeutic relationship; and (5) the capacity of the parents to support the treatment of, and resulting changes in, the child. Few therapists report success with the severe obsessional child where the onset was at a very early age except through long-term analysis. This type of treatment is also considered by several authors to be essential to personality change in the latency age, ego-intact, obsessive-compulsive neurotic(15, 16).

A review of the literature reveals no actual research on the follow-up of obsessive-compulsive children as such, but one study(20) includes these children in its treated "neurotic" group who were reevaluated at the termination of treatment and again a year afterward. A control group of referred and diagnosed but untreated children was used for comparison, but no figures on the incidence of specific neuroses are included in the research report. The literature abounds with case descriptions of obsessive-compulsive childhood histories in adult paranoid schizophrenics. It is likely, also, that many moderately neurotic obsessive-compulsive children may become the obsessive-compulsive characters well-known among adult scientific scholars when anxiety has been wholly or partially relieved through therapy, through sublimation, or through defensive reaction formation. These particular character formations are outstanding examples of what Reich refers to as "a suit of armor"(21, p. 44).

The whole question of prognosis for childhood obsessive-compulsive disorders awaits more definitive answer through follow-up research. One of the usual problems in this kind of research, differential diagnosis of the population to be followed, would not be as serious a problem in studying this particular disorder.

BASIC CONSIDERATIONS INVOLVED IN THE TREATMENT OF THE DISORDER

Some of the considerations involved in the treatment of obsessive-compulsive disorders are considerations which are common to the treatment of children in general. They involve (1) the recognition that the child is still in his primary family unit and that the plan for treatment must address itself both to his family milieu and to the intrapsychic forces within his own personality; (2) the correlative consideration that the vehicles of psychotherapy—that is, transference, resistance, identification, and so on—will, because of the child's continuing relationship with parents and parent-substitutes, present particular problems, different from those encountered in the therapy of adults; and (3) the fact that the patient is still in the process of continuing ego development and psychosexual change where both regression and autonomous growth are more readily available to the therapeutic process.

Family Involvement

Where the child is very young and the illness is mild and clearly reactive to a family situation such as one of extreme disciplinary pressures or undue oedipal stimulation, casework with parents may be the only intervention needed. Melanie Klein(16) attributes these manifestations to anxiety produced by parental suppression of oral and anal aggression. Wulff cites one case in which an overly strict father heeded her "advice" and his child's compulsive symptoms were gone "in a few days" (23, p. 174). In the severe obsessional child, even if he is very young, psychoanalysis seems to be required. Melanie Klein describes the analysis of a six-year-old obsessional girl who showed "marked signs of illness" before she was quite a year old. By the time she was between two and three years old, her character was already abnormal and she was suffering from a definite obsessional neurosis(16, p. 81).

The more frequent obsessive-compulsive disorders in children, however, are neurotic in nature and, in these cases, individual psychotherapy of the child and casework with one or both of his parents are the usual recommendations, with "intensity" of his treatment dictated by many considerations. One of these is the ability of the child to tolerate anxiety between sessions. The highly anxious child must usually be seen more than once a week to allow the alliance between his ego and the therapist's to develop and deal with the anxiety. Less frequent therapy sessions are indicated with the psychologically flexible and ego-intact child who can carry the treatment process over from one week to the next. Where defenses are rigid and long standing, more frequent sessions may be called for, especially in the early stages of therapy when the defenses are dealt with. These distinctions are not always apparent in the diagnostic study and it is often necessary to experiment with the frequency of therapy in any particular case. It is sometimes necessary, moreover, to change the frequency of therapeutic sessions during the course of treatment according to the needs of the process. For example, therapy may, through the weakening of defenses, allow expression of impulses at home which, in turn, heightens the child's anxiety level. More frequent sessions may then be necessary.

Transference

Transference is the most important vehicle for psychoanalytically oriented psychotherapy with children, as it is with adults. There has been, right from the time that child psychotherapy was first attempted, much controversy as to whether or not a "true transference neurosis" is possible within the therapy of children. Anna Freud(11, p. xii) defines this phenomenon as "the giving up of the original neurosis during treatment and replacing it by a new neurotic formation in which the original objects disappear and the therapist takes their place in the patient's emotional life." She believes that this process is not possible in a child since he still possesses the original objects, the parents. There is, she maintains, no motive for the formation of the transference neurosis in children. Selma Fraiberg(9, p. 306) concurs in this viewpoint and presents her logic for arriving at this conclusion. She argues that since the original objects which are primary in the childhood neurosis are still available, the child, in therapy, will relive his neurosis in relation to these objects.

Melanie Klein(17) is the chief proponent of the opposite viewpoint. She believes that the oedipus complex has occurred and has been largely repressed, even in the very young child, and that he is far removed, through repression and feelings of guilt, from his original objects and can, therefore, establish a transference neurosis in therapy. She describes such a transference in her analysis of Erna, an obsessional child, and points out that it was accompanied by a concomitant alleviation of her acting-out in relation to the parents. Whether the phenomena observed in analysis and in less intensive psychotherapy are true "transference neuroses" or only "transference reactions," there is some agreement that the child does transfer or, at least, does "generalize" his impulses and the defenses against them into the therapeutic situation. Fraiberg refers to this generalization as "extension" of defenses into therapeutic situation while they continue to exist in the child's daily life(9, p. 300).

Because the child-patient is still realistically involved in family relationships, transference resistance is also quite different from that encountered in the therapy of adults. When defenses are crumbling within the therapy process, the child is likely to act-out the original impulses at home, hopefully, however, with more awareness than was possible in their original activation. Parents who are being seen in casework are usually warned of the possibility of this "acting-out." Because of the physical imminence of his parental objects, however, the child must redefend against these impulses, and then the therapist's interpretations of the defenses are met with resistance. It becomes necessary, in a child's therapy, to deal with his fears of the consequences of his defenseless-ness—that is, with the parental reactions to his new impulse-freedom. As Fraiberg points out, this task will be gravely complicated when the child's worst fears are justified—that is, when the parent actually does respond punitively to the child's acting out(9, p. 293). This possibility is one of the prime reasons for the need for collaborative casework in child therapy.

Development of Ego and Psychosexuality

The third consideration in differentiating child from adult therapy is of special importance when the disorder is an obsessive-compulsive one. This consideration is that the child's ego and psychosexuality are still in the process of development and that, as a consequence, both regression and autonomous growth are more susceptible to therapeutic forces. Obsessive-compulsive neuroses in adulthood are notoriously refractive to therapy, even of an intensive kind. Fenichel lists eight difficulties specific to the analysis of compulsion neurosis(8, p. 309). While many of these same difficulties are encountered in the psychotherapy of child-patients to some degree, the chances of therapeutic effect are greater because crystallization of defenses is, except in near-psychotic obsessional chil-dren, less advanced. Moreover, the obsessive-compulsive adult has usually undergone two regressions to the anal-sadistic level before he comes to therapy: one in the oedipal period and another in adolescence. The superego, solidly established during latency, may be, by the time adulthood is reached, severely sadistic; intellectualization and reaction formation are likely to be permanently entrenched through reinforce-ment. Even in the child, the two media most important to the work of psychotherapy, thought and speech, are usually themselves affected by the illness. In the adult, as Fenichel points out, these functions have become the faithful slaves of the powerful superego.

BASIC PROBLEMS IN THE TREATMENT OF OBSESSIVE-COMPULSIVE CHILDREN

Psychoanalytically oriented psychotherapy with children takes place within a therapist-patient relationship and uses transference as the chief medium of treatment. Its purpose, like that of adult psychotherapy, is to relieve the patient of his burden of delimiting and incapacitating defensive reactions and the anxiety which occasioned them and, thus, to free his energy for natural growth toward more mature levels of psycho-sexual development and of ego integration. This relief comes about through the interpretation of the transference reactions which occur within the therapeutic relationship. At first the transference is likely to consist almost entirely of the defensive measures which have been adopted to ward off the anxiety associated with basic conflicts. The interpretation of the defenses is especially important in the treatment of the obsessive-compulsive child whose defenses are likely, because of their nature, to have been strongly reinforced even at a young age. Only then can the patient, through becoming aware of his defensive maneuvers and through experiencing that he can, in this situation, survive without them, begin to let his formerly unacceptable feelings and thoughts slip past the repressive barrier. As these feelings are expressed and, at times, re-enacted in reference to the therapist, the therapist can perceive and interpret them to the child. Here again, the obsessive-compulsive child has a special difficulty in that his illness represents not only a repression of his anxiety-producing oedipal wishes and their accompanying sexual and aggressive feelings but involves, as well, the contradictory anal sadistic anger and anal erotic wishes against which his superego has had to defend. If the child is to be freed of these conflicts and his energy released for healthier growth processes, he must have, in the therapeutic relationship, the experience of reenacting these repressive emotional patterns with their love and hate, passivity and aggressivity, dependence and rebellion, and of finding that the therapist does not react in the manner that the child, in his fantasy, expects.

Dealing with Negative Phases of Transference

Many therapists find the negative phases of the transference espe-cially difficult to accept and deal with. One of the points of disagreement between Melanie Klein and Anna Freud is over this issue. In describing the technique of psychoanalysis of children, Anna Freud advocates that the therapist "demolish or modify" the "negative tendencies directed toward the analyst" which she finds "especially inconvenient." "The really fruitful work always takes place with a positive attachment"(11, p. 31). Melanie Klein, operating on exactly the opposite premise, finds that interpretation of the transference, positive and negative, is absolutely necessary and that failure to allow and interpret the negative transference may be one reason why children act-out at home instead of within the therapeutic relationship. In discussing her treatment of the obsessional child, Erna, Klein tells of the force with which Erna's anal-sadistic impulses were being liberated and how they sought gratification outside the analysis. "I realized that I had failed to resolve the resistances in the analytic hour and to release in its fullness the negative transference"(17, p. 175).

When, in directing his negative feelings toward the therapist, the child finds that they do not bring on the emotional reaction he had expected, an expectation which had forced the initial repression, the child is faced with the realization that the feelings are wholly his own. If the relationship with the therapist is, by this time, a strong alliance, child and therapist can, together, look at these feelings and at the unreality of the expectations. Feelings which the obsessive child has had to isolate because of their potential danger can now be reintegrated into his total functioning and brought back under the control of the ego to be used in more constructive ways.

These principles are often implemented through play therapy when the obsessive-compulsive child is of latency age or younger. This medium provides, for the young child, a "natural," more primitive means of expression with, in some cases, more freedom for regression than he finds in conversation. Thoughts and feelings can be "played out" which the child might have great difficulty in verbalizing directly to the therapist. This latter consideration is especially important in the initial phase of treating an obsessive-compulsive child who usually has a problem in relating interpersonally. He is likely either to avoid talking or to use speech copiously but to please or divert the therapist rather than to express emotions or seek a relationship.

Initially, the compulsive child will choose the kind of play which is best suited to maintain the height and strength of his defensive barrier. He may engage in solitary, repetitious play with little bits of clay; or he may use the blackboard to produce for the therapist's approval little bits of knowledge in the form of word-spelling or arithmetic problems; or he may line up toy soldiers and equipment endlessly without ever having them engage in action. Older children often want the therapist to take part in highly intellectualized games of skill like chess or checkers. In all of these cases, for play therapy to be psychotherapy, the therapist must recognize the defensive nature of these activities and treat the play not as an end in itself nor only as catharis, but rather as a medium through which defenses can be enacted by the child, perceived by the therapist, and, in time, interpreted. Usually this interpretation is made only after a relationship has begun to jell; however, the process can also occur in reverse. It is sometimes the therapist's understanding of the dynamics of the play and his communicating this understanding to the patient that break the ice and allow the relationship to develop.

> *Example:* Tommy had spent many therapy hours in highly intellectualized conversation which amounted to a display of his detailed knowledge of atomic research. The therapist listened for several weeks, then began to comment about Tommy's use of this subject to avoid talking about other things, "like feelings." Tommy seemed not to "hear" these comments but, after a time, asked the therapist to play checkers with him. The therapist wondered why Tommy had thought of checkers just now. "I learned a new system and I want to show you how I can beat you." The therapist agreed to play, seeing in this situation the possibility that Tommy might feel and become aware of his feelings in a way that had not emerged in his precocious conversation.
>
> In the first few games, Tommy's "system" worked and the therapist was beaten. The therapist noted Tommy's pleasure in beating her and casually commented upon it after each game, wondering aloud what it was about winning that was so necessary to Tommy. He replied that it made him "feel good" to know how to play the game and to make it come out the way he wanted. The therapist said it seemed Tommy needed to be in complete control. What would he expect to happen if he couldn't control and didn't win? Tommy ignored this attack on his defensive structure.
>
> Finally, Tommy lost a game. He began to complain and whine a little. Then, as if the dike of control had sprung a small leak, he lost several games in succession. His behavior became very babyish. He threw the checkers down, accused the therapist of cheating, and whimpered his disappointment. The therapist did not respond at all to Tommy's accusations but only said that she could now understand Tommy's earlier need to control and win. What was happening to Tommy was what he had been unable to talk about.

In this example, several principles are worth noting. Tommy employed intellectualization as a means of control and an avoidance of emotions. Specifically, speech and logical thought were his defensive tools. The therapist's first comments about this defense seemed to be ineffective, possibly because the interaction was, at this point, devoid of emotional significance for Tommy. The patient's wish to play checkers might even be viewed as an additional resistance to the therapist's interpretations

and a wish to use a less direct mode of interaction. Tommy chose
checkers, moreover, over games of a less intellectual nature. Here,
however, in his affective need to win, the patient could verbalize the
nature of his defense, i.e., its controllingness.

When, in the highly charged competitive situation, Tommy's defenses
failed and he regressed to a dependent, angry, and uninhibited child, the
interpretation of defenses could be completed. With the patient's experiencing "in the flesh" the impulses of anger and dependency toward the
therapist, he was no longer able to ignore the connection between defense
and impulse, between thought and feeling.

This example greatly oversimplifies the therapeutic sequence. Actually,
in the course of therapy, the movement is back and forth over the terrain
of defenses, interpretation, resistance, acceptance of interpretation, lifting
of the repressive barrier, expression of impulses, integration of affect into
functioning, and so on. Therapy, to be successful, however, shows an
overall progressive development from the loosening of defenses (because
they are no longer essential in the accepting atmosphere of therapy), to
the bringing of the impulse, or at least the thought of it, into consciousness (with initial anxiety around its expression gradually diminishing
through finding that the expectations of dire consequences are unwarranted) and, finally, to the reacceptance of the impulse into consciousness on a realistic basis with tolerable anxiety that allows for its
constructive use; for example, in learning and in the making of relationships.

Where ego development is actively halted, as in the pervasively
obsessional young child, it is, however, unlikely that out-patient psychotherapy of the kind just described can succeed. The obsession, in these
cases, is merely the most observable aspect of a total maldevelopment of
personality.

Example: Alan was brought to Child Guidance at three years of
age with complaints of severe temper tantrums, sleeplessness, and
fecal smearing. He was completely obsessed with the thought of
trains. He spent his days in drawing them in remarkable detail for
his age, talking about them, and pressing his parents to take him to
see trains of all kinds. His language had become solely "train
language" and his knowledge in this field was prodigious. The only
positive affect Alan showed was a kind of transfixed elation when
absorbed with his obsession. Otherwise he was a sullen, unhappy
child given to frequent and uncontrolled anger. Object relationship
was solely at the level of narcissistic gratification.

Out-patient psychotherapy of a year's duration proved to be totally ineffective. Anxiety, initially severe and pervasive, was only increased by interpretation. No therapeutic relationship could be established. When Alan became actively suicidal, in-patient treatment was recommended. It was four years later, however, and after much "shopping around" for other recommendations, that the parents were forced, because of Alan's behavior, to follow the original recommendation. In the in-patient hospital setting, Alan's sadistic behavior could be tolerated and, when his anxiety was heightened in his psychotherapeutic sessions, it could be recognized and alleviated within the therapeutic milieu of the hospital. Alan made a little progress toward socialization and some of his symptomatic behavior decreased. Practical considerations caused termination of his hospitalization, however, and, after a short period in the community during which his sadistic behavior at school became intolerable, Alan had to be committed to the State Hospital. There was, in addition to the extremity of Alan's near-psychotic illness, severe pathology within the family which added to the barriers to treatment in this case.

Psychoanalysis in the Treatment of Children

Several reports in the literature describe relative success with psychotic or near-psychotic children where the therapy is psychoanalysis(2, 14, 16). All of these reports, however, refer to the extreme difficulty of the treatment and to the probability of residual pathology after the treatment. Certainly, this use of child analysis is a departure from its traditional use (that is, in the neuroses), and the implications of this departure can be assessed only after reviewing the indications for child analysis in the neuroses, in general, and in obsessive-compulsive neuroses, in particular.

The number of child analyses are, of course, narrowly limited by the shortage of analysts and analytic time. Because of this shortage and the equally important considerations of the cost, time, and commitment required of the patient and his parents, very few children are actually analyzed even when this is the treatment of choice. In addition to these weighty practical considerations, however, this "choice" is increasingly complicated by changing concepts and techniques in modern child analysis itself and in its relationship to other types of treatment.

When child analysis was first attempted, the choice of patient was governed by prior experience with adult analyses. Thus, selection (except in the cases of those few analysts who believed analysis was good for practically "all" children) was confined mainly to those children who were suffering from a neurosis severe enough to have interfered with normal development; analysis was usually not recommended where the child had never established object relationship within the family and where anxiety was not available to the therapeutic process—for instance, in character disorders(9, 18). These criteria for the early or "classical" child analyses would fit most of the neurotic obsessive-compulsive children but would exclude obsessional psychotic children and those with character disorders.

Currently, however, child analysis has been affected significantly by two major developments within the field of child therapy: (1) the appearance of another treatment possibility through the widespread application of psychoanalytic principles to treatment media other than analysis; and (2) the realization by analysts of the need to modify their techniques to accommodate the large number of children with more severe disturbances in ego and character development.

The growth of psychoanalytic psychotherapy as an alternate treatment mode has prompted child analysts to consider those distinctions between this mode of treatment and analysis which would dictate the use of one or the other mode in a particular case. The Committee on Child Analysis of the American Psychoanalytic Association, after much deliberation, published this opinion as to the distinction.

Psychoanalytically oriented psychotherapy, although it utilizes the unconscious productions of children, is essentially a manipulative and focal type of therapy aimed at the solution of immediate conflicts. It attacks a specific problem. No deep systematic investigation of the unconscious fantasy is undertaken. Interpretation is confined to the preconscious productions. . . .

On the other hand, psychoanalysis may employ all the above types of therapy during the course of treatment, but only in psychoanalysis is the genetic investigation and interpretation of the unconscious fantasies carried out together with the analysis of ego defenses. Psychoanalysis aims at the resolution of fundamental or basic conflicts which have involved and impaired the child's development, past and present. . . . (4, p. 34).

More recently, in a 1964 publication, Sylvia Brody(3) has repeated this distinction in terms of both the aims and the techniques of the two treatment forms. She restricts the aim of child psychotherapy to the "alleviation of a specific neurotic symptom or of a specific form of emotional distress and the reduction of related anxiety, through interpretation of the most dynamically relevant unconscious conflict. . . ." By contrast, "in child analysis, . . . the unconscious conflicts underpinning a neurosis are interpreted systematically . . . the oedipus complex is reached, worked through, and resolved according to the psychosexual maturity of the child at the termination of treatment" (p. 386). The central techniques used in psychotherapy, according to Brody, are those which "in analysis, would constitute only basic preparation for the interpretation of instinctual-drive derivatives and their working through." These techniques include interpretation of affect and defense. The "abbreviation" that is psychotherapy "may have to by-pass nuclear psychosexual conflicts" but may achieve significant therapeutic gains, including increased reality testing, strengthening of object relations, and lessening of fixations.

From their very beginnings, reports of child analyses have included many of obsessive-compulsive neurotic children(e.g., 2, 16). Even now, since the advent and increasing availability of psychotherapy, many child therapists still hold that analysis is the treatment required for this illness.

Brody(3, p. 406) lists obsessional neuroses as one of several conditions which "cannot be expected to yield to techniques of psychotherapy. It is a grave problem that many of the children referred for psychotherapy belong to this category. So much effort must be made to engage them in an affective relationship and to develop their insight into the existence of unconscious resistances, that the limited period available for psychotherapy usually ends in frustration for both partners." In this viewpoint, the importance of the length and intensity of analytic treatment lies in providing the "scope in which to comprehend the elaborate and myriad ways that symptoms, defenses, and character traits of the patient have become enmeshed and are mutually supportive." She feels that psychotherapy, in its failure to provide both this "scope" and an opportunity to work through the instinctual wishes, allows the oedipal conflict to remain "like a tight vessel in which related neurotic conflicts can continue to grow"(3, p. 404). The changes usually claimed for analysis, on the other hand, are "structural" changes. They include gaining insight into defenses and freeing the ego to understand and handle the unconscious material against which it has been defending(19).

These distinctions in aims and techniques suggest, in a general way, the criteria for analysis in obsessional neuroses. Kramer and Settlage(19, p. 535) cite as the "prime indication" for child analysis, "the arrest of, or gross interference with, normal development." The assessment of this interference is made through determining the presence, degree, and severity of regressions and fixations. This assessment is admittedly complicated, however, by the changing pattern of children's symptoms, the overlapping of stages, and the susceptibility of the child's normally weaker ego to temporary disturbances. What would undoubtedly be seen as regression or fixation in the adult may, in a child, be only temporary set-backs which might respond to less intensive treatment. The more practical analysts concede that "when less intensive treatment will suffice, psychoanalysis is not the treatment of choice"(19, p. 533).

This clarification of the task which child analysts set for themselves in the treatment of obsessional neurosis throws light on the reason why they have, until recently, avoided the treatment of obsessional children with serious ego defects. Prerequisite to the analysis proper are enough ego strength to withstand anxiety, and enough capacity for object relationships to make transference possible and to provide the cushion for anxiety reactions. Where analysts have reported success with "borderline" or psychotic children, they have reported, also, a modification of their analytic technique. Ekstein and Wallerstein describe, in clear relief, the child whose ego functions fluctuate from primitive, "psychotic manifestations to advanced achievement. . . ." They describe how their usual technique, interpretations aimed at "giving insight," that is, pressing an association between primitive fantasy and objective reality, cannot be applied to this child whose weakened ego is incapable of handling the anxiety which the interpretation incurs. When the child has regressed to the primary process, it is necessary, instead, to give "an interpretation within the regression" and to actively strengthen weakened ego through direct assurance of protection. "Such interpretation rests upon the temporary willingness to assume that the patient's grossly distorted perceptions reflect outer reality, because they accurately reflect his inner psychological reality and the state of his ego which has temporarily lost the capacity to differentiate inner and outer reality"(6, p. 309). Only with the therapist's acceptance of the child's regressive fantasy, interpretation within the regression, and assurance of protection by the therapist from the terrible dangers within the fantasy, will panic be avoided and the ego be gradually strengthened to the point where secondary process interpretation is possible. The sequence, so clearly described by these analysts, amounts to gradually decreasing the regressive (psychotic) trends and stabilizing the neurotic aspects of the child's ego. Then analysis can proceed in a manner generally comparable to that used with neurotic children.

Even in the neurotic obsessive-compulsive disorders, some ego functions and ego organizations are likely to be affected. Where this effect is pervasive, total functioning may be so disrupted that attendance at school is impossible and, in some cases, the child cannot be maintained at home. Such was the case of 13-year-old Frances whose symptoms finally became so incapacitating that hospitalization on an emergency basis was required.[1]

> ***Example***:   Many of Frances' rituals were associated in a direct way with her religion. The whole family were strict Catholics whose close adherence to the rules of the church had taken on a sacrificial, ceremonial nature. Frances had become so obsessed with the idea of sin that she could not go into the kitchen on Friday for fear that there might be meat in the refrigerator. She had to substitute other words in her prayer for each "dirty" word in the prescribed prayer, for example, the word "fruit" in the Hail Mary. She walked with her legs wide apart and her hands held high over her head to avoid possible contact with the genital area. She could not wipe herself after a bowel movement. She had to wash her legs after urinating and washed her mouth out with soap after defecating. These symptoms made attendance at school impossible; moreover, she had been having a hard time in her schoolwork for a long time since she had to erase each word that she wrote while she was having a "dirty" thought.
>
> The therapeutic milieu of the psychiatric ward can tolerate the bizarre symptoms and help alleviate the panic which the child experiences when his defenses fail. It was necessary, in Frances' case, for someone to sit with her part or all of the night when her anxiety was so great that she could not let herself fall asleep. She felt she had to stay awake to hold her nightgown away from her body lest it touch her and tempt her to masturbate.
>
> Frances was seen three times a week in psychotherapy during the year she was hospitalized. At first her therapy was characterized by excessive rumination, constant doubting, isolation of affect, and recounting of her rituals. She tried to seduce the therapist into acting-out some of her forbidden impulses as, for example, through trying to get the therapist to talk about sexual matters and then rejecting her help because she could now accuse the therapist of being "contaminated" like herself.

It is most important that the therapist recognize the defensive nature of the ruminative material that this kind of patient brings into therapy. Relating to the content would only serve to reinforce the symptoms. The

---

[1] The author wishes to express appreciation to Elizabeth Nettles for supplying the account of this patient's treatment.

therapist points, instead, to their defensive use and, finally, turns the patient's attention to the wish behind the symptom. These wishes, usually at first anal-sadistic and, later, oedipal, will appear in transference to the therapist.

After her defenses were interpreted, Frances was helped to recognize the wishes behind her symptoms and to accept thoughts and feelings as her own and not the "works of the devil." She became aware of her anger at her parents and her teachers. She brought the same anger into the transference where it could be recognized and interpreted.

His characteristic, defensive, intellectual approach to life is quick to make its appearance on the therapeutic scene even in the more moderately disturbed obsessive-compulsive child. Talking, which the therapist usually counts on as the main avenue for therapeutic interaction, is used by the patient instead for compulsive and detailed accounting replete with numbers, names, places, and repetitive events. The child is obviously talking to avoid feeling.

Example: Eight-year-old Danny began his hour by telling about his walk to the clinic. He had noticed how some of the cars had six inches of snow on top of them; some of the limbs on the trees were only one inch in diameter and couldn't hold quite as much snow as those that were two inches thick; these, in turn, couldn't hold as much as those that were three inches. . . . Last night there were supposed to be 15 children at the Boy Scout den meeting but only 8 showed up because of the weather. The Bear den had only two kids there; and his den, the Wolves, had only six instead of the nine that should have been there. Danny stopped, out of breath, and when after a few minutes, the therapist asked for his thought, Danny said, "I'm just sitting here thinking what we're going to talk about and I wish you'd ask me some questions."

Other compulsive talking may exhibit a wealth of knowledge about highly specific matters usually of only academic interest. Sometimes the isolation of affect from thought is directly observable in the process.

Danny had spent most of the hour sitting silently, looking at the therapist suspiciously through half-closed eyes, or telling how the other children at school had been trying to "dig things" out of him to get help with their school work. Finally, he looked at the clock

and said, "Now, now's the time." He had decided this was the exact
moment in time when he could begin to "spend the rest of the hour"
in playing with the toy soldiers and guns that were in the room. He
lined the men up and then told all about each soldier: what rank he
had, which war he fought in, the costume that would be most
appropriate, the vehicles used for each purpose, and the place of
camouflage and other techniques in the fighting. Then he wanted
the therapist to "guess which of the soldiers don't fit" in the scene he
had set up.

The therapist must avoid responding to the content of these intellectual discussions and to the invitation to compete with the patient in a
struggle for intellectual superiority. If his defensive intellectualization is
to be dethroned, it must first be relieved of its magical power.

The therapist said that she guessed Danny had some idea about
which soldiers these would be (that didn't fit). He said, "Yes."
Therapist said she supposed Danny was wondering if she could
guess what was in his mind. Danny looked at her suspiciously and
insisted that he "just wanted" her to guess. Therapist said she could
not know what was in Danny's mind without his telling her. Danny
tried again to draw her into competitive guessing by letting her
have "a little more information." When the therapist again refused
to "read his mind," Danny became noticeably anxious. It was to be
many hours of therapy later before Danny could show anger as well
as anxiety.

The question naturally arises as to what has happened or is still
happening in the parent-child interaction, to contribute to the child's
need to avoid expression of emotion. Most case reports cite some extreme
castration threat or parental explosiveness which support the oedipal
fantasy. Often the compulsive child has one or both compulsive parents
whose own tendency to isolate affect allows it to break through in
unexpected and shattering blasts.

The social worker who was treating Danny's parents reported
infrequent but volatile fights between them. Father, an extremely
compulsive and usually passive man, would let mother dominate
and depreciate him until he suddenly "got fed up"; then he attacked
her verbally and, on rare occasions, physically. Danny would turn
his back to this upsetting scene and literally "shut it out." The
parents, ashamed of this behavior which was so out of keeping with

their usual sophistication and compulsive control, were glad to have Danny ignore it.

Obsessive-compulsive children are usually subject to the same threat of extreme emotional upheaval, and many have temper tantrums beyond the appropriate age. The strength of their defenses is but evidence of the power of the impulses which necessitated their construction. The thera- peutic situation allows and supports the expression of affect in whatever amplitude and frequency the child can finally allow himself.

> *Example:* Kris had been barely passing in school during his first four grades, in spite of bright normal intelligence and much con- scious motivation to succeed. He was a conforming, compulsive, and rather effeminate boy who had not identified with his bright but not very successful father. After nearly a year of weekly therapy in which Kris's defenses of isolation and reaction formation had not yielded to interpretation to any noticeable extent, Kris asked if he could use the dictaphone. Then, he took little cars and enacted "accidents" which he recorded in vivid sound effects on the dicta- phone. He loved to listen to these records and spent months in once- a-week alternate dictating, and playing back what he had dictated. The "accidents" became noisier and more destructive. At first the voices were those of adult drivers. Then, Kris added "Junior," a little boy with a feminine voice who had been kept locked in his room and who was afraid to come out. After much urging (from Kris in his own role), Junior emerged and began to take part, gingerly at first, in the recorded fanfare. Junior sometimes retreated to his room but, over the next months, spent increasingly greater amounts of time in the symbolic struggle which by now was clearly an oedipal one and could be interpreted. Finally, the day came when Junior dropped the effeminate voice and interacted vigor- ously. Kris announced, "He's never going back into the locked room again." In the meantime, Kris had begun to succeed in school and was becoming more aggressive socially.

SUMMARY

The psychotherapy of obsessive-compulsive children is as complex and varied as are the many different manifestations that go into this group of disorders. The type, setting, and frequency of the treatment chosen will depend upon many factors, important among which are the severity, time of onset and duration of the illness, the extent of ego functions involved, the assets for therapy, and the availability of parental cooperation. The characteristics which mark the dynamic interrelationship among the several disorders within this group are also the characteristics which pose particular problems for the therapist. These include the anal regression or fixation, the isolation of affect, and the involvement of those tools upon which therapy most depends—speech and thought—in the service of the illness itself.

REFERENCES

1. ARTHUR, HELEN. A comparison of the techniques employed in psychotherapy and psychoanalysis of children. *Amer. J. Orthopsychiat.*, 1952, 22:484–98.

2. BORNSTEIN, BERTA. Fragment of an analysis of an obsessional child. *Psychoanalytic study of the child*, Vol. VIII. New York: International Universities Press, 1953.

3. BRODY, SYLVIA. Aims and methods in child psychotherapy. *J. Amer. Acad. Child Psychiat.*, 1964, 3:385–412.

4. BUXBAUM, EDITH. Technique of child therapy: A critical evaluation. *Psychoanalytic study of the child*, Vol. IX. New York: International Universities Press, 1954.

5. DAWES, LYDIA G. Comments of the committee for psychoanalysis in childhood and adolescence. *Bull. Amer. Psychoanal. Assn.*, 1949, 5(1):33–35.

6. EKSTEIN, R., and WALLERSTEIN, J. Observations on the psychology of borderline and psychotic children. *Psychoanalytic study of the child*, Vol. XI. New York: International Universities Press, 1956.

7. ERIKSON, ERIK H. *Childhood and society.* New York: W. W. Norton & Co., 1950.

8. FENICHEL, OTTO. *The psychoanalytic theory of neurosis.* New York: W. W. Norton & Co., 1945.

9. FRAIBERG, SELMA. Clinical notes on the nature of transference in child analysis. *Psychoanalytic study of the child*, Vol. VI. New York: International Universities Press, 1951.

10. FREUD, ANNA. Indications for child analysis. *Psychoanalytic study of the child*, Vol. I. New York: International Universities Press, 1945.

11. FREUD, ANNA. *The psychoanalytical treatment of children.* London: Imago Publishing Co., 1946.

12. FREUD, S. Notes upon a case of obsessional neurosis. *Collected papers*, Vol. III. London: Hogarth Press, 1933.

13. FREUD, S. The predisposition to obsessional neurosis. *Collected papers*, Vol. II. London: Hogarth Press, 1946.

14. GELEERD, ELIZABETH. Psychosis in childhood. *Psychoanalytic study of the child*, Vol. II. New York: International Universities Press, 1946.

15. HAMILTON, GORDON. *Psychotherapy in child guidance.* New York: Columbia University Press, 1947.

16. KLEIN, MELANIE. *Contributions to psycho-analysis.* London: Hogarth Press, 1948.

17. KLEIN, MELANIE. *The psycho-analysis of children.* London: Hogarth Press, 1932.

18. KNIGHT, ROBERT P. Management and therapy of borderline patients. *Bull. of the Menninger Clinic,* 1953, 17:1–12.

19. KRAMER, S., and SETTLAGE, C. On the concepts and technique of child analysis. *J. Amer. Acad. Child Psychiat.,* 1962, 1:509–35.

20. LEHRMAN, L.; SIRLUCK, H.; BLACK, B.; and GLICK, S. Success and failure of treatment of children in the child guidance clinics of the Jewish Board of Guardians. New York: *Research Monograph,* Jewish Board of Guardians, 1949.

21. REICH, WILHELM. *Character-analysis.* New York: Orgone Institute Press, 1949.

22. WEIL, ANNEMARIE P. Certain severe disturbances of ego development in childhood. *Psychoanalytic study of the child,* Vol. VIII. New York: International Universities Press, 1953.

23. WULFF, M. The problem of neurotic manifestations in children of preoedipal age. *Psychoanalytic study of the child,* Vol. VI. New York: International Universities Press, 1951.

5

James T. Proctor

The Treatment of Hysteria in Childhood

TYPICAL HYSTERIA in childhood is an uncommon neurosis, although the frequency with which it is seen by different observers varies considerably. It tends to be seen more often in primarily medical settings, or in psychiatric facilities associated with pediatric medical services, since the disorder frequently mimics physical illness and a medical evaluation usually is sought first. Where there is easy communication between the medical and psychiatric facilities, referral is frequently accomplished. Otherwise, the cases are often treated medically, symptom relief obtained, and the patient discharged without either psychiatric consultation or follow-up. In addition, childhood hysteria seems to appear more frequently in primitive socio-cultural groups, and thus tends to be concentrated in certain geographic locations. The maximum incidence reported recently is from the University of North Carolina, where one series of cases studied in the child unit revealed that 13 percent of the cases were diagnosed as hysteria. Dissociative reactions accounted for 20 percent of that hysteric group, and conversion reactions for the other 80 percent. In many areas and facilities the incidence is so much lower that the illness is rarely seen(10A).

However, hysteria is particularly interesting and instructive as throughout history it has attracted more attention and study by physicians and philosophers than any other psychological disorder. Indeed,

121

our dynamic understanding of neuroses evolved from study of this archetypal form(2), which remains the prototype of the relatively treatable neurosis. In this paper, something of the dynamics of hysteria and the symptoms of conversion and dissociation in childhood will be discussed, along with several treatment techniques, the emphasis being on the briefer treatment methods which are so often dictated by necessity. For the purpose of this paper, "childhood" encompasses youngsters through 16 years of age, even though there is obviously great difference between the pre-oedipal, latency, and adolescent periods, and considerable difference in the significance of symptoms in each period. These differences are functions of maturation and development, and the structural balance achieved between the psychic agencies (id, ego, superego). However, the general principles apply throughout and, as many child psychiatrists or other child therapists see children of all ages, the arbitrary inclusion seems functional.

THEORETICAL CONSIDERATIONS

It is difficult to formulate a simple, generally acceptable model for the neuroses, and a detailed exposition would require a sizeable monograph which is far beyond our present scope. However, certain considerations need to be discussed as a foundation for the clinical examples, even though the present discussion must assume considerable prior knowledge and many important issues must be simply ignored.

The Oedipal Complex in Neuroses

Psychoanalytic theory consists of the proposition that the oedipal complex, the culmination of infantile sexuality, is nuclear in the neuroses and that it represents the essential part in their content. Mastery of the oedipus complex leads to normality, and a failure to master leads to neurosis. Thus, neuroses are disorders of the ego or organizational aspects of the personality in which the immature and relatively weak ego of the child is unable to discharge or master the flood of libidinal and aggressive excitation associated with the oedipus complex, which is unacceptable to the emerging superego or judgmental aspects of the personality. To put the matter another way:

1. The neuroses are due to an intrapsychic conflict between unacceptable libidinal or sexual impulses (and associated aggressive impulses) and the organizational aspects of the personality, the ego;

2. The conflict has been solved neither in favor of one side or the other, nor by a suitable compromise; but, as the impulses are unacceptable to the ego, the conflict has become unconscious through the process of repression which blocks their discharge;

3. The repression has been unsuccessful or failed in that the impulses have only been expelled from awareness and not rendered innocuous, but indeed the repressed libidinal impulses press for discharge and actually obtain conscious manifestation and partial discharge in disguised form; i.e., symptom formation.

To elaborate (and recapitulate), regression plays an important role in this scheme. In the normal course of development the child acquires fixation points to which part of his instinctual energies remain attached, while the main quantity progresses into later stages of development. Thus, in the beginning of a neurotic conflict when the ego is confronted with an internal or external danger producing unmanageable anxiety in relation to libidinal discharge, the libido flows backward (regresses) and attaches itself to earlier libidinal fixations, wishes, or discharge routes. The child (his ego) then finds himself confronted with primitive oral, anal, aggressive wishes which his relatively more mature ego will not tolerate. The child (his ego) then defends himself by various mechanisms of defense such as repression, reaction formation, displacement, and perhaps others. However, if such defense is unsuccessful, neurotic symptoms arise which represent gratification of the wish in a distorted, compromised form compelled by the repressive forces. These symptoms then represent the central libidinal discharge routes. At this point it should be emphasized that actual conflict between the child (his ego) and an outside agency, or between his ego and an impulse is not neurotic conflict. Neurotic conflict arises only when the conflict is between the ego and a repressed impulse.

Neurotic Conflict and Repression

Repression may fail and neurotic symptoms emerge for several reasons. First, there may be an increase in the drives or impulses which exceeds the repressive forces. This may be in an absolute sense, as at puberty. Often, however, the increase in the drives is relative and caused by excessive stimulation or seduction, by keen disappointments which stimulate regressive longings for forbidden and previously relinquished gratifications, or the intrapsychic balance may be upset by blocking of current gratifications or displacements which give at least some instinctual gratifications and discharge. Again, repression may fail due to a decrease in ego strength from fatigue; intoxications of whatever source;

or debilitation through illness, fever, and so on, or, especially in younger children, through the relative or absolute loss of external ego-supporting objects or agencies, notably a parent or parents.

It is instructive to emphasize that all neurotic phenomena are based on an insufficiency of the normal control apparatus to manage current excitation, neurotic symptoms being involuntary emergency discharges which supplement the normal discharge modalities. The interruption of homeostasis is brought about either by too much excitation or by a blocking of the normal discharge routes. Of course, both these factors may operate simultaneously, and usually do. It is clear here that we are dealing with quantitative factors concerning the internal and external disposition to neurosis. Actually, the internal and external are complementary and in reciprocal relation to each other. With a stronger inner disposition, particularly a strict conscience or superego which blocks even impulse derivatives, less external excitation is required to precipitate a neurosis or an acute symptomatic phase in a previously fairly well-compensated neurotic state; while with less inner disposition, more external excitation is necessary to disturb the equilibrium as the system is able to discharge larger quantities of excitation. The nearer a neurosis is to the traumatic end of this spectrum (that is, too much excitation) the better the prognosis in general, as it indicates the patient's control-discharge apparatus is relatively intact and overwhelmed only by major excitation. Only a few of the cases we see are truly traumatic, but the closer the precipitating factor comes to a real trauma, the easier it is to assist the patient to reestablish a relative equilibrium, as simply removing the excessive excitation will often allow the patient's fairly adequate discharge modalities to reestablish homeostasis. The greater the element of actual neurotic blocking, the use of extensive, relatively chronic ego defense, the more difficult the case, as we must direct our attention to internal change, undoing the neurotic blocking of discharge routes.

The actual etiology of neuroses is not uniform, but two major factors are important: the biologic and the social. The biologic includes the instinctual disposition with all of the hereditary, congenital factors, and all other factors which affect the biologic system—for example, illness or fatigue. The social factors depend on external conditions such as the immediate family, the birth of siblings, economic conditions, and other environmental considerations. The oedipus complex seems to stand between the two; that is, viewed from one vantage it is biologic, from another vantage it is social.

The specific neurosis of hysteria in its pristine sense is a focal neurotic disturbance (i.e., the essential pathology is oedipal in origin) in which the primary ego defense is repression. When repression of the unacceptable sexual impulses or oedipal wishes fails, the repressed returns in the symptoms of conversion or dissociation, although the exact form of the symptoms is extraordinarily diverse and can mimic almost any organic process(8).

Conversion Symptoms

In conversion, the genital oedipal impulse is displaced onto another part of the body, and finds plastic expression and partial discharge in alterations of physical function. Conversion symptoms are thus compromise substitutes for an instinctual satisfaction, an affect-laden somatic expression that has specific thought representation which can be retranslated from its somatic language to the word language. At times the specific conversion seems to be determined by the ability of the affected organ to give expression to the unconscious sexual fantasy; for example, the eye and blindness where scoptophilia is involved or a rigid paralysis of a finger or limb where erection and penetration require expression. At other times, a constitutional weakness of an organ or some acquired disease seems to predispose that part (somatic compliance) and, in fact, hysterical superimpositions onto or prolongations of actual physical symptoms are common. At other times, the choice of the organ and thus the specific conversion depends on the situation in which the decisive repression occurred, those parts being predisposed which were under the highest tension at the moment of repression; for instance, the eye in witnessing the primal scene, the ear in hearing sexual sounds, and so forth.

In dissociation, repressed daydreams (which are derivatives of the further repressed oedipal conflict) break through seeking at least partial discharge, and the patient reacts to these daydreams rather than to reality, resulting in a disturbance of consciousness, although alteration in consciousness may have specific meanings of its own. These events so briefly stated are complex phenomena, but a detailed exposition again is beyond the scope of this paper. However, Freud's(2) description of hysteria in adults seems to exactly fit children's symptomatology and dynamics, and the reader is also referred to the reviews (1A, 1B, 10A) for a detailed exposition and bibliography.

It should be noted here, though, that analysis of conversion or dissociative reactions leads to daydreams and then to masturbatory fantasies which are themselves highly disguised or distorted remnants of the oedipal fantasies along with condensed pregenital fantasies. These pregenital components are practically very important, as they are guilt-laden accessories of the oedipal complex which serve as intermediary links and working them out in treatment can be tedious and difficult. The pregenital components are further important in that it is implicit in analytic theory that it is the neurotic character structure which, when it decompensates, sets the field for the particular symptom neurosis. The oral components in the character structure of the hysteric are well known, and indeed when the pregenital components or fixations are extensive (particularly orality) the diagnosis is at times confused with schizophrenia.

Conversion and dissociation may be symptoms of: (1) an acute traumatic state, or more prolonged states of excessive excitation which are not really neurotic, but represent more of a problem in immediate adjustment where there is an actual conflict between the child's ego and an impulse which is not repressed; or (2) they may be the symptoms of a classic, focal, circumscribed, neurotic conflict with the primary pathology located in the oedipal phase, with secondary disturbances extending into the pregenital phases; or (3) they can be symptoms of a diffuse disturbance combining primary pathology in the pre-oedipal phase with the nuclear pathology of the oedipal phase. In the latter instance, the diffuse disturbance results from the effects of a disturbed and disturbing pregenitally fixated mother (or perhaps other early childhood deprivations) on the pregenital functioning of the child. The nature and extent of the precipitating or sustaining trauma and the pregenital fixations determine whether we are dealing with an immediate adjustment reaction (an acute or even relatively chronic traumatic state), a focal neurosis, a characterologic disorder, or a more diffuse disturbance, even of psychotic proportions.

A brief clinical example to illustrate our theory seems in order here, although it is no substitute for the detailed case histories referred to elsewhere in this paper. Likewise, the later clinical examples of treatment merely serve to illustrate, and can in no way substitute for careful supervision by an experienced therapist and teacher.

Example: A 14-year-old boy, John, developed an acute anxiety state in which he feared he would lose his mind. This was associated with a horizontal head-nodding tic and nocturnal enuresis. The symptoms appeared acutely about 72 hours earlier without any apparent external precipitant. John was in great distress, well motivated, and innately psychologically oriented. He was seen three times a week for the first two weeks and achieved rapid symptom alleviation. He then was continued on a twice-a-week basis for the next year, during which time he worked very hard and many of the details of his illness were revealed. His dramatic and at times agonizing therapy revolved around two screen memories, a terror dream that had been repetitive from his fifth through seventh year, his current dreams, and transference relationship to the therapist.

The first of the screen memories was a pleasant, bright, detailed visual image of the patient at age five riding on his father's shoulders while his father waded in a stream, getting wet in the process. The other memory was a vivid but emotionally neutral one of himself at about age five standing in the hall on an early spring morning and seeing his mother and father quietly asleep in bed, covered with a sheet. The repetitive terror dream was of the patient in a room in which the only openings were four windows, through each of which a gorilla with horrible teeth stared at him.

The history from the mother revealed that John, who was an only child, had had in early childhood a very warm, satisfying relationship with both his parents. However, during his fourth year, the father became progressively more erratic in his general behavior and somewhat abusive to John. When the patient was about five and one-half years old, the sheriff had come to the home and in John's presence taken the father to the State Hospital on a commitment order issued on the basis of central nervous system syphilis (paresis). For some months prior to his father's removal, John had had the nightmare noted, and also had an eye-blinking tic of moderate but diminishing severity which persisted about a year in all. Following his father's departure he became nocturnally enuretic which persisted until it was corrected by an alarm device at age eight. His mother and other relatives supported him warmly and were very compassionate about his difficulties and the loss of his father. By age eight John was symptom free and was a reasonably conforming child who did well in school and was well liked by adults and his peers. His acute neurosis was a surprise to his family and friends, who had suspected no psychological problems of consequence.

Analysis of his screen memories and the early dream revealed them to be closely interwoven and related to the four-and-one-half- to five-and-one-half-year period. The memory of his parents quietly in bed covered by a sheet emerged as an observation of vigorous sexual intercourse between his nude parents, which had flooded him with a variety of emotions and may have triggered a loss of bladder control at the time, although this particular aspect was never adequately clarified. The memory of riding on the shoulders of his father expanded into an episode in which John urinated on his father while riding on his shoulders—an act of hostility which he explained at the time as an accident, but for which his father severely berated him.

The early dream revealed several important elements. He had been involved in sex play with neighbor children in an unused woodshed in the back of his home, which was the distorted dream scene (there were no windows in the woodshed, but four in the dream building). In association to the dream, he recalled an episode in which he asked his father, who was shaving with a straight razor in the bathroom at the time, about circumcision, the question having been stimulated by observation of a circumcised male peer during the sexual play noted. His father replied that "they take off a little bit," the patient reacting as though he gestured menacingly with the razor in his hand. John immediately and in regressive evasion of the threatening razor, converted the term "bit" into "bite," which then served as dream material resulting in a gorilla watching him in his sex play and threatening to bite off his penis.

The exact sequence of internal and external events was never exactly known. This was due partly to the lack of historical confirmation, but was also due to a somewhat vacillating and unstable transference state. This latter represented, I think, a mild ego disturbance of traumatic origin (i.e., rather than faulty technique), and while it nicely revealed John's tumultuous state at the onset of his neurosis, it precludes certain precision in reconstruction. John's neurosis can, however, be fairly adequately reconstructed from his recollections, complicated associations, and transference reactions to the therapist.

At about four and one-half years of age, when his sexual impulses, activity, and curiosity were high, his father became progressively more irritable, which John reacted to as a progressive disapproval of himself and his sexual impulses. His sexual impulses and overt incestuous fantasies were further heightened by what seemed an accidental observation of parental intercourse which evoked enormous rage at both parents, but particularly his father. John probably reacted to this trauma by a regressive loss of bladder control at the time of the observation. The only direct expression of anger toward the father (although passive in nature and couched as an accident) was the episode of urinating on his father, the aggressive impulse needing to be suppressed because of his father's strong disapproval of the act.

John's rage at his father, however, resulted in the wish to be rid of him, which in his child's mind was poorly differentiated from killing him. As John feared retaliation of like kind, according to the talion law of the unconscious (an eye for an eye), even tender contacts with his beloved mother evoked fear of his father. In addition, as John genuinely loved his father in spite of his fear of him, he also worried that any direct confrontation would cause father to stop loving him. This situation resulted in a partial withdrawal from both parents and thus a concurrent reduction in ordinary gratifications, with a regression to fantasy and an attempt to gain some satisfaction in this way. At this point John was in considerable inner turmoil over this actual conflict, and the more primitive (anal, largely) fantasy systems that became regressively activated. Even more important, both his sexual-aggressive impulses toward his parents and the regressive fantasy system activated were progressively more intolerable to his rapidly crystallizing superego, the internalized parental (especially paternal) demands and prohibitions. Consequently the entire sexual and aggressive impulse-wish system was repressed. The impulses continued, however, to press for discharge and did gain permanent representation in disguised or screen memories of both the primal scene and his hostile urination on his father.

His wish to look at and vicariously participate in his parents' sexual activity, as well as the superego prohibition, were converted to a physical symptom, the eye-blinking tic which was a compromise between the impulse to look (eyes open) and the prohibition (eyes closed). John seemed to master events to this point fairly well, at least with only minimal symptom formation (the eye-blinking tic). He was able to maintain the discharge routes of masturbation and sexual play with his peers until he inferred a horrible castration threat from his father when he asked about circumcision. This further terror resulted in cessation of masturbation and sex play, and rapid repression of the impulses. Thus, there was concomitant damming up of his libidinal and aggressive forces which, however, continued to press for discharge, but could only find expression in the symptomatic terror dream.

Fate then intervened in John's affairs and actually effected the removal of his father, giving form to his impulse to be rid of father. The sorrow attendant to losing his father, and his heightened fear of retaliation by the father evoked further regression and symptom formation, namely nocturnal enuresis. This was an intrapsychic passive-feminine yielding to his father, a compromise between his urethral hostility and the superego prohibition against it. At this point the repression of the entire oedipal conflict was firm, but John was able to obtain some fairly direct although highly disguised (to him and mother) instinctual gratification through mother's attention to his enuresis, and occasional times in her bed when the terror dream would emerge.

By virtue of his own basic ego strengths, mother's warm support, firm repression of his sexual and aggressive drives, and the spontaneous forward surge of the libido in the growth process, John was able to progress to a symptom-free state by eight years of age. Characterologically he was somewhat compulsive about schoolwork and his personal appearance, and hostile aggression was notably absent in his interpersonal relationships, as was any direct sexual expression. John was, from 8 to 14 years, almost the ideal child. Neither the death of his father (from heart disease) at age 12, nor the onset of puberty at about 12 and a half had disturbed this equilibrium. John managed his conflicts during these years by firm repression, mild compulsive devices, reaction formations, and avoidance of stimulating or seductive situations, including masturbation. He thus carried his latency organization over into full puberty at the time we would expect adolescent disruption of that organization.

In working with the terror dream of the gorilla from his earlier childhood, the event precipitating his neurosis emerged. The evening prior to the onset of John's acute illness, he had been baby-sitting with the five-year-old son of neighbors, and observed the boy masturbating in the bathroom. While John had dealt benignly with the boy, this seduction simultaneously contacted several points crucial in the onset of his own neurosis: age five, masturbation and the associated fantasies (the sexual impulse system), the bathroom (father and castration—the prohibition). At the time, although vaguely uneasy about the matter, John seems to have denied its emotional significance and considered it inconsequential, hence it had not been reported earlier (although there is pertinent question whether the precipitating event was also repressed and only emerged into consciousness after a period of treatment). However, this episode activated and stimulated John's libidinal impulses beyond his capacity to keep them repressed. His character defenses (the "ideal," nonsexual, nonaggressive latency child) thus collapsed and an acute symptomatic phase of his neurosis began.

It is interesting to note that some of his symptoms were very similar to those at the onset of his neurosis at age five. The enuresis seemed to have identical dynamic organization. The horizontal head-nodding tic was closely related to the eye-blinking tic in that it was a conversion symptom condensing the impulse to look (turning the head toward) and the prohibition against the impulse (turning the head away). The head shaking itself was an important element in this symptom and was a condensation of father's habit of shaking his head when saying "no" (the superego prohibition), and his own habit of shaking his penis as a child (masturbation and the associated fantasies—the impulse-wish system). Thus, the head-shaking aspect of the symptom was an upper displacement of the impulse to masturbate and a compromise with the prohibition, expressing both the impulse and defense against the impulse. These symptoms, however, failed to bind large quantities of his anxiety. This tension was then felt as an incipient dissolution of the ego or personality, the fear of going crazy.

Another element in this symptom concerned his identification with his father's insanity. John's reactivated wish to take his father's place with his mother (or in identification with him, to obtain like instinctual pleasures) produced enormous guilt as he imagined he had actually driven father crazy and into an institution. He had also learned at age 12, when his father died, that the insanity was the consequence of sexual actions. Because of this guilt, John could only partially identify with, and suffer something of, father's craziness, rather than obtain any instinctual gratification.

A ten-year follow-up was obtained. John graduated from college as an engineer, married, and now has a two-year-old son. He has no symptoms, although he is somewhat overcompliant with authority figures, and tends to be a bit passive in his relationship with men. John and his wife are both happy in the marriage, and the son is reported to be a delight.

Somatic Disturbances

To digress, the affect-laden somatic expressions seen in the pre-oedipal child should be considered. Transitory, unstable symptoms such as stomach-aches, headaches, and various sensory and motor disturbances occur frequently in the pre-oedipal child. Occasionally gross disturbances such as blindness or paralysis may occur. Many such cases appear descriptively identical with a classic hysteric disturbance, but these symptoms—affect-laden somatic expressions which appear before the presence of adequate language—seem to be reversions to the somatic foundations of speech in which emotionally expressive gestures, pantomimic movements, and condensations of identifications with fantasy elements play a prominent role. These symptoms are primitive conversion mechanisms used by the immature psychic apparatus to achieve a compromise discharge of pent-up affects, where the opposition to discharge is largely external; i.e., from parents or other important adults. As they are the direct result of an external excitation or prohibition, or frequently a combination of these factors, they respond well to support, to suggestion, and to reduction in excitation and external prohibition. Direct work with the mother or parents to achieve these goals is the most expeditious approach, as they (especially the mother) supply crucial ego and superego functions for the child, and can both reduce excitation and mitigate the prohibitions to assist the child achieve homeostasis. If the child's symptoms are aggravated or fairly prolonged, and careful assessment reveals significant ego or libidinal retardation or arrests, direct psychotherapy with the child as well as his parents is certainly in order.

It should be noted, at least in passing, that the problem of diagnosis and prognosis in the pre-oedipal child is not simple. Fixed, pre-oedipal neuroses exhibiting affect-laden somatic expressions, conversion-like symptoms, probably do not occur, as a true neurosis which is relatively independent of external forces cannot occur before consolidation of the superego under the impact of the oedipal conflict. A self-sustaining or true neurosis only becomes possible with this internalization and independent perpetuation of parental injunctions. However, at times pre-oedipal conflicts and symptoms can be consolidated under the impact of the oedipal complex and emerging superego, and become self-sustaining in unchanged form. In addition, the organ neuroses or psychosomatic syndromes which begin in the infantile period (i.e., literally the period before speech), but which may persist throughout life, are in fact indistinguishable from conversion reactions before the emergence of adequate speech, even when the symptoms are in the so-called involuntary neuromuscular or sensory-perceptive systems (1C).

THE TREATMENT CHOICE

To return to our main theme, it is therefore urgent when confronted with a picture of conversion or dissociation, to adequately understand the nature and extent of the pathology. This can only be achieved by careful synthesis of a comprehensive anamnesis with a thorough psychiatric evaluation of the patient; the type, duration, and severity of symptoms; the impulse-defense system; the fantasies or current solutions to the conflicts; and the behavior exhibited. The tenacity of libidinal fixations, the relative fluidity of the libidinal organization, and the neurotic interference with important ego functions should be carefully scrutinized. The milieu (especially the immediate family) is crucial and should be evaluated as a major factor in the living instinctual conflict, its accessibility, and plasticity or rigidity.

The initial goal then is to achieve the best practical understanding of the intrapsychic forces and ego strengths, in relation to the emotional milieu of the child, and thus the relative balance of factors which tend to maintain the illness or which will permit modification. An appropriate estimate of this kind is the most important to determine where we can achieve some therapeutic leverage, and indeed to determine what type of therapy is to be instituted. The better our dynamic understanding of our patient, the better we can predict the outcome of our interventions. Treatment techniques, from simple environmental manipulation to analysis, may be instituted, but the limitations of our diagnostic and therapeutic methods should also be kept in mind. We must realize that any particular therapeutic maneuver or series of maneuvers will succeed only insofar as they offer therapeutic leverage and the opportunity to shift the balance of forces in the instinctual conflict. Appropriate, well-timed interpretation of the impulse-defense system is very effective, and indeed, interpretation is the therapeutic intervention of choice in childhood hysteria. On the other hand, the spontaneous maturational forces operate in the child's favor, and at times minimal intervention to support the child and reduce excitation is enough to favorably shift the balance of instinctual forces. In fact, spontaneous recoveries (which we should always suspect) do occur in children, especially at adolescence (and of the "infantile neurosis" at the onset of the phallic phase at four to five years) where the forward thrust of the maturational wave is at times strong enough to overcome the libidinal fixations.

In the focal hysterical neurosis where, (1) the conflict is at the oedipal level, (2) the anxieties are castration anxieties, (3) the object relations are fairly secure, (4) regressions are secondary to blocking at the oedipal level, and (5) there is little or no hope for a spontaneous recovery with lesser effort, psychoanalysis or intensive psychoanalytic psychotherapy are in general the treatments of choice. There are several excellent reports in the literature concerning the indications for analysis, and the actual analysis of hysterical neuroses in children. The reader is particularly referred to A. Freud(5), Kaufman(9), and Dawes(3). However, as A. Freud has pointed out, we can rarely select cases for analysis or intensive therapy on our own judgment according to the need of the child. The question of analysis or intensive therapy is often decided by the parents' conscious and unconscious attitudes about therapy itself. Children who badly need intensive therapy are frequently withheld, while at times children with relatively mild disturbances are brought for intensive treatment. Even when analysis or intensive analytic psychotherapy is indicated and accepted by the parents, it cannot usually be implemented due to the lack of a suitable therapist and the limitations imposed by time, money, geographic distance, and the limitations to human endeavor.

Therefore, briefer psychotherapy and other therapeutic interventions are a practical necessity. These shorter term measures are technically more difficult and require all of our knowledge, technique, and art to achieve the best therapeutic results possible under existing conditions. This is not compromising treatment, but rather recognizing and working within the framework of reality and giving the child some help which he would not otherwise receive. We may have to settle for symptom relief with some (often substantial) decrease in the potential for symptom formation in the face of ordinary life stresses, although our goals may be more ambitious. Short-term therapy should not be despised, as it has a long and honorable history. For example, Freud presented a famous case of brief psychotherapy, that of "Dora," which lasted only three months. It is pertinent to my thesis to note that Freud was not very apologetic that Dora had "fallen ill again from other causes" over 20 years later(6).

It should be emphasized again that as a rule we do not select a treatment technique theoretically and ideally suited to the pathology of the child, but rather insidious circumstance usually dictates the treatment form, the duration and intensity of treatment that can be accomplished. We are frequently coerced into creative therapeutic improvisation to meet the needs of the child. A word of caution should be injected at this point. Hysterical symptoms in children frequently respond readily and rapidly to the support and suggestion implicit in brief psychotherapy or hospitalization. Some care must be exercised to assure that our interventions, of whatever kinds, have achieved a relatively stable asymptomatic state or homeostasis, and that the symptoms, or some new creations, will not recur as readily as they were banished, as follow-up studies on children diagnosed as hysterical reveal a subsequent history of unnecessary hospitalization, operations, and other illnesses(11, 12).

CLINICAL APPLICATION

Emergency Psychotherapy and Catharsis

Even when it is fairly clear that we are dealing with a circumscribed neurosis, immediate help may be urgent to relieve severely disruptive symptoms such as gross dehydration and disturbed metabolism (ketosis) in cases of hysteria with vomiting, or severe and incapacitating tics, and so forth. Emergency psychotherapy, hypnosis, or intravenous barbiturates may be indicated to obtain symptom relief, and more intensive and extensive psychotherapy may have to wait until physiologic homeostasis is achieved, or the patient is calm enough to participate in psychotherapy. The following brief case summary is presented to illustrate emergency psychotherapy.

Example: An 11-year-old white female was admitted to a university hospital, after 30 days in two other hospitals for intractable vomiting, which kept her in moderate dehydration and other metabolic imbalance in spite of good medical management. After several days further in the university hospital, during which time this pattern persisted and the patient again did not respond to medical management, psychiatric consultation was obtained. At this point the family's finances were critical, intravenous infusions to maintain nutrition and physiologic balance were becoming extremely difficult, and everyone involved in the case agreed that interruption of the symptoms was urgent.

Several pertinent factors in the patient's situation were immediately obvious. First, the child was very angry about the continued intravenous infusions and the sharp restrictions on her food intake by mouth. Also, her menarche had occurred a few weeks prior to the onset of the present illness. In discussing her family relationships it was clear from her manner that she was very angry at her mother for the not unusual controls imposed, although this anger was denied and was in no way conscious. She vociferously denied sexual concerns or interests. In addition, the patient had recently been having two recurrent anxiety dreams. In one, she was swimming and something bit off one of her toes. In the second, her abdomen would swell.

Due to the pressures noted, three therapeutic maneuvers were elected: (1) to discontinue the intravenous infusions and allow the patient to eat whatever she wished, which was (to the pediatrician's horror) potato chips, hamburgers, and coke; (2) to interpret the patient's hostility toward her mother, along with her fear of pregnancy, and her castration concerns; (3) to get the patient out of the hospital as quickly as feasible and transferred to another therapist for continuing outpatient psychotherapy, this latter because I surmised her hostility would be mobilized and directed to me.[1] The

---

[1] It is interesting to note that several weeks later, while I was passing down the hall, she sprang at me from hiding and shot me in the eye at point-blank range with a dart gun. Perhaps her painful accuracy was no greater than mine had been.

patient's hostility toward her mother for the controls mother imposed was interpreted, along with her concern about the imagined loss of her penis, and her conflict about being a woman, bearing children, and competing with mother. The vomiting disappeared immediately and the patient was in physiologic balance within 48 hours. She was promptly discharged from the hospital and taken into therapy on a twice-a-week basis by another therapist. She settled down fairly rapidly and found methods of peaceful co-existence with mother. Treatment was continued for several months, during which time the patient gained some insight into her conflicts and the sources of her anxiety. A follow-up one year after treatment revealed the patient to be asymptomatic and happy, and adjusting well in all areas.

In this case, due to the various pressures noted, the patient's focal conflicts were immediately interpreted, which the patient perceived as an assault. This facilitated the development of an intense, negative maternal tranference to me (as anticipated) which allowed her to resume a more satisfying relationship with her mother and relinquish her symptoms for the moment. She then went on in outpatient therapy to ventilate something of these negative affects, and modify the blocks to her normal discharge routes.

Hypnotic or Drug-Induced Catharsis

Hypnotic or drug-induced catharsis certainly still has a place in the therapy of traumatic states, although catharsis alone has no permanent effect as the patient's ego is by-passed, and thus there is no decisive alteration in the impulse-defense discharge system. To achieve permanent alteration in the instinctual conflict, the ego must face, work through, integrate, and find new solutions for the conflicts. However, catharsis does discharge previously blocked affects and in this way produces an at least temporarily better ego state, or more salubrious balance of forces. This factor, associated with verbalization and thus better definition of the traumatic events, fantasies, and affects, can put the patient and therapist in a stronger position from which to deal with the traumatic complex. The method of inducing catharsis does not seem to matter much, the essential factor being the presence of the therapist to act as a focal point and transference figure around whom the conflicts can be mobilized, and with whom they can be faced and worked through. When dealing with ordinary conditions in which the traumatic elements are minimal, the cathartic method usually meets with poor success, and there are a number of cases where catharsis may actually be harmful.

The possible deleterious effects of catharsis, whether induced by hypnosis or drugs, certainly must be considered. However, with proper support of the patient and uncovering of highly charged experiences in controlled "dosage," there would seem to be no great risk. That is, the therapist should exercise some caution not to overwhelm the patient by allowing too rapid awareness of the previously repressed experiences which would exceed the patient's ability to master and reintegrate the traumatic complex. This requires nice clinical judgment and constant evaluation of the patient's current ego strength and the amount of support or ego reinforcement he needs at any given moment.

The following example is presented to illustrate the use of hypnotherapy in a case of "Grand Hysteria of Charcot."[2]

Example: A 15-year-year-old white, female sophomore in high school from a small town in Oklahoma, was admitted as an emergency to the medical service of the university hospital after the onset of opisthotonic seizures: a condition in which there are sustained spasms of the back muscles resulting in the head and limbs being bent back and the trunk arched forward so that only the top of the head and heels touch the bed—a symptom well known in major hystero-epileptic attacks. There was some delay in formulating a diagnosis, but psychiatric consultation was obtained on the third day of a 14-day hospitalization. The parents were initially noted to be clinging, overconcerned, and found it difficult to abide by hospital rules—for instance, visiting hours.

When first seen, the patient's bed was surrounded by anxious personnel attempting to calm her as she thrashed aimlessly about, terrified of her visual hallucinations.[3] Sedatives (barbiturates) had been unsuccessful in quelling her anxiety. Pelvic thrusts and visual hallucinations occurred simultaneously. Her eyes were rolled back in her head and she clung to the hands of personnel who surrounded her. The consultant was introduced by the ward doctor,

---

[2] I am indebted to Gary C. Aden, M.D., for this case example and summary. The treatment was supervised by Eugene Pumpian-Mindlin, M.D.

[3] The phenomena of hysterical hallucinations and hysterical psychosis are fascinating, but subjects unto themselves. Suffice it to say here that in this case they are not defense maneuvers in the ordinary sense, but rather are manifestations of an ego disruption under acute stress. Other cases seem to present simultaneous indications of psychosis, neurosis, and healthy ego function, and are perhaps best categorized as borderline personalities. The reader is referred to Hollender and Hirsch's article(7) and Abse's monograph(1B) for a more comprehensive discussion of these matters.

but the patient paid no attention, continuing her movements. Someone asked her to look at something with no apparent response, whereupon the consultant's first contact with the patient was to say, "Maybe she doesn't feel like looking," on which the patient grabbed the consultant's hand and said seductively, "I like you." At this point the consultant assumed responsibility for the patient's psychological management and ordered a tranquilizer (chlorpromazine) to reduce the patient's restlessness and the staff's anxiety about the patient.

The examiner succeeded in establishing excellent rapport, introduced himself as a kind of magician who dealt with people who heard and saw frightening things, and told the patient he was going to help her. Over the next couple of days the patient became quieter, but her symptoms included blindness, seizures, frontal headaches, paralysis of the lower extremities, and various anesthesias and other distorted skin sensations. Her auditory hallucinations were of voices which called her "dirty." Her visual hallucinations consisted of her father attired in a big black hat, coming at her with a black stick while she attempted to defend herself with a knife held in her left (nondominant) hand which was bent back at the wrist in dorsal contracture.

The psychiatric consultant and medical staff agreed that it would be disadvantageous to send the patient to a state hospital, but that active intervention was urgent. Despite the presence of an untrained psychiatric staff and limited precautionary facilities, the patient was treated on the medical floor. Because of the patient's florid symptoms and the possibility that suppressed or repressed traumatic elements were present, hypnosis was used as a tool in conjunction with a form of psychotherapy. The patient was not ordered to give up symptoms, but rather encouraged to talk about herself. The atmosphere of treatment therefore could be described as semicathartic and semisupportive. This allowed the patient to bring out obvious, pressing, conflictual sexual material of which she was quite ashamed, but at the same time allowed her to partially evade responsibility for having related the guilty thoughts.

Significant past history involved the patient's being the third of five children born to a rather sadistic, alcoholic, father who had a moderately advanced lung disease (emphysema), and a rather masochistic, religious mother who had in recent years embraced the teachings of Jehovah's Witnesses. The patient had, prior to this hospitalization, had episodes of conversion hysteria involving sustained spasms of the jaw muscles, paralysis of the lower extremities, and may have had an unnecessary abdominal operation.

Under hypnosis, the patient first revealed she had been involved in heavy petting with her brother-in-law for the month prior to admission, consciously wishing to revenge herself on her eldest sister in this way. This seems to have been the precipitating stress. Later under hypnosis, the patient recounted with considerable affect an incident at age nine in which she was raped by a deranged, elderly man; however, from the description it was apparent that she had courted such an attack. Also, the patient reported that at age 11, her father assaulted her mother during one of his alcoholic rages, then turned on the patient, beating her around the breasts. In reaction to this she started to stab him in the back, only to have her sister intervene. The patient recalled running when her attack failed, and having a pain in her left side. The most significant conflict appeared to be her perception of intercourse as a violent, sadistic act with her the passive, masochistic object. Correspondingly, her masturbatory activity involved fondling her breasts and the midline of her abdomen, while she imagined herself a bullfighter who was being gored by a bull (father), which produced pain in her left side.

After her masturbatory conflicts had been extensively discussed the patient could walk, and her ward behavior improved. Only the pain in the left side remained, and an anesthesia over the back and scalp. This latter symptom was hypnotically induced and maintained by the psychiatrist as a precaution. The patient's symptom formation was complex, but in the course of contact with the psychiatrist in both trance and waking states she was able to discharge affect-laden material which helped elucidate the situational origin of her symptoms. This made them somewhat understandable to her so that a degree of mastery was achieved and she could return to her own milieu.

In this case, hypnotherapy as the treatment of choice in a medical ward allowed the patient to return to school without having to face the stigma of being a mental patient. The difficulty of keeping teenagers in intensive psychotherapy and dealing with the cultural maladjustment that sometimes occurs when teenagers from rural cultures enter psychotherapy were further considerations in the use of hypnosis in this case. The prognosis here appears to depend in the long run upon the patient's ability to achieve homeostasis by utilizing religion as an external or artificial neurosis, and also upon the ability of her father to control his drinking, his impulses toward, and excitation of, the patient. The use of hypnosis in this case is similar to the way that Breuer and Freud report its use in *Studies in Hysteria*(2). Fenichel, in "Brief Psychotherapy"(4), discusses the hysterical types who are ready for a dramatic transference and for "magical" influences as being candidates for the type of brief psychotherapy that was accomplished in this case.

As might be expected from the above remarks, this girl's family rejected any notion that she had an emotional problem, saying that "God would provide," and that her real problem was low blood sugar. They refused continued treatment by the psychiatrist, but it was learned later that the patient was being counseled by her school psychologist while not rejecting the low socio-economic and primitive religious values of her parents—a reasonably good outcome.

Although the case presents a number of interesting areas for discussion and much information is deleted for the sake of brevity, hypnosis proved to be of value in effecting catharsis, in elucidating the onset of the seizures, obtaining historical information, overcoming the patient's propensity toward drowsiness while on tranquilizers, and removing the disabling symptoms while allowing the patient to keep minimal symptoms (scalp and back anesthesia) to partially discharge some of the still-repressed affect. Following discharge from the hospital she was able to obtain the only psychotherapy available to her.

Brief Psychotherapy

Brief psychotherapy promoting verbalization of conscious interpersonal conflicts, manipulating the transference, and using limited interpretations can be a very effective tool. This is particularly true if the milieu can be altered to reduce excitation or temptation. Direct work with the parents can often be effective here.

Example: Susan was an attractive, nine-year-old female and an only child. Her past history revealed a generally good adjustment with adequate peer relations and excellent school work. For several months prior to the onset of her illness, she had favored her father and been slightly hostile and negativistic toward her mother. She was visiting a friend's home when a hurricane struck, separating her from her parents without communication for several hours, during which time violent, elemental forces raged. The patient was frightened for her own safety and that of her parents, although realistically neither was in any consequential danger. Susan became histrionic, wept, cried, and was inconsolable.

In just a few hours she was reunited with her parents and regained control, but then complained of a severe headache, toothache, and abdominal pain. The abdominal pain disappeared quickly but the headache and toothache persisted so that she was taken to a dentist. A tooth was extracted without relief, so that two further teeth were extracted, but again without relief. These three teeth were all normal as well as could be determined subsequently. Susan was enraged at her mother by this time and, along with tantrums, threatened to kill her mother or commit suicide. She was admitted to the pediatric service of the university hospital on an emergency basis, where careful examination revealed no positive physical findings.

Her parents seemed genuinely interested in her and appropriately concerned, but the pediatric house and nursing staff complained that the father made them very uneasy when he was with the patient. The patient would affectionately curl up in her father's lap, and he would affectionately place his hand inside her pajama pants and rub her buttocks. Susan was somewhat hostile and negativistic toward ward personnel, but was otherwise asymptomatic within 48 hours. She was seen on her second hospital day for a psychiatric diagnostic evaluation, following which she avoided the psychiatrist as much as possible. As there was some pressure to admit more severely ill patients, Susan was promptly discharged to be followed on an outpatient basis.

When first seen as an outpatient she refused to see the therapist, but was pressed to go into his office. As soon as the door was closed, she began extraordinary and horrendous screaming—to the point it was actually painful to the ear. It seemed that any verbal intervention only increased the volume of her shrieks. She screeched that the therapist was a "mean, wicked, ugly old man" and that she hated him. It is interesting to note that she could have left the office at any time, but did not attempt to do so. The therapist tried to appear calm and proceeded to model clay to interest Susan, but to no avail. Finally he drew a picture of a stick man which he called himself, and to which he set fire, letting it burn in an ash tray. This maneuver caught Susan's attention, and useful contact was thus established around the therapist's dramatic play demonstrating his understanding and lack of fear of her aggression toward him. The screaming abruptly ceased, and although Susan remained wary, she began to examine the therapist's toys with him. She was subsequently seen weekly over a period of about six months, for a total of 20 interviews. Her parents were also each seen weekly for 30 minutes by a social worker, in traditional collaborative therapy.

During the first hours Susan was distant, guarded, and somewhat hostile in her long silences. The therapist gently led her to discuss the hurricane, her conversion symptoms, and the other factors leading to hospitalization. She preferred to draw in therapy, repetitiously making excellent heads of a king and queen, particularly of the queen. These latter drawings were of a formally pretty, but too precise and cold woman. Susan gradually progressed to some discussion of her everyday discontents in school with her teacher and peers. Throughout this phase her relationship to the therapist was fairly formal, although he was supportive and ingratiating, attempting to facilitate a positive relationship. Simultaneously the parents were supported and assisted to understand and rationalize their daughter's illness. Father was directly advised to reduce body contact with her, and to be circumspect otherwise in the display of his affection for her. Fortunately, he was able to follow this advice. This regime proved very successful, and although Susan was remote in therapy, she was said to be "her old self" by the 10th interview. The parents, because of the excessive distance they had to travel (about 150 miles each way, and truly a hardship) and her asymptomatic state, were considering discontinuing.

At this point the therapist cancelled an appointment to attend a professional meeting. Although he sent Susan two postcards to maintain contact with her, there were frantic messages from her parents when he returned to town after an absence of seven days. Susan had been vomiting frequently for a week, had eaten little, and had lost five pounds of body weight. An appointment was arranged at the earliest time. Susan was wan, denied psychological problems, and emphasized her vomiting. Her hostility to the therapist for his desertion was interpreted, which brought forth further denial, but also a stream of vituperation about her hate for him, disinterest in him, that he was dirty and wicked, and so on. However, Susan's vomiting disappeared immediately and the weekly therapy with her and her parents was resumed.

The same general pattern in therapy persisted, but the reexperience of separation (which had been a major factor in the precipitation of her illness) and verbalization of the hostility in the transference resulted in further improvement. She became warmer in therapy, her drawings were less stylized and shifted to broader subjects such as animals and pastoral scenes. She became very much interested in a boy (the first) at school, and this relationship was encouraged in therapy. Her hostility toward her mother was dealt with only superficially around everyday discontents, and sexual themes were not broached at all. However, her parents reported glowing improvement at home and school, and noted better peer relations than she had ever had. In view of these circumstances, they insisted on discontinuing. The therapist agreed to exchange letters with Susan when she wished to write, and a half dozen letters over the next year were exchanged. At first Susan wrote that she loved the therapist (which was never stated in therapy) and missed him. The therapist responded that he too missed her, hoped all was going well with her, and assured her he would be pleased to see her at any time she wished. Susan's last letter was to report the birth of a baby brother that she loved so much she "could just eat him up."

This case represents many of the dilemmas of brief therapy. No psychiatrist would think that this was adequate treatment. The basic hostility toward the mother was hardly touched. Sexual themes were not broached at all, much less the oedipal conflict itself. Therapy consisted essentially of supporting the patient; facilitating verbalization of hostile affects toward the therapist when they became intense; reducing external stimulation (father's seductions); increasing parental support; facilitating and maintaining a positive relationship to the therapist and to a male peer—and this for only 20 interviews over a period of six months. On the other hand, Susan is known to have remained asymptomatic for 18 months after treatment was discontinued by her parents. In addition, there was no further word from Susan, her parents, or any professional person during a subsequent six and one-half year period (until the therapist left the area) when Susan would have been 17 years old. In view of this it seems reasonable to assume there were no further major difficulties; had there been, Susan and her parents would likely have sought help. These gains are hardly to be disparaged, although long-term follow-up studies on cases such as this (and the others reported in this paper) are certainly needed.

Somnambulism in children, dissociative states arising during sleep in which a dream is partially put into action and some pantomimic discharge achieved, is fairly common, but does not usually present a problem; it seldom comes to clinical attention except as one symptom in a more extensive complex. The discharge achieved in sleepwalking may be diffuse and nonspecific, but more often the discharge is highly specific, the typical goal being the parents' bedroom and the dissociated impulse-wish to participate in the adults' sexual life. Occasional somnambulism in the absence of other symptoms is not a cause for concern, as in this case the fantasies seldom achieve motility, and then only during a sleep state, which is not usually symptomatic of a neurosis, although in extreme conditions it can be. A brief clinical note will suffice to demonstrate somnambulism in an otherwise normal child.

Example: John, a 13-year-old boy fairly advanced in puberty, was well adjusted, and had always functioned effectively in all areas. To the best of his parents' knowledge he had never walked in his sleep before. One night while alone in the house with his attractive 18-year-old sister who was "baby sitting," John retired early, leaving his sister reading alone in the living room. Some two hours later he came to the living room in his pajamas, slowly disrobed in front of his sister, left his pajamas lying on the living room floor, and returned nude to his bed. The next morning he was perplexed by the absence of his pajamas, but was deeply chagrined by his amused sister's explanation, which he refused to accept although he had no explanation of his own.

This example certainly reveals the boy's exhibitionistic impulses and seductive invitation to his sister to return to bed with him, a conclusive demonstration to the "baby sitter" that he was not a baby. Somehow, the dream had gained access to motility during sleep, and in his parents' absence from home. There was no known recurrence in the next five years.

Dissociative reactions which are precipitated in the seemingly fully awake individual are uncommon, only about one in five cases of hysterical neuroses in children having major dissociative components. The dissociative episodes are often bizarre and tend to frighten people, as the child is usually not in contact with those about him and cannot be readily contacted. In addition, the fantasy may achieve motility which, coupled with the expression of frightening affect, dramatizes the child's distress. Hysterical amnesia in children prior to puberty is very rare, and the more prolonged dissociative states reported in adults (for instance, lasting weeks or even years, with assumption of another identity, and so on) are unknown. The following brief case summary illustrates a dramatic dissociative reaction.

Example: A 12-year-old white male in early puberty was admitted to the orthopedic service of the university hospital for a fractured elbow which was promptly set under general anesthesia, and the arm casted. The surgeons planned to observe the boy's arm for perhaps 72 hours before discharging him to his home which was at some distance. When the patient began to arouse from the anesthetic he was restless. Without apparent provocation he sprang from his bed and ran up and down the ward holding his testicles, screaming in terror. He was obviously out of contact, and was captured and calmed only with difficulty. The surgeons were not particularly disturbed by this reaction as the patient emerged from his anesthetic, but when the patient twice more exactly repeated the performance at about 12 hour intervals the surgeons were upset along with the entire ward and its personnel.

Psychiatric consultation was sought, and it was learned that the patient, who was from a marginal, rural socio-economic setting, had had similar or identical episodes every couple of months at home since the age of six. The family adhered to a fundamental religious sect, and had never been too concerned about the boy's dissociative episodes. It was not possible really to interest the family in psychotherapy for the boy, but it was possible to see him for six therapy hours over a period of about six months, the therapy hours coinciding with his return visits for orthopedic care and physiotherapy instruction. He related well, but was initially guarded about his fantasies and personal thoughts. He was very fond of his father, and somewhat effeminate in his manner with the therapist. He denied masturbation, sexual interests, or hostile affects except for rather conventional negative feelings toward two younger male siblings.

As I did not know from one appointment to the next, how many times I would be able to see the lad, or whether I would even see him again, I was very active in treatment. During the first hour he revealed upon direct questioning that he had seen his father castrate farm animals on several occasions since early childhood. This had always made him "sick at the stomach," and at least once the patient had a night terror the content of which was identical to the farm castration scene. His castration fears were directly interpreted in relation to his fear of his father and the hospital as an agent of his father. During the second hour, he added the information that he had been very distressed by the surgeons' original concern that his elbow might "get stiff." At that time his fantasy had been that if his elbow got stiff it would be necessary to amputate his arm. Supplying some of the probable associative links, I suggested that the "getting stiff" was related to his erections and the fear that if he had erections and sexual thoughts, father (or the doctors) would totally castrate him. This evoked considerable discomfort and squirming, but he seemed to integrate the interpretation.

At subsequent interviews the patient revealed moderate anger toward his siblings and fear that his parents might have more children, thus further impoverishing him in what was already a realistically difficult family and economic situation. He knew that farm animals were castrated to make them more tractable, and so "they couldn't mate." I suggested that he had considered castrating father to prevent him from mating with mother and having more children, but he was horrified by this and protested vigorously that he could never think such a thing. At this point he precipitously had to leave therapy to go to the toilet. On his return, I suggested he had really gone to check his equipment. This was met with a blank stare, so that I went on to connect his need to check his genitals as a reassurance in the face of the frightening matters we had been discussing. We spent the last two hours essentially reworking the material already elucidated, with some greater mastery by the patient as indicated by his diminished anxiety. It should be noted that he remained somewhat effeminate throughout. A brief interview with the mother at the last session revealed that he had had no dissociative episodes in the last six months (the maximum asymptomatic period in six years), and that in some ill-defined way he seemed happier and "less troubled."

There is unfortunately no follow-up on this case, but it is presented to elucidate the dynamics which seem to speak fairly well for themselves. The patient, who I suspected had witnessed the primal scene many times in his crowded rural home, seemed to have had his hostility heightened by this and the birth of siblings. His own fantasies of castrating and destroying his father were given further form by the observation of farm animals being castrated, and his concept of father as the terrifying castrator was reinforced by observation of the father actually castrating animals. It seems that he toyed with a homosexual solution, the wish to be castrated, but this was too terrifying to bear. When these fears were triggered by some event (for example, the injury to his arm and hospitalization) he could only react to the fantasies and their terrifying affects, thus dissociating. Dissociation seems to be, in this and other cases, a transitory elimination of consciousness and perhaps an archaic pattern of repression evoked when all other devices (except perhaps fainting) fail.

Pharmacotherapy

It is beyond the scope of this paper to discuss in detail the use of drugs in the therapy of childhood hysteria, which has been the subject of another communication(10B). To summarize, however, (and even omit discussion of the "anti-hysterics" such as musk and valerian, which may activate repression through the similarity of their odor to sexual and toilet odors), the pharmacologic properties of psychoactive drugs may be very useful adjuncts in therapy to minimize anxiety, but have no curative properties within themselves, and pharmacologic treatment alone is of little value. Let it suffice to say here that, in addition to any pharmacologic action, the administration of a drug is an important transaction between the doctor and patient. This transaction should be recognized as not only a pharmacologic intervention, but also as a very important psychodynamic intervention with various possible psychologic implications. The suggestion implicit in administering a drug is ordinarily considered to be positive in nature; that is, that the doctor administers a drug with the expectation that the patient will at least symptomatically benefit, and the patient takes the drug anticipating at least symptomatic improvement. However, this is only one of many possible variations. The physician can administer a drug as a "last resort" when psychotherapy has failed; or when he considers the case hopeless to begin with; or he can administer a drug in a hostile, or punitive, or rejecting way. The patient can receive and incorporate the drug as a helpful agent of the good physician, as a punitive agent of an ambivalently conceived physician, or the patient can conceive the drug as a direct symbolic substitute for the physician, and so forth. Aside from any pharmacologic action of a drug (or the lack thereof) there can be an overriding positive or negative psychologic influence, depending on the meaning of the transaction to the physician and the patient, and even to the patient's family. Occasionally even more remote people such as schoolteachers must be considered.

Many different drugs have been used in the treatment of hysteria. To mention a few: asafetida, valerian, musk, sumbal, camphor, bromides, chloral, paraldehyde, barbiturates, amphetamines, phenothiazines, hydroxozine, and such. However, no drug seems to hold particular advantage, except insofar as it pleases the physician.

With mild or even essentially transitory hysteric symptoms that occur under stress, pharmacologic intervention (and its dynamic significance) may shift the balance in such a way that the patient can reestablish his previous (perhaps neurotic) equilibrium. In fact, such results seem to be frequently achieved in the clinical practice of pediatricians and general practitioners. However, most mild cases are screened out in this way and are rarely referred to a child psychiatrist. By the time a child comes to psychiatric attention, psycho-pharmacologic intervention alone is seldom sufficient to achieve even symptom relief, although the administration of a sedative or tranquilizer in a crisis may minimize anxiety, serve as a vehicle for the physician-patient relationship, and facilitiate early rapport and positive transference in selected cases. This may be very useful when a child in a hysteric crisis is ready for a positive transference and needs to recurrently incorporate the good, controlling physician, but can only be seen infrequently and irregularly because of geographic or other limiting factors. A drug (or a letter for that matter) can prove a real sustaining force until further alteration in the conflict can be achieved; that is, hopefully through psychotherapy and interpretation, at the least through environmental manipulation. To conclude the discussion of drugs, pharmacologic intervention can be useful to minimize anxiety and assist the patient achieve better control in a crisis, but is rarely sufficient alone. Success with drugs, as with all therapeutic interventions in childhood hysteria, depends largely on the physician's understanding of his patient's current dynamic organization, and the manner in which the drug will effect homeostasis, and facilitate (or impede) psychotherapy or other maneuvers to favorably shift the balance of forces in the instinctual conflict.

Group Therapy

While consideration of analytic group therapy does not fit well into the context of this paper, which is primarily oriented to brief individual therapy, some comment seems justified as the group therapy of neuroses in children is not much discussed. However, group therapy in which group defenses, content, and transferences are interpreted seems to be well suited to the treatment of hysteria in childhood. Children seen briefly (perhaps 20 times) in open groups as inpatients (i.e., completely free admission to and discharge from the group, the only criterion being the child's presence in the hospital) have responded well and seemed to use the group process effectively. However, with inpatients where there is a tightly integrated milieu, including individual therapy a minimum of three times each week, occupational therapy, recreational therapy, art therapy, daily therapeutically oriented school, as well as group therapy once or twice each week, it is impossible to delineate the role of group therapy itself.

My personal experience as well as the collective experiences of my immediate colleagues is limited in the actual treatment of children with hysteria in closed or semiopen outpatient groups where treatment is carried to a reasonable conclusion (perhaps 18 months), although neuroses in general seem to respond well. However, there is no hesitation in assigning an hysteric child to an analytic group (as opposed to an activity group), and a six-year-old child who has had frequent dissociative episodes for the past three years is now in outpatient group therapy. It should be made clear here that I refer to group therapy in which: (1) the goal is treatment of the individual patient, but the medium of treatment is the group; (2) all members take an active part, and all communications and relationships (verbal and nonverbal) are treated as the equivalent of free associations of the group and a part of the group process; (3) there is a relaxation of censorship concerning verbalizations; (4) no directions are given except that it is therapy and the patients are encouraged to say whatever comes to mind; (5) the therapist's role is to clarify and interpret group defenses, content, process, behavior, and relationships; and (6) the parents are engaged in collateral analytic group therapy; that is, separate groups for the mothers and fathers.

SUMMARY

It should be emphasized that childhood is a period of rapid development and maturation, and that the forward thrust of the libido itself compensates for many minor regressions and fixations. Minimal therapeutic intervention is often effective in reinstituting the main stream of the growth process. The effectiveness of such brief intervention depends on the therapist's understanding of the living instinctual conflict, and using environmental manipulation (including brief therapeutic work with the parents), drugs, catharsis, suggestion, and brief psychotherapy alone or in combination with these other maneuvers to favorably shift the balance of forces and achieve homeostasis stable enough to withstand ordinary life stresses. Brief techniques depend on assisting the patient to verbalize conscious conflicts, using limited interpretation, provoking certain types of transference, and providing or assisting the patient to find and use socially acceptable outlets while avoiding either excessive temptations or prohibitions. The chief technical problem is that we have no real system of brief therapy, so that it is more demanding and difficult in many ways than the traditional uncovering psychotherapies.

REFERENCES

1A. ABSE, D. W.   Hysteria, in *American handbook of psychiatry,* Vol. I New York: Basic Books, Inc., 1959. Pp. 272–92.

1B. ABSE, D. W.   *Hysteria and related mental disorders.* Bristol, England: John Wright & Sons, Ltd. In press.

1C. ABSE, D. W.   Personal communication.

2. BREUER, J., and FREUD, S.   Studies in hysteria. Nerv. Ment. Dis. Monogr. Ser., 1950, No. 61.

3. DAWES, L. G.   The psychoanalysis of a case of "Grand Hysteria of Charcot" in a girl of fifteen. *Nerv. Child.*, 1953, **10**:272–305.

4. FENICHEL, O.   Brief psychotherapy. *The collected papers of Otto Fenichel*, 2d series. New York: W. W. Norton & Co., 1954. Pp. 243–59.

5. FREUD, A.   Indications for child analysis. *Psychoanalytic study of the child*, Vol. I. New York: International Universities Press, 1945.

6. FREUD, S.   Fragment of an analysis of a case of hysteria. *Collected papers*, Vol. III. London: Hogarth Press, 1953.

7. HOLLENDER, M. H., and HIRSCH, S. J.   Hysterical psychosis. *Amer. J. Psychiat.*, **120**(11):1066–74.

8. JANET, P.   The major symptoms of hysteria. (2d ed.) New York: Macmillan, 1929.

9. KAUFMAN, I.   Conversion hysteria in latency. *J. of Amer. Acad. Child Psychiat.*, **1**(3):385–96.

10A. PROCTOR, J. T.   Hysteria in Childhood. *Amer. J. Orthopsychiat.*, **28**(2): 394–407.

10B. PROCTOR, J. T.   Drug therapy in childhood hysteria. In HARMS, ERNEST, and KLINE, NATHAN S. (eds.), *International series of monographs on child psychiatry*. New York: Pergamon Press. In press.

11. PURTELL, J. J., ROBINS, E., and COHEN, MANDEL E.   Observations on clinical aspects of hysteria: A quantitative study of 50 hysteric patients and 156 control subjects. *J.A.M.A.*, 1951, **146**(10):902–9.

12. ROBINS, E., and O'NEAL, P.   Clinical features of hysteria in children, with a note on prognosis: A two to seventeen year follow-up study of 41 patients. *Nerv. Child*, 1953, **10**:246–71.

6

Lucie Jessner

Psychotherapy of Children
with Psychosomatic Disorders

PSYCHOSOMATIC DISORDERS are defined as the bodily manifestations of constant or recurrent emotional states, transmitted mainly via the autonomic or hormonal system. Intrapsychic and interpersonal conflicts are contributing, and perhaps even necessary, factors in the genesis or the course of these illnesses.

Certain psychophysiological disorders tend to occur at specific ages: for example, rumination, colic, celiac disease, eczema during infancy; asthma in early childhood; ulcerative colitis and rheumatoid arthritis in latency; obesity and anorexia nervosa in adolescence. This temporal relationship reflects the importance of developmental phases in the field of psychophysiological disorders; with maturation there is a change in regard to avenues of discharge of tension, in regard to tolerance for and mastery of emotions, and in regard to available defenses against anxiety.

The fact that psychophysiological responses can be observed to lead to specific dysfunction later in life makes the topic of psychosomatics in childhood an exciting area for investigation and preventive endeavor. Bodily signs of displeasure can be observed (for instance, the infant's reactions to mood changes in the mother), and one becomes aware of the fact that the term psychosomatic means a unit, not a duality. The infant's world is less complex than the adult's. Therefore it lends itself more readily to the study of adaptive and maladaptive patterns and ultimately to suggestions in regard to fostering the former.

151

DISTURBANCES IN EARLY CHILDHOOD

The infant depends for survival and for well-being on mothering, which fulfills his needs and attenuates his tensions. The transactions in the mother-child relationship and its emotional climate have therefore been a focus of research and therapeutic intervention during the last 25 years.

Mother-Child Relationship

Impaired physical functioning of the infant as a consequence of a disturbed mother-child relationship has been described by many investigators, among them Benedek(6), Fries(31), Rank(62), Ribble(63), Spitz(73, 74). Infants with anxious or tense mothers have been observed to reflect this communicated tension with vomiting, diarrhea, and feeding difficulties(77). Marked somatic manifestations related to lack of motherly care during the first months of life or to separation during critical periods has been well documented(13, 34, 71). René Spitz(73), in attempting to correlate infantile experiences with somatic disorders, found that mothers of babies with colic were primarily anxious and over-permissive; mothers of babies with infantile neurodermatitis were hostile under the surface of anxiousness. Margaret Gerard(34) and her co-workers studied 38 children with various psychosomatic disorders and observed the detailed behavior of their mothers to determine the influence of minute variations in the mode of feeding, of holding, bathing, talking or singing, smiling or frowning, as well as the consistency or lack of consistency of these actions, and of the child's exposure to different modes of behavior and the "separation trauma," when a substitute person displaced the mother. Such data might help in finding an answer to questions of choice of symptoms which have evaded explanation from gross descriptions of environmental influences, and might provide guidelines for a therapeutic approach to the mother. In Gerard's study, each child presenting a psychosomatic disorder had experienced frustrated dependence at a stage when body needs are dependent upon the mother for satisfaction.

Attitudes and feelings transmitted from mother to child are to a large degree not conscious. Melitta Sperling(72), through psychoanalysis of mothers and simultaneous treatment of young children, was able to show how the modification of the unconscious needs of the mother resulted in changes in the somatic responses of the child. Psychosomatic disorders were reversible if the relationship between the mother and patient improved.

Earlier studies in this field focused observation and therapy on the mother as a "noxious agent." Over the last 20 years it has become clear that the interaction between mother and child is effected by the contributions of both participants. Studies now have taken into account the endowment of the child and his special ways of experiencing(8, 31). For example, Arthur Mirsky(55) pointed out:

Although Spitz may be right in stating that infants with neurodermatitis have anxious mothers with "unusually large amounts of unconscious repressed hostility," it is just as probable that such infants contribute something to their mother's attitude as well as to the pathogenesis of their lesion. . . . It is possible that an infant with a low rate of sebum secretion may require a different kind and quantity of tactile stimulation for his particular skin. . . . In order to delineate the contributions of the infant to the mother-child unit it is essential to develop methods for the quantitative evaluaion of the physiological capacities of infants during the phase of biological dependency.

Mirsky's work with peptic ulcer patients led him to postulate the presence of hypersecreters among infants.

The baby with gastric hypersecretion has a stomach which is behaving constantly like that of a hungry normosecreting infant. Therefore, infantile dependent demands persist. Their degree depends on the extent of the mother's integrative capacity as well as on the rate of gastric secretion. Thus gastric hypersecretion plays a role in the persistency of infantile-receptive wishes which then act as ulcer-precipitating factors when mobilized by meaningful environmental events.

Constitutional Makeup

Another example of relevant investigations is Julius Richmond's study of the neurophysiology of the newborn and its implications for child development and especially for the genesis of psychophysiological disturbances. Richmond(65, 66) and his co-workers investigated the "functional constitution" of the individual in terms of the autonomic reactivity of the newborn and, in particular, the development of cortico-autonomic relationships. Their findings indicate that the wide individual variation among newborns in regard to heart rate and skin temperature, and in regard to the responses of the autonomic nervous system, calls for great flexibility of the mother in order to respond to the individual needs of her infant. Aside from quantity and quality of need-gratifying experiences, the *timing* of tension-reduction is relevant for the achievement of somatic and psychological homeostasis. Due to the helplessness of the infant, the patterns of physiological responses are dependent on the quality of mothering in the beginning of life. The repetition and modification of these patterns in a widening horizon of relationships to a variety of human beings appears relevant for the development of psychosomatic reactions in later life.

How this comes to pass is as yet not clearly seen in cases of adults or children. Retrospective studies can seldom uncover the minute variations in the infant's constitutional makeup nor can they reconstruct the subtle nuances of the environment's responses to the child.

Closest to a clarification of the processes involved is the investigation George Engel(25) and his co-workers carried out with Monica, an infant with a gastric fistula, begun on the fourth day after birth because of esophageal atresia. At the age of 13 months, Monica was hospitalized because of marasmus with a history of marked reaction to tensions within her family and to her mother's second pregnancy. Monica improved during her short hospitalization, but at home after the birth of a sister showed a sharp decline and was readmitted to the hospital where she was observed from the 16th to the 21st month of age. The aim of the investigation was to examine how—if at all—the secretory activity of the stomach is correlated with the total behavior of the infant.

Concomitant observations of behavior in different settings (with the doctor to whom she was attached, with strangers, and so on) and examination of the gastric secretion led to the following conclusions: Affective states which are expressive of social communication, libidinal or aggressive, are associated with rising rates of secretion of hydrochloric acid. Depressive affects, involving a relative reduction in the degree and rate of communication with the environment, are associated with decrease or cessation of gastric secretion. When the infant was confronted alone by a stranger, the depression-withdrawal reaction—muscular hypotonia, inactivity, and sad facial expression—and reduction of gastric secretion predominated; eventually a sleep state occurred. This reaction vanished when the child was reunited with a familiar person. The highest secretions occurred during rage and during a joyful reunion with the love object. In this specific case the connection between "affects, object relations, and gastric secretions" is convincingly documented and inspires further exploration of what Felix Deutsch(20) called "the mysterious leap from mind to body."

Therapeutic intervention for infants with minor or major variations from the biological norm would consist mainly in helping the mother to recognize and respond to the child's special needs and to deal with her own feelings: A child who is difficult to satisfy frustrates and disappoints her mother.

This is unavoidable, but it might be possible to prevent the following chain reaction: The mother begins to resent the child and then feels guilty for angry and hostile impulses towards him; she excuses herself for being a bad mother or tries to justify herself, blaming the child. These conflicting feelings lead some mothers to a masochistic surrender to the difficult child, and others to reject him. Frequently an atmosphere of tense anxieties pervades the home, increasing the child's discontent and apprehension. To prevent such disturbances in the mother-child relationship, it is important to give the mother an opportunity to express and work through her feelings.

Childhood Events

The infant's difficulty in achieving homeostasis through motherly response to his specific needs seems, to many investigators, the basis for later psychosomatic disturbances, whereas immediate conflicts, preceding the outbreak of the illness, appear as precipitants(35). In addition to constitution and earliest experiences, meaningful events in childhood play a role in the manifestation of psychosomatic illness.

Example: Dorothy, at the age of two, went with her older sister through a pile of leaves which covered a fire. Her sister ran through while the patient stopped in the pile of leaves and screamed in terror for her mother, who didn't realize immediately what went on. Dorothy got third degree burns on her foot while her sister was not hurt. After this episode she became fussy about eating and started to soil. Gradually she developed diarrhea. When she was four years old, ulcerative colitis was diagnosed.

The frightening experience seemed a factor in the development of her illness, not only because one followed shortly after the other, but also because of the content of her fears and fantasies, when she was seen in psychotherapy at the age of 11. At this time she was depressed and had made a suicidal attempt. She complained that her sister is healthy, strong, and can do everything. The sister fights back at father but Dorothy is too afraid of what he might do to her. For quite some time she has had "a fear of something about to happen." She always wants somebody to watch her. In one interview, she told the story of a girl who leads a blind girl into quicksand and then the blind one dies. Whenever she gets excited or worried—for instance, when the doctor suggests doing something to her, or when she hears mother and father fighting, or whenever she is away from home—she gets the feeling she ought to run to the bathroom. Play interviews centered around Dorothy's concept of her illness: a doll, whom she named Patty Ann (Ann was Dorothy's middle name) wore a bandage on her stomach, after an operation on the doll had revealed two objects which Patty Ann might have swallowed a long time ago.

Dorothy said mother and father used to keep dangerous things within Patty Ann's reach when she was a baby. Once Patty Ann got some matches to play with but her father took them away just in time. There was also a box of small toys which should have been a larger size so that they could not be swallowed. Patty Ann might have swallowed some of them. Dorothy had told Patty Ann's parents that they were careless and would have a lot of misery if Patty Ann died.

It appears that Dorothy, overwhelmed by the sudden onslaught of anxiety resulting from the trauma at the age of two, regressed to an earlier level when she had not yet been able to control her bowel functions. She avoided all pleasurable activities (for example, playing or eating), aways fearful that something might happen to her, whereas others would get away with it. She wanted to be protected but had no confidence that anybody would or could help her. It seemed that her resentment of the traumatic experience was perpetuated and expressed in her unwillingness to take food, and in expelling whatever she had accepted.

In psychotherapy, she became gradually less suspicious and to a certain degree affectionate towards the therapist, and trusting too. At that stage it was noticed that at times of stress—for example, before an X-ray examination—Dorothy would rub her stomach with her hand. She commented once that the rubbing made her fear and pain go away. She recalled that her mother used to do that for her when she was little and could not eat, or had a pain in the stomach, or felt like going to the bathroom. It became obvious that Dorothy was longing for this early, tender, mother figure who could allay her discomfort. The return of early memories of her mother's care was an essential element in her improvement, insofar as it brought back the original trust in her mother.

Felix Deutsch(20) postulated that the choice of a particular organ often was due to an illness of this part of the body (for instance, the upper respiratory system), which had occurred during a critical period in childhood.

SPECIFIC PSYCHOSOMATIC DISORDERS

It is not possible to include the whole gamut of psychosomatic illnesses in one chapter. Having to make a choice, I will present the more intensely studied ones.

A. Eating Disturbance

1. *Rumination.* Rumination has been defined as the regurgitation of previously swallowed food and the rechewing and reswallowing of it. As the reswallowing is incomplete, there is considerable food and fluid loss; inanition, electrolyte disturbance, and death may result.

Most authors(33, 45) found the earliest onset at three months of age. The infants ruminated when left alone, and also showed other self-stimulating behavior; for example, rocking, head-banging, genital and fecal play, excessive finger-sucking. They seemed depressed. Their mothers appeared to keep an affective distance from the baby(32) and were, in general, immature. Richmond(67) and his co-workers do not suggest that specific maternal psychopathology results in rumination, but that many factors which deprive the infant of intimate, stimulating relationships may predispose to the disorder.

All investigators found that a striking reversal of symptoms occurred when a warm, stimulating environment was provided. Therapy thus consisted in providing the infant with a mother-substitute, until psychotherapy of the mother brought about changes in her attitudes.

2. *Nutritional Dwarfs.* These are children who fail to grow because they consistently refuse to eat. Poor or finicky eating has been a frequent complaint in the past. This symptom has decreased, since pediatricians and mothers are less rigid about feeding.

There are, however, children whose rejection of food seriously endangers their health and growth. A variety of psychological factors may lead a child to be fearful of or disgusted with food, instead of enjoying it. Most frequently, his refusal reflects the child's mistrust of his mother's care. A typical example will illustrate the underlying dynamics.

Example: Michael was admitted to the pediatric ward at age four because of refusal to eat, vomiting, and loss of weight. He was found dehydrated, undersized, and underweight, and was referred to child psychiatry because he was seen gagging after he was fed. He gave the impression of a quiet, unhappy child, apprehensive and suspicious, obliging, without spontaneity, infantile in speech and manners. Past history revealed that he was the only child of parents who divorced when he was six months old. He was breast fed for one month by his tense and irritable mother. Her milk was considered not sufficient and he was weaned to a bottle. From this time on, he vomited after each feeding. When Michael was five months old, his grandmother recalled that he screamed in his crib, whereupon his mother threw all his toys on him. The patient yelled once, then was absolutely silent, and the mother explained to grandmother that this was the way to teach him good behavior. From age six months on, the patient was boarded with his maternal grandmother, as the mother began working after her divorce; but she took the patient during weekends. Grandmother described the patient as very "good," obedient, well-behaved, often near tears, but never crying or complaining. He had no friends. Children always beat him up. He liked to listen to stories and every so often asked his grandmother to tell him that she loved him, to which she routinely answered, "Yes, if you are a good boy." Once every night he went into his grandmother's bedroom to see whether she was still there. She occasionally asked him what he would do if she died. She told him that children who use bad words are taken away by the police. She liked him, but felt him to be a burden, because she was in her sixties; and she displaced much of the anger toward her daughter on to him. We recommended casework with the grandmother and psychotherapy with the child. Work with the grandmother had mainly two goals: (1) To eliminate this displacement of hostility. She was encouraged to express her resentment against her daughter and to have empathy with the traumatized child. (2) To realize the child's fear of abandonment and of annihilation. She became aware that her threatening Michael with being taken away by police or witches increased his anxiety and confusion. This enabled her to be more encouraging to Michael and less punitive.

Psychotherapy with the child was indicated, because much of his conflict was internalized. His fear of mother and grandmother was heightened by his own destructive impulses and fantasies, for which he expected retribution.

In psychotherapy the patient at first restricted himself in his play. He didn't know what to do, but after a few interviews, he messed

up the whole room with water and fingerpaint, then became afraid
that someone would find out. He then began freely using four-letter
words. He made a cake of clay, called it shit, and asked the
psychiatrist to eat it, commenting that other boys make him eat
sticks and stones and dirt. When he goes home, he will make them
eat shit. If one eats what others have eaten, one gets germs and is
sick and has to go to the hospital. He then told me that grandmother said witches come at night to give candy to boys and then
cook them in a stove. (Grandmother had told the social worker with
great anger that mother feeds patient candy when she has him for
weekends). After this interview the patient did not vomit anymore,
was discharged from the ward, and treated in the child psychiatric
clinic. Meals at home were still ordeals of several hours duration. In
psychotherapy, he continued to express a fearful preoccupation with
eating; for instance, talking about his games with a girlfriend, he
said that if they are found out doing bad things they will be killed,
chopped up in little pieces, ground up, and eaten. In play he finally
distinguished on his own between bad and good food, e.g., swallowing dirty water and spitting it out and then swallowing clean water
and retaining it. After a prolonged stretch of swearing, destroying,
and attacking in play interviews, he became able to control himself
and to be active and boyish at home.

Michael's refusal to eat was due to his concept of food as poison and
feces, a gift of hatred rather than love. This concept grew out of his
experience as an infant, fed by a hostile mother, overcome by rage in
which he wanted to eat up his enemies as he expected to be devoured by
his "witch" mother. The intensity of his helpless fury and the fear of
punishment had led to an inhibition to express any aggression, lest he
would be abandoned and destroyed. The aims of psychotherapy were:
(1) to provide the child with a person whom he could trust and who
could accept the expression of his intense oral and anal aggressive drives;
(2) to alleviate the child's rage and fear by allowing him to express his
fantasies in words and play so that in the later stages of psychotherapy he
could be helped to master his aggression.

3. *Anorexia Nervosa.* Anorexia nervosa, a different form of self-
starvation, is characterized by the refusal to eat, vomiting, frequent use of
drugs recommended for losing weight, and hyperactivity. It is quite often
interrupted by bouts of overeating. The cessation of menses sometimes
precedes weight loss in adolescent girls.

In contrast to the nutritional dwarfism of childhood, anorexia nervosa most frequently begins around puberty or in adolescence. It is characteristically an affliction of that period when the existence as a child comes to an end physiologically, psychologically, and sociologically; when the struggle for a new identity begins, and a conflict between reaching for and rejecting the genital phase of development becomes acute.

At this late stage of childhood, food has taken on a variety of symbolic meanings; most prominently—consciously or preconsciously—eating is perceived as oral impregnation and getting fat as being pregnant—conditions desirable, but frightening and unacceptable. The roots of this illness also can be found in early mother-child interaction. My co-worker D. W. Abse and I learned from intensively studied patients that they had suffered a period of early traumatic feeding, followed by a time of satisfaction, weight gain, and intimacy with their mothers. Separation, jealousy, and rivalry regularly brought the ambivalence to the fore, until the precarious mutual adjustment broke down in the crisis of adolescence.

Hilde Bruch(17) has stressed the disturbances of perception in this condition: the failure to recognize the nutritional need, the lack of awareness of exhaustion during overactivity (this lack of fatigue was stressed by Janet), and the unconcern with their gruesome appearance, indicating a disturbance in body image.[1]

In studying the family background, the author concluded that the clues for need fulfillment originating in the baby were not adequately responded to by the mother, which led to failure of recognizing body functions and needs (such as hunger) in the child. These families did not encourage self-expression. The outcome is compliance and negativism when progressive development demands more than obedience; the absence of reliance on inner resources and autonomous decision then becomes critical.

In regard to therapy, Dr. Bruch stresses the necessity of making the patients aware of the impulses and sensations originating within themselves so they may learn how to control them.

Anorexia nervosa, in the beginning of the illness or in the milder cases, where hysterical features are prominent, responds well to psychotherapy.

---

[1] My observations of anorexia patients do not show a lack of perception; for example, several of them complained about hunger and achieved weight loss through vomiting. The female patients were aware of their ugliness; for instance, an adolescent girl drew a portrait of herself as a scarecrow and a picture of herself as she sometimes wished that she would look: a round bosomy, graceful dancer. The urge for self-destruction rather than lack of perception seemed to me the underlying disturbance.

In the more severe cases where obsessive neurotic, depressive, or schizophrenic trends predominate, the main difficulty is to establish a therapeutic alliance with these extremely ambivalent and basically suicidal patients—with a mortality rate of 7.8 percent.

Hospitalization often is imperative, not only to safeguard survival by constant medical supervision, but also for psychological reasons. The patient's involvement with her parents—the conflict between the wish for infantile dependence and the rebellious struggle against it—is so intense that only a separation from them makes it possible to alternate the intensity of affects and to transfer her ambivalence to the personnel of the hospital. The first phase of treatment, we found, is best carried out if the hospital care can be tailored to the patient's infantile and anaclitic needs, wherein the patient may find "the rescuing mother" in her therapist. Strengthening of the restitutional forces against the constantly emerging regressive tendencies is, in this phase, the aim of therapy. When the danger state of actual starvation and electrolyte imbalance has passed and the relationship to the therapist is positive, psychotherapy can begin. It usually challenges the therapist to the utmost, because the transference feelings are most intense and infantile. Love and hatred alternate rapidly, and the therapist has to deal with his counter-transference in order to tolerate the onslaught. The last aim becomes not only the relinquishment of self-starvation, but the acceptance of individuation and sexual maturity.

4. *Obesity.*   While food has come to be a dangerous substance in the two syndromes discussed, for children obese from overeating, food represents comfort, security, protection. Oral gratification is used to relieve tensions and feelings of loneliness, emptiness, and boredom, usually heightened at times of self-devaluation or lack of narcissistic supply from other people. These patients actually are in a state of affect-hunger. Hilde Bruch emphasized the type of the fat boy, who is afraid of competition and of fight. In her later publications she stresses the inability of these patients to recognize the physiological messages from the body; that is, they take a feeling of inner emptiness as a signal from an empty stomach. The roots of this oral fixation also can usually be traced to infancy, to times of either oral frustration or (sometimes alternating with) overgratification, and most frequently when feeding is used as the universal method for soothing the child.

Therapy, needless to say, has to be directed not to the symptom, but to the child's personality and motives. Most obese children have been teased to a point where they consciously are eager to lose weight, where, indeed, their self-esteem depends on a presentable figure. But only a few are able to follow a diet—a difficulty similar to that of giving up other addictions, such as to alcohol or drugs. Therapy more often than not calls for intensive work with the parents: (*a*) Parents who themselves are either overeating or overvalue food—as a means of health, strength, or pleasure, or as sign of their providing love and care. This is more frequent in some cultures (for instance, some Italian or Jewish groups) than in others. For these people a reorientation to eating might have to penetrate to their own unfulfilled needs. (*b*) Parents who cannot provide or allow the child other satisfactions of libidinal or aggressive drives. Group therapy has been shown to be effective—with groups of parents (or mothers) and groups of youngsters. Members of such groups can borrow strength from each other. Therapy usually has to go through a stage of dealing with the child's image of himself and his usually low self-esteem, before his specific conflicts and longings can be expressed and finally solved through gratifications other than eating.

5. *Pica.* Pica means the ingestion of inedible substances. It is the most frequent source of lead poisoning in children. It is related in origin and in dynamics to obesity, but with a stronger emphasis on oral biting tendencies.

In a recent investigation of children treated for pica at Children's Hospital of the District of Columbia, Frances Millican(**52, 53**) and her co-workers studied the personality of these patients and their mothers. They seemed to fall into three groups:

1. Those where the mother herself has pica or where certain forms of it (e.g., eating of clay, soil, or laundry starch) was considered beneficial in their special cultural group.[2] In these cases, guidance of the mothers would be the therapy of choice.
2. Children where the crucial factor was emotional deprivation that led the child to act in the manner of "nobody loves me, I am going to eat worms." Therapy here would have to aim at a restitution of emotional supply.
3. A group of children with poor reality testing in general, due to brain damage or to psychosis of mother and/or the patient.

B. Disturbances of Gastro-Intestinal Functions

1. *Colic.* Colic is defined as a state of paroxysmal loud crying of the infant with his legs flexed, seemingly connected with abdominal pain. No

---

[2] For example, in several rural communities in North Carolina, red clay is thought to be good for one's health.

demonstrable cause has been found, but several explanations are preferred(77).

1. The immaturity of the gastro-intestinal system, which is one aspect of the incompleteness of the newborn, could account for some of the symptoms and for their disappearance in the third or fourth month of life, when the nervous system becomes more mature and is capable of taking on the exigencies of normal demands.

2. A food allergy, which would account for the improvement which often occurs when the infant is put on a different formula.

3. A constitutional predisposition to hypertonia, consistent with the idea of vagotonia, which implies a low threshold for sensory stimuli. H. I. Meyer(50) described the type of the energetic active infant, who later on develops into a forceful leader.

4. Most investigators believe that the colicky difficulties of the infant are related to the emotional state of the parents, and that what Wessel(77) termed "paroxysmal fussiness" can be engendered by tension in the family. This would explain the common experience that the symptoms subside when the colicky baby is moved to the care of a mature woman or transferred to a hospital. In a review of 654 charts, recorded from 1944–47 in the New York Foundling Hospital, Levin did not find a single case of colic reported; close scrutiny of the charts revealed eight possible cases(77). These data lend support to the assumption that colic of the infant is related to the interactions within the family.

In regard to the treatment, what matters most is to relieve tension and anxiety in the home atmosphere. Meanwhile, for the sake of infant and mother the more immediate remedies should not be left out: giving a pacifier; patting and rocking, which have proven to sooth; with some babies, changing the formula has relieved the infant as well as the mother's self-accusations for doing something wrong. Antispasmodic medication (atropin or a mixture of amphetamine and phenobarb) was found helpful.

2. *Constipation.*   Chronic constipation and megocolon are fairly frequent disturbances in childhood. Alexander(2) and his co-workers found in adult patients with chronic retention of bowel movements an attitude of distrust, and frequently the feeling of being rejected. Their emotional undertone is described as "I cannot expect anything from anybody and therefore I do not need to give anything. I must hold on to what I have." He found that an underlying unconscious, aggressive, and deprecatory attitude toward others is severely inhibited and extends to the excretory function, which unconsciously signifies a hostile attack.

Children suffering from constipation had, as Melitta Sperling(72) described, parents with compulsive traits, ambivalent attitudes toward the child, and a need to control him, with emphasis on toilet training. The children revealed a variety of motivations for retention of stools:

1. Feces were conceived as a part of the body, and defecating seemed a loss of a part. This fear increased when constipation caused painful bowel movements, which were dreaded, but also enjoyed; this added libidinal importance, and also interfered with physiological function.

2. There was fear of the toilet or the noise of flushing, as something that can make something disappear; these children had the wish of flushing siblings or parents down, expecting the same to happen to them in retribution.

3. Having incorporated the mother's disgust of excrements, defecation seemed unbearably dirty and a disgraceful activity one had to avoid.

4. Anger was expressed in spiteful withholding, and often became a successful weapon in a power struggle with the parents.

Therapy preferably deals with the antagonists, parents and child. In working with the parents, it is helpful to discuss their attitude in regard to toilet functions. Some are convinced that a daily bowel movement is required, though they may have been instructed to the contrary by their pediatrician. Some harbor an excessive disgust of the sight and smell of excrements, imparting it to the child, but can be helped to take a more tolerant attitude. Such changes in attitudes often are not possible and not sufficient without the parents' understanding of the child's anxieties or his need for self-assertion as underlying the symptom of constipation. Such understanding also can become effective in decreasing hostility against the child. Psychotherapy with the patient should give him the opportunity to express his needs, fears, conflicts, and fantasies in words or play rather than in psychosomatic reactions.

3. *Diarrhea.* Anger and fear also can be expressed by defecating, a common experience amply reflected in the vernacular.

> *Example:* George M., age five, had been hospitalized several times because of chronic diarrhea since he was a year old. The pediatric service noticed a cessation of diarrhea during hospitalization and a recurrence on his return home. The pediatrician suspected that the gastro-intestinal symptoms related to tensions between the patient and his mother and referred him to child psychiatry.
>
> The patient appeared frail, wiry, and undernourished, overactive and aggressive, excited and full of noisy bravado, with an apprehensive look in his eyes.
>
> *Medical History:* During the first three months of life, he was a "colicky" baby, but then thrived till the age of 11 months, when he

began to refuse food. This occurred at the time when his mother resumed a job outside of the home. From age 12 months on, he had five to six watery bowel movements a day. Celiac disease was diagnosed and he was put on a fat-and-sugar-free diet.

Family Background: Both parents suffered from "irritable colon" when under pressure. Mrs. M. had felt deprived in her childhood. When she was three years old, her mother died after giving birth to a boy. This younger brother was considered a genius and an older sister and Mrs. M. sacrificed their free time, their education, and their money in order to raise this brother and to send him to college. The brother became an outstanding scientist but alienated himself from his sisters. Mrs. M. felt extremely bitter about his ingratitude and wished she would never have a son. After a scene with her brother she had her first miscarriage. After George, the first living child was born, she had severe diarrhea when told the baby was a boy. She had a few more miscarriages afterward, but when George was seven she gave birth finally to a girl. She was over-attached to her baby daughter and diffident toward George; he reacted to her indifference by attention-seeking obnoxious behavior and she then treated him with frank hostility.

Therapy: Mrs. M. was seen by a social worker, while George was in psychotherapy with me. Mrs. M. was in the beginning extremely anxious, insecure, and overprotective: she constantly asked which food and how much to give to the patient who asked for huge meals, followed by diarrhea. In the course of casework, Mrs. M. was able to realize that she displaced the anger she felt against her ungrateful brother on to her son, who in many ways reminded her of his uncle. She finally could accept George as an individual in his own right and the tension between mother and child lessened till the birth of her daughter upset the balance.

The patient in psychotherapy immediately transferred his hostile dependency on to me. He explained his tremendous greed for food, which his mother was reluctant to give him and which he knew was doing him harm. Whenever he ate, he had to think of diarrhea; and whenever he thought of it, he got it. He was outspoken in words and in play that he wanted to kill me and threatened to kill himself by climbing on the windowsill, ready to jump. When these maneuvers failed to frighten me, he became aware of the difference between his murderous fantasies and the reality of an ambivalent relationship where impulses are not acted-out. The relationship with his mother improved; diarrhea subsided, but his aggression and the need for attention persisted, and were aggravated by resentment of his mother's pregnancy and then jealousy against his sister. Instead of a psychosomatic disorder he presented a behavior disturbance for several years.

4. *Ulcerative Colitis.* That changes in function of the colon occur under the impact of emotions was directly observed by Grace, Wolff and Wolf(36) on four patients with fistula, through which a part of the colon could be seen. If these patients were in a state of marked anger, resentment, and hostility, the colon "blushed," became engorged and hypermobile. In life situations provocative of "object fear and dejection," pallor, relaxation, and hypofunction of the colon appeared.

Similar findings on color changes of the mucosa as effected by food and psychic stimuli were reported on three children with colostomies. Prugh(59) was able to measure the correlation of emotional tension and disturbed bowel activity in children with ulcerative colitis. Melitta Sperling(71) described the dynamics and the unconscious meaning of ulcerative colitis in two analyzed children. The impact of unconscious urges rather than overt affective reaction on the colon has been demonstrated in several adult patients psychoanalytically treated. Engel(23) in his critical survey found a consistency of certain characteristics in ulcerative colitis patients which he regards as possibly contributory or even necessary, yet not sufficient in themselves for the development of this illness which seems to be a reaction of mucosa and submucosa of colon and ileum to a noxious agent. Studies based on psychoanalytically treated patients establish "that the major psychodynamic trends long antedate the development of clinically manifest ulcerative colitis." The assumption that these characteristics are the consequence of the severe and debilitating disease finds no support when patients are studied for years.

Most patients with ulcerative colitis show obsessive-compulsive trends, an uncanny perception of hostility, dependence on one or two key figures, and an inability to establish genuine friendships.

The affective state of these patients, preceding the onset or relapse of ulcerative colitis, is described as a feeling of helplessness and despair in a situation where the tenuous relationship with the person on whom they depend is lost or threatened. Several observers, especially those working with children(60) are impressed by the intense violent rage in this setting which is too frightening to be expressed in actions, play, or words.

The basis of this psychological condition has increasingly been assumed to stem from the mother-child relationship. Engel(24) speaks of an impressive consistency in the description of mothers of ulcerative colitis patients. They are perceived as rigid, controlling and perfectionistic, worrying and occasionally paranoid, often martyrs, arousing guilt feelings in the child.

Finch and Hess(27) describe the children as constricted, defensive, guilty, covertly hostile, and with obsessive-compulsive character traits.

In a study of 12 children with ulcerative colitis at Massachusetts General Hospital, Boston,[3] my co-workers and I found that experiences from early childhood onward aroused special interest in the gastrointestinal tract, and played a considerable role in the choice of the colon as an organ for expressing emotion. Compulsive and rigid parental attitudes were reflected in the way toilet training was handled, or were demonstrated in other ways, as by emphasis on goodness, neatness, control of feelings, and regularity of bowel movements. Larry (age 5) had constipation twice during treatment, and both times his mother became anxious and administered suppositories; her need to have the bowels move every day was quite apparent.

In other parents, preoccupation with the bathroom and anality was striking. Michael's mother always suggested that they go to the bathroom at the end of the hour, before leaving the hospital. When Michael had severe nightmares, his mother took him to the bathroom to relieve his anxiety. The following characteristics were observed in these patients:

1. Suspicious and sometimes paranoid attitudes toward the world.

2. Fear and hostility which intensified each other to produce a state of helpless fury.

3. A vulnerable and wounded narcissism, with shameful feelings for being a coward.

4. Hypochondriacal concerns about the body.

5. Extremely aggressive impulses, often too dangerous to be expressed, even in words.

6. Depressive moods.

7. Through projection of their own destructive fantasies, the children regarded every aspect of medical therapy as a hostile attack, and there was tremendous resentment of any medical manipulation.

8. In their violently destructive fantasies, food and feces symbolized the persons to whom these children were attached with such strong ambivalence. Figures of speech, such as "I'll bite your head off" or "I could eat you up," were taken literally, and carried connotations both of hatred and love, which were felt to be devouring forces. The "stomach" was treated with almost parental solicitude as a precious organ from which enemies and harmful substances must be eliminated; eating and straining hence became forbidden, dangerous pleasures.

---

[3] This study was partly supported by a Research Grant (MH–66 from the National Institute of Mental Health [USPHS]).

A psychodynamic constellation common among these children was found: disillusionment in parents or their care, leading to a general distrust of people; hostile, destructive impulses without the capacity to express or master them, leading to projection of hostility and a feeling of helpless humiliation; and, outstandingly, struggle with rage against the beloved person.

This is reflected in therapy: Engel(24) states that remissions seem to occur when an effective relationship is again achieved. For our patients this statement could certainly be confirmed, but it became obvious that the establishment of such a relationship usually came only after cruel fantasies and hostile feelings were expressed and tolerated. Thus psychotherapy of these children is a severe challenge. Finch(28) describes that the illness often is utilized as a means of omnipotently controlling the therapist and frightening him into avoiding anything which would upset the patient. Because of the enormous need for oral-dependent supplies, the patient continually felt disappointed in the therapist and exercised demands which could never be met. This was our experience too. Any interruption—through the therapist's absence, illness, or a vacation—was resented as an insult and abandonment by the child, disrupting the tenuously positive, trusting relationship; it frequently coincided with an exacerbation of intestinal symptoms. The therapist is harassed from two sides: from his countertransference aroused by the passionately ambivalent and primitively destructive patient; and by the seriousness of the somatic situation, which may end fatally or lead to malignancy.

Ulcerative colitis patients should always be simultaneously under pediatric care for medical therapy and sometimes surgical intervention. Particularly with a hospitalized child, it is most relevant that pediatrician and psychotherapist have a common understanding and plan for management, because the child usually is eager and apt to perceive disharmony and tension in this team, as he does in the relationship between his parents(47).

In spite of great difficulties, psychotherapy can be successful and rewarding with these children. O'Connor(56) and his co-workers surveyed 114 ulcerative colitis patients, half of them treated with psychotherapy and the other half without psychotherapy. Groups were matched for severity of disease, sex, age of onset, and use of steroids. The effects of treatment were evaluated over eight years. By the end of the eighth year, the proctoscopic rating and the clinical symptoms had improved considerably in the psychiatrically treated group but only minimally in the control group.

As a general strategy, it is good to keep in mind that in the beginning of therapy all depends on finding channels of communication and ways of relating to these patients, without stirring up too much emotion(22). One has to take into account that these children are extremely sensitive to rejection, to disappointment, and to separation. It therefore matters to be consistent, predictable, and reliable, qualities the patient usually has missed in his parents. Every so often, one has to be a buffer between child and parents, avoiding the position of being a participant in their mutual struggle. The patient should be permitted to express his hostility to the doctor, the nurse, and others, in transference where guilt feelings are less intense than to the original objects of rage. The patient has to feel accepted without having to fear retaliation or abandonment. When the acute illness subsides, it may be possible to give interpretations and to deal with basic conflicts. After recovery, therapy may be essential to help the child back into action and reality concerns. These severely sick children have been deprived through their illness of means to deal actively with their environment. They often have no other mode of communication than through bowel function. Helplessness and dependency have been resented as well as enjoyed. Attention has been focused on the body, its function and its sensation, and a transition to a less narcissistic way of life is often difficult.

C. Rheumatoid Arthritis

Children with rheumatoid arthritis have some characteristics in common with ulcerative colitis patients, and rheumatoid arthritis not infrequently is associated with or follows ulcerative colitis in the same patient as an infectious disease. G. E. Blom et al.(11, 12) stressed the depressive character of both mother and child in rheumatoid arthritis cases; both were unable to express feelings, particularly hostility. In these mothers masochistic trends were outstanding. Most of them had suffered the loss of a key-figure during pregnancy with, or during the infancy of, the patient, which had revived deprivations experienced in the past. These mothers were usually slavishly devoted to the child and no sacrifice seemed too great. One may assume that the self-sacrificing attitude of the mother makes it extremely difficult for the child to feel resentful towards her and to express anger. This inhibition of aggressive activity may lead to tensions of the musculature of the extremities.

Psychotherapy then aims mainly at enabling child and mother to accept the ambivalence in their relationship, to permit awareness and expression of hostility and greater independence from each other.

D. Bronchial Asthma

Bronchial asthma was considered a psychosomatic illness even before this word was coined and was called "asthma nervosum" in the 19th century. With the findings of allergic reactions, emotional precipitation of asthma attacks were considered like conditioned reflexes; for instance, in MacKenzies' example of a lady, sensitive to roses, getting an attack when paper roses were brought into her room.

Later investigators agreed that asthmatic patients had an allergic predisposition, but did not always develop attacks when exposed to the allergens to which they were sensitive, and conversely often developed typical attacks when the provoking substance was not present(30).

More specific characteristics either in the personality, the life history, or the conflict of these patients have been elucidated during the last 15 years.

French and Alexander(30) studied 27 asthmatic patients psychoanalytically, 11 of them children. They found:

1. The attack was a reaction to the danger of losing mother's love. Not the actual loss of the mother through death or separation, but the fear of it, was decisive. This anxiety arose particularly when sexual or aggressive impulses or the wish for independence became strong.
2. The lives of the patients were dominated by attempts to guard against abandonment, either through suffering, confession, avoidance of temptations, or occasional revolt against their bondage.
3. The asthmatic patients differed from each other in their personality structure, but had in common a lack of independence and an overattachment to mother figures.
4. The attack appeared as an equivalent of a suppressed cry—in fear or anger.
5. The attack at times subsided when the patient could cry or confess. Patients did become free of attacks when they could achieve independence and when they lost their fear of abandonment, although the allergic condition was unchanged.

Early upper-respiratory infection also seems relevant for the genesis of asthma. Felix Deutsch assumed that the occurrence of bronchitis, whooping cough, and so forth, during an emotional or maturational crisis, established a link between distress and respiratory difficulty. Upper-respiratory infection also precipitates attacks in children who seemed already asthma free(42).

In our study(38, 44) of 65 asthmatic children at Massachusetts General Hospital, Boston, my co-workers and I also saw the fear of alienation from the mother as the central core, reflected in play, daydreams, and behavior. That it is the fear and not the fact of separation seemed confirmed by the observation (ours and others) that the majority of these children became asthma free when hospitalized, sometimes also at camp, and relapsed shortly after their return to their home. While away from their parents they appeared sad and homesick.

The asthmatic children seemed to need a union with their mothers mainly for protection and shelter. Many among them regarded the world as full of dangers; the wind, the rain, fire, strangers, and so on were experienced as forces that might harm or destroy them. Fantasies of being in a cave or under water came up spontaneously and in response to projective testing, interpreted as symbols for the wish to return into the womb. These enclosures were enchanting but at the same time threatening with suffocation and death.

The majority of these children had been described as oversensitive, vulnerable infants demanding an unusual amount, as well as subtlety, of care. This tended to keep the mother close, but also aroused in her frustration, anger, and rejection. In some mothers, it revived the wish for a symbiotic existence, which they once had with their mothers or with a sister. The question of why this nuclear conflict—namely, persistence of infantile dependency and the struggle against it—should influence respiration has been answered by Alexander(2) with the explanation that the cry is the infant's way of getting to his mother, and that sighing is the expression of sorrow and longing.

In summary, the factors leading to asthmatic attacks were found to be:

1. An allergic propensity (established by skin tests and by the frequency of allergic disorders in members of the family).
2. A symbiotic mother-child relationship.
3. An aura of anxiousness about the child, not only in connection with asthmatic attacks.
4. Respiratory illnesses at critical periods during infancy.
5. The first and also later attacks often were precipitated by an experience conceived by the child as a threat to his closeness with his mother.

The interaction between constitutional and emotional factors necessitates the cooperation of the psychotherapist with the allergist or pediatrician.

In severe cases, hospitalization may be unavoidable not only for medical but also for psychological reasons. Separation from parents as a successful therapeutic device for children with intractable asthma (that is, not responding to the traditional medical treatment) has been demonstrated on a large population in publications from the Children's Asthma Research Institute and Hospital at Denver(64). Peshkin(58) has called this use of separation "parentectomy." Abramson(1) reports the recovery of about 40 percent of the children removed from their homes. Bernstein and Purcell(9) differentiated between such rapidly remitting children and another group which depended on the administration of steroids. They suggest that among rapidly remitting children, asthma "more often serves as a means of coping with conflict and anxiety." Asthma among steroid-dependent children, on the other hand, is viewed primarily as a response to genetic, infectious, and allergic, rather than psychogenic, factors.

When the emotional factor is predominant, asthmatic children usually respond well to psychotherapy because most of them develop a positive transference sooner or later. The therapist has to guard against letting the child become overattached and overdependent. His task is to develop a relationship with the child which can tolerate ambivalence without the threat of alienation.

This gradually attenuates the child's conflict between the fear of losing the beloved person and the fear of losing his own identity. This eventually liberates the child from the bondage of dependency(39). The younger the child, the more essential it is to enable the mother to find a new relationship to her child. By working through her own need for symbiotic closeness and her struggle against this encroachment, she might be able to release the child and herself from the old ties.

Caution in psychotherapy is important because an asthmatic attack can be precipitated if defenses are suddenly removed, or if the child feels rejected by the therapist. To give an example: an asthmatic nine-year-old boy in analysis with me(39) had improved insofar as his attacks were infrequent and he had become less fearful. His formerly overprotective mother had been encouraged to support his strivings for masculine self-assertion. She was glad when he asked her to make him a costume for Halloween. When the evening approached he did not want to go. His mother did not hide her disappointment and her notion that he was a sissy. He promptly got an asthmatic attack. A few days later, during his analytic hour, he attempted to masturbate my dog. I was caught by surprise and showed my indignation. The following night he had an asthmatic attack.

The oversensitivity of these patients to any loss of love has constantly to be kept in mind. Status asthmaticus or death during an attack are potential dangers.

E. Diseases of the Skin

1. *Eczema.* Eczema, a frequent lesion of infants, often precedes asthma. Both illnesses have certain characteristics in common: allergic predisposition and a psychodynamic constellation related to an over-involvement between mother and child. There is a similarity also in regard to separation from parents. Finch(29) notes the frequency of improvement when the child is hospitalized, that is, temporarily removed from the scene of major emotional conflict, followed by a flare-up on return home.

The interplay of emotional and physiological factors in the course of eczema works in a primary and secondary way: primarily, through changes in the skin in affective states (e.g., blushing in shame, redness in rage, pallor and sweating in fear, gooseflesh in fright); secondarily, through the consequences of eczema for child and mother: both are deprived of tactile pleasurable communication (cuddling, touching, kissing). Instead of this intimate contact, the mother has to take care of the skin through medications, which are often painful to the patient and disgusting to his mother. Tension in both is heightened through the child's wish to scratch and the mother's task to prevent it. It is not clear whether the sado-masochistic tendencies in eczema patients (Alexander [2]) precede the illness, are a reaction to its discomfort, or, most likely, are aggravated by it. The sado-masochistic aspect was well expressed by one of our patients, a four-year-old boy, who sang one night in the hospital: "I want a new mommy, I want a new nurse, I want a new itch."

2. *Urticaria.* Urticaria (hives) also seems to have an intrinsic relationship to asthma, clinically and psychodynamically. Alexander(2) described that inhibited dependent longing for a parental object is a conspicuous finding. Saul and Bernstein(67) suggest that the urticaria attack is the expression of suppressed weeping as an analogy to the suppressed cry of the asthmatic patient.

3. *Atopic Dermatitis* Felix Deutsch and Nadell(21) studied children with atopic dermatitis and their allergic relatives and found strong obsessional trends in these patients in contrast to those with urticaria. The psychotherapeutic approach should be guided by the same considerations as in asthma.

Therapy should best be done in collaboration with a dermatologist or pediatrician. Psychotherapeutic intervention should include the mother, because the interaction between her and the patient is crucial. The patient often can be helped if new avenues are opened for receiving affection and for expression of anger and frustration on other objects than his own skin. To scratch a teddy bear or to bang a doll may be adjuncts to psychotherapy.

F. Headaches

Headache is a not infrequent complaint in childhood. Medical or neurological evaluation is necessary in order not to overlook pathological conditions such as brain tumor, subdural hematoma, or hypertension. The most common headaches, however, stem either from dilation of cerebral vessels or from contraction of the skeletal muscles of the head and neck. In either of these conditions emotional tensions may play a decisive part.

In a study of nine children with migraine and persistent or recurrent headache, Sperling(72) found that the onset of the headache could be traced back to a situation in which intense rage impulses had to be repressed suddenly. The original traumatic situation often related to the birth of a sibling. The headache seemed to be the somatic expression of the unconscious impulse to kill the hated object through an attack upon the head. One of my patients, an 11-year-old girl, was admitted to the pediatric ward with the suspicion of brain tumor, because of headaches of one-half year duration. Martha was one of nonidentical twin sisters. She was tremendously jealous of this sister, a brighter, more easy-going and better-liked girl than the patient. Martha's only asset was a "sweet composure," occasionally interrupted by a fit of rage in which she would box her sister's ears. Psychotherapy led to the patient's awareness of her smoldering hatred against her twin and to the possibility of expressing it in words to the therapist. Finally she accepted herself as a person in her own right, instead of an inferior twin.

G. Endocrine Disturbances

1. *Hyperthyroidism.* The relationship between an apparently stressful situation and the onset of hyperthyroidism has been known and recognized since the earliest clinical descriptions of the disease.

One can summarize the points of view expressed by Ham(37), et al., as, "A cardinal feature of the developmental history appears to be the need to build a defensive structure against repetition of unbearable feelings of rejection and isolation that occurred in early childhood."

The mechanisms by which this is primarily achieved are by taking on responsibilities, by doing for others, by assuming a mother's role in essence, and thereby being loved. These patterns have been more clearly worked out for female than for male patients.

Ham, Alexander, and Carmichal(37) have proposed a phylogenetic precedent to explain why the thyroid may be especially affected in persons who appear to strive for precocious maturity. They point out that the thyroid gland in animals primarily serves the function of accelerating metamorphosis. For example, artificial stimulation of the salamander results in phylogenetic advancement from gill to lung breathing. They postulate that hyperthyroid patients, whose primary adaptation to insecurity appears to be a precocious "maturity," may excessively stimulate the thyroid when some stressful life event causes their previous adaptation to be inadequate, Lubart(46) found that patients with toxic goiter (in contrast to those with nontoxic goiter) showed a defensive pattern of denial of dependence, identification with the strong parent, and an attitude of pseudo independence. These patients take the role of caretaker of the individual upon whom they have fixed their own dependency. This frail counterphobic device breaks down upon threat or loss.

> *Example:*   Nine-year-old Tonio was admitted to the hospital for thyrotoxicosis. His mother had immigrated with the patient and his sister, two years his junior, from Sicily, after the father had deserted the family. In the new environment, the patient was the first to know his way around and to learn the English language. He established himself as paterfamilias, earned money after school or while truanting from school, and ran the household, whereas previously he had been a playful, rather immature, little boy. He constantly asserted that he could take care of himself and his family. After hyperthyroidism had developed, hyperactivity, restlessness, and irritability became prominent features. In conjunction with medical treatment, the patient was seen in psychotherapy. His urge to replace his father and to be himself a much better provider and protector was worked through. Tonio gradually could accept his status as son and brother and as a youngster.

2. *Diabetes Mellitus.*   Stewart Wolf(79) among others has demonstrated the influence that psychological stress can have on the metabolic adjustment in diabetes.

In the predisposing personality, "oral" features are frequently mentioned: "It is not possible to conjecture from past studies how often the passive oral character structure and the ensuing emotional problems play an etiologic role in diabetes. The personality structure, it is true, is noted frequently; however, because of the problems diabetes creates, it can perpetuate preexisting immaturity and foster regressions"(26). Mirsky(54) emphasized the factor of heredity and speculated that some children have constitutionally a limited capacity to regulate sugar metabolism, which would result in diabetes after prolonged stress, which could be emotional. Harold Wolff(80) speaks of "stress diuresis" in connection with intense interpersonal conflict, which then might precipitate ketosis and lead to diabetes.

The relevance of emotional factors in the genesis of diabetes in children has been documented by several investigators(7, 26).

Swift and Seidman(76) investigated 40 diabetic children in regard to their adjustments. They found significant relationships between control of diabetes and social and emotional adjustment. In their judgment, "children with diabetes have greater anxiety, a less adequate self-image, a more disturbed dependence-independence balance, and greater oral preoccupation than do children without diabetes." Because of the high correlation of poor diabetic control and psychosocial maladjustment, the authors urge that a child with poorly regulated diabetes be referred for psychiatric consultation.

Psychotherapy, in conjunction with the medical regime, has two goals: one would be toward attenuating the underlying psychological stress; the other one would be towards accepting this chronic disease and the problems which the medical treatment is likely to arouse.

The diagnosis of diabetes in a child, fatal in pre-insulin days, is frightening for most parents, and this in turn is bound to arouse anxiety in the child.

The first step in psychotherapy may be to help parents cope with their apprehension and to suggest ways to tell the child about his condition which are neither alarming nor denying the necessity to follow the medical regime. This regime, at present still consisting mainly of urine tests, diet, and insulin mostly by injection, touches sensitive areas of the child; it never lets him forget his body and his being different from other children. It deprives him of much oral gratification, it makes him dependent on a drug, and arouses the fear of injection. Many children react to the management of diabetes as an invasion of privacy and a loss of integrity. Rebellion, self-devaluation, and self-destructive tendencies may seriously interfere with the medical management of diabetes. An example may illustrate the interplay of underlying emotional tension, adjustment to the regime with the help of psychotherapy, and the breakdown under the impact of a traumatic experience.

Example: An 11-year-old diabetic girl was referred to psychiatry because she would not adhere to her diet but would sneak candies and sandwiches from her classmates. On first encounter she complained that she was not getting what everyone else had: sweets and goodies. After arranging that she got diabetic candies, I asked her whether she did feel in general that she was not getting what everyone else had. The patient then told about her distress being in a foster home instead of living with her father. Her mother had died during her infancy and the father had promised to take her, after getting remarried and settling down. In working through her longings for a reunion with her father, she could accept waiting in the foster home and following the diet without much difficulty. Suddenly the patient died in a diabetic coma, after having received the notification that her father had requested that she should become a ward of the state.

HOSPITALIZATION

Since Spitz(73), Bowlby(13), and others(49) demonstrated the potential traumatic effect of hospitalization for children, there has been a trend to avoid it, or at least to attenuate the experience of separation from the mother, by having her stay with the child or visit frequently and letting her participate in the care of the child. These recommendations certainly are beneficial for the majority of sick children and especially the very young ones. For many of those with psychosomatic illness, however, individual scrutiny should be used(40). The therapeutic effect of "parentectomy" for the asthmatic child has been mentioned. We also observed serious relapses in children with ulcerative colitis after the visit of parents on the ward, or when the child had a weekend at home. One ought to keep in mind that feelings between mother and child are the most intense ones and that sick children are not able to cope with ambivalence, rage, fear of loss of love, and jealousy. If, during hospitalization, these feelings are transferred to parental substitutes like doctors and nurses, they are less threatening and can be worked through. In some cases, separation thus may be in the service of finding a new relationship to the parents; there is also often a good opportunity to work with the mother while she is not acutely involved in the care of the sick child.

Group therapy with parents of hospitalized children has been explored by Lewis(43).

SUMMARY

A. Preventive Aspects

It is to be expected that in the near future more will be known about the constitutional conditions which, later in life under the impact of emotional factors, lead to psychosomatic illness. At present, it seems that preventive intervention is indicated and possible, when the mother is not able to respond adequately to an infant who shows unusual sensitivities which can hardly be satisfied or soothed. Observing mother and infant in their transaction will give relevant clues toward recognition of the forerunners of disturbed psychophysiological reactions; helping the mother to be alert to the special needs of such children and to respond to them, would be one attempt at prevention.

B. Management

Psychotherapy with the child needs the parents as allies. It is essential to avoid heightening their guilt feelings, but it is equally important to indicate their role in the course of the illness.

It is essential for the psychotherapist to work closely with the pediatrician and to establish a harmonious and decisive management on which the child and his parents can rely.

Psychotherapy with the child may have either the immediate goal of: (a) adaptation to the illness and its sequelae by strengthening the capacities of the child's ego. This can be achieved by stimulating his resources to find compensatory satisfactions (for example, for restraint of motility or for oral deprivations), a support for self-esteem, the avoidance of neurotic reactions to the illness, regression, and invalidism. The universal conflict of childhood between the wish to be taken care of and the wish for independence and mastery is heightened during illness and convalescence; psychotherapeutic assistance may be necessary to strengthen the progressive potential. Another frequent problem is the secondary gain of the illness: the possibility to dominate the parents, to keep them close, to frighten them, is relished by many of these children, as well as the avoidance of competition which the illness permits. (b) The more far-reaching goal of psychotherapy extends into the area of the basic emotional difficulty which has contributed to the genesis of the psychosomatic disorder. The most common difficulty consists in the child's inability to separate himself as an individual from the mother and still to retain trust, intimacy, and reliance.

What matters most in any psychotherapeutic approach is to establish just this kind of relationship with the child. This tack is a major challenge for the therapist, because these children are prone to react to him with suspicion, hatred, and negativism (especially those with ulcerative colitis) or with clinging, demanding, and withdrawing behavior (especially those with asthma). They have difficulties in expressing their feelings in words or play instead of somatizing them.

The therapist has continuously to be aware of the vulnerability of these patients to separation, disapproval, or probing, lest he precipitate an exacerbation of the disease. After physical improvement, the child may show depressive trends or neurotic acting-out, which require continuation of psychotherapy. For all his exhausting efforts the therapist can, however, be rewarded not only by the child's recovery from his acute illness, but also by a spurt in the patient's development as a person.

REFERENCES

1. ABRAMSON, H. A. Some aspects of the psychodynamics of intractable asthma in children. In SCHNEER, H. (ed.), *The asthmatic child.* New York: Hoeber, 1963.
2. ALEXANDER, F. *Psychosomatic medicine.* New York: W. W. Norton & Co., 1950.
3. APLEY, J. Psychosomatic disorders in children. *Lancet,* March 28, 1959, 1:641–44.
4. APLEY, J. Psychogenic disorders in children; an experiment in management. *Brit. med. J.,* January 16, 1960, 1:191–92.
5. BATTEN, Z. W. Psychosomatic disorders in children. *Brit. med. J.,* April 25, 1959, 1:1109–10.
6. BENEDEK, T. The psychosomatic implications of the primary unit mother-child. *Am. J. Orthopsychiat.,* 1949, 19:642.
7. BENEDEK, T. An approach to the study of the diabetic. *Psychosom. Med.,* 1948, 10:284.
8. BERGMAN, P., and ESCALONA, S. K. Unusual sensitivities in very young children. *Psychoanalytic study of the child,* Vol. III/IV. New York: International Universities Press, 1949.
9. BERNSTEIN, L., and PURCELL, K. Institutional treatment of asthmatic children. In SCHNEER, H. (ed.), *The asthmatic child.* New York: Hoeber, 1963.

10. BLOM, G. E.   Ulcerative colitis in a five-year-old boy. In S. CAPLAN (ed.), *Emotional problems of early childhood*. New York: Basic Books, 1955.

11. BLOM, G. E., and NICHOLLS, J.   Emotional factors in children with rheumatoid arthritis. *Am. J. Orthopsychiat.*, 1954, **24**:588.

12. BLOM, G. E., and WHIPPLE, B.   A method of studying emotional factors in children with rheumatoid arthritis. In JESSNER, L. and PAVENSTEDT, E. (eds.), *Dynamic psychopathology in childhood*. New York: Grune & Stratton, 1959.

13. BOWLBY, J.   Separation anxiety. *Int. J. Psychoanal.*, 1960, **41**:89.

14. BRODY, S.   *Patterns of mothering*. New York: International Universities Press, 1956.

15. BRUCH, H.   Psychological aspects of obesity. *Psychiatry*, 1947, **10**:373.

16. BRUCH, H.   Physiologic and psychologic interrelationships in diabetes in children. *Psychosom. Med.*, 1949, **11**:200.

17. BRUCH, H.   Perceptual and conceptual disturbances in anorexia nervosa. *Psychosom. Med.*, 1962, **24**:187.

18. COBB, S.   Mind-body relationships. In LIEF, H. J.; LIEF, V. F.; and LIEF, V. R. (eds.), *The psychological basis of medical practice*. New York: Hoeber, 1963.

19. COBB, S.   *Emotions and clinical medicine*. New York: W. W. Norton & Co., 1950.

20. DEUTSCH, F.   *On the mysterious leap from the mind to the body*. New York: International Universities Press, 1959.

21. DEUTSCH, F., and NADELL, R.   Psychosomatic aspects of dermatology. *Nerv. Child*, 1949, **5**:339.

22. ENGEL, G. L.   Psychologic aspects of the management of ulcerative colitis. *New York State J. Med.*, Sept. 15, 1952.

23. ENGEL, G. L.   Studies of ulcerative colitis; the nature of the somatic processes and the adequacy of psychosomatic hypotheses. *Amer. J. Med.*, 1954, **16**:416.

24. ENGEL, G. L.   Studies of ulcerative colitis III. The nature of the psychological process. *Amer. J. Med.*, 1955, **19**:231.

25. ENGEL, G. L., and REICHSMAN, F.   Affects, object relations and gastric secretions; the study of an infant with a gastric fistula. *Psychosom. Med.*, 1956, **18**:374–98.

26. FALSTEIN, D. I., and JUDAS, J.   Juvenile diabetes and its psychiatric implications. *Amer. J. Orthopsychiat.*, 1955, **25**:330.

27. FINCH, ST. M., and HESS, J. H.   Ulcerative colitis in children. *Amer. J. Psychiat.*, 1962, **118**:819.

28. FINCH, ST. M.   The treatment of children with ulcerative colitis. *Amer. J. Orthopsychiat.*, 1964, **34**:142.

29. FINCH, ST. M.   *Fundamentals of child psychiatry*. Chap. VIII. New York: W. W. Norton & Co., 1960.

30. FRENCH, T. M., and ALEXANDER, F.   Psychogenic factors in bronchial asthma. *Psychosom. Med. Monogr.* No. 4 (Washington).

31. FRIES, M. E., and WOOLF, P. J.   Some hypotheses on the role of the congenital activity type in personality development. *Psychoanalytic study of the child,* Vol. VIII. New York: International Universities Press, 1953.

32. FULLERTON, D. T.   Infantile rumination. *Arch. gen. Psychiat.,* 1963, 9:593.

33. GADDINI, R., and GADDINI, E.   Rumination in infancy. In JESSNER, L., and PAVENSTEDT, E. (eds.), *Dynamic psychopathology in childhood.* New York: Grune & Stratton, 1959.

34. GERARD, M.   Genesis of psychosomatic symptoms in infancy; the influence of infantile traumata upon symptom choice. In DEUTSCH, F. (ed.), *Psychosomatic concepts in psychoanalysis.* New York: International Universities Press, 1953.

35. GOSLINER, B. V.   Psychosomatic diseases in children and adolescents. *J. Amer. psychoanal. Assn.,* 1960, 8:152.

36. GRACE, W. J.; WOLF, S.; and WOLFF, H. S.   *The human colon.* New York: Hoeber, 1951.

37. HAM, J. C.; ALEXANDER, F.; and CARMICHAEL, H. T.   A psychosomatic theory of thyrotoxicosis. *Psychosom. Med.,* 1951, 13:18.

38. JESSNER, L., *et al.*   Emotional impact on nearness and separation for the asthmatic child and his mother. *Psychoanalytic study of the child,* Vol. X. New York: International Universities Press, 1955.

39. JESSNER, L.   From the psychoanalysis of an eight-year-old boy with asthma. In SCHNEER, H. (ed.), *The asthmatic child.* New York: Hoeber, 1963.

40. JESSNER, L.   Some observations on children hospitalized during latency. In JESSNER, L., and PAVENSTEDT, E. (eds.), *Dynamic psychopathology in childhood.* New York: Grune & Stratton, 1959.

41. JESSNER, L., and ABSE, D. W.   Regressive forces in anorexia nervosa. *Brit. J. med. Psychol.,* 1960, 33:303.

42. KNAPP, R. H.   The asthmatic child and the psychosomatic problem of asthma. In SCHNEER, H. (ed.), *The asthmatic child.* New York: Hoeber, 1963.

43. LEWIS, M.   Management of parents of acutely ill children in hospital. *Amer. J. Orthopsychiat.,* 1962, 32:60.

44. LONG, R. T., *et al.*   A psychosomatic study of allergic and emotional factors in children with asthma. *Amer. J. Psychiat.,* 1958, 114:809.

45. LOURIE, R. S.   Treatment of psychosomatic problems in infancy. *Clin. Proc. Children's Hospital of D.C.,* 1955, 9:142.

46. LUBART, J. M.   Implicit personality disorder in patients with toxic and nontoxic goiter. *J. nerv. and ment. Disorder,* 1964, 138:255.

47. LINDEMANN, E.   Modifications in the course of ulcerative colitis in relationship to changes in life situations and reaction patterns. *Proc. Assoc. Res. nerv. Disorders,* 1950, 29:706.

48. MAHLER, M. S.   Thoughts about development and individuation. *Psychoanalytic study of the child,* Vol. XVIII. New York: International Universities Press, 1963.

49. MASON, E. A.   The hospitalized child—his emotional needs. *New Eng. J. Med.,* 1965, 272:406.

50. MENDELSON, M., et al.   A critical examination of some recent theoretical models in psychosomatic medicine. *Psychosom. Med.,* 1958, 18:364.

51. MEYER, H. F.   A clinical interpretation of the colicky infant. *Postgrad. Med.,* 1958, 24:627.

52. MILLICAN, F. K., *et al.*   The prevalence of ingestion and mouthing of nonedible substances by children. *Clin. Proc. Children's Hospital of D.C.,* 1962, 18:207.

53. MILLICAN, F. K., *et al.*   Study of an oral fixation—pica. Presented at meeting of Amer. Psychoanal. Assn., December, 1964. (To be published.)

54. MIRSKY, J. A.   Emotional factors in the patient with diabetes mellitus. *Bull. Menninger Clin.,* 1958, 12:187.

55. MIRSKY, J. A.   Psychoanalysis and the biological sciences. In ALEXANDER, F., and Ross, H. (eds.), *Twenty years of psychoanalysis.* New York: W. W. Norton & Co., 1953.

56. O'CONNOR, G. E., *et al.*   Psychotherapy and ulcerative colitis. *Amer. J. intern. Med.,* 1964, 60:587.

57. NEMIAH, J. C.   Anorexia nervosa. *Amer. J. Digest,* 1958, 3:249.

58. PESHKIN, N. M.   Intractable asthma of childhood, rehabilitation at the institutional level with a follow-up of 150 cases. *Intern. Arch. Allergy,* 1959, 5:91.

59. PRUGH, D. G.   Influence of emotional factors on clinical course of ulcerative colitis in children. *Gastroenterology,* 1951, 18:339.

60. PRUGH, D. G.   Variations in attitudes, behavior and feeling states as exhibited in play of children during modifications in course of ulcerative colitis. *Proc. Assoc. Res. nerv. Disorders,* 1950, 29:692.

61. PRUGH, D. G.; WERNER, H.; and LORD, J. P.   On the significance of the anal phase in pediatrics and child psychiatry. In GARDNER, G. E., *Case studies in childhood emotional disabilities,* Vol. II. New York: American Orthopsychiatric Assn., 1950.

62. PURCELL, K., *et al.*   A preliminary comparison of rapidly remitting and persistently "steroid-dependent" asthmatic children. *Psychosom. Med.,* 1961, 23:305.

63. RANK, B., and MacNAUGHTON, O.   A clinical contribution to early ego development. *Psychoanalytic study of the child,* Vol. V. New York: International Universities Press, 1950.

64. RIBBLE, M. A.   Infantile experience in relation to personality development. In HUNT, J. M. V. (ed.), *Personality and the behavior disorders,* Vol. II. New York: Ronald Press, 1944.

65. RICHMOND, J. B., and LUSTMAN, S. L.   Autonomic function in the Neonate; implications for psychosomatic theory. *Psychosom. Med.*, 1955, 17:269–75.

66. RICHMOND, J. B., and LIPTON, E. L.   Some aspects of the neurophysiology of the newborn and their implications for child development. In JESSNER, L., and PAVENSTEDT, E. (eds.), *Dynamic psychopathology in childhood*. New York: Grune & Stratton, 1959.

67. RICHMOND, J. B., *et al.*   Rumination, a psychosomatic syndrome of infancy. *Pediatrics*, 1952, 22:49.

68. SAUL, L. and BERNSTEIN, C.   The emotional settings of some attacks of urticaria. *Psychsom. Med.*, 1949, 3:349.

69. SHANDS, H.   Change in a mother-child relation in asthma. In SCHNEER, H. (ed.), *The asthmatic child*. New York: Hoeber, 1963.

70. SIFNEOS, P. E.   *Accent from chaos; a psychosomatic case study*. Cambridge, Mass.: Harvard University Press, 1964.

71. SPERLING, M.   Psychosomatic medicine and pediatrics. In WITKOWER and CLEGHORN (eds.), *Recent developments in psychosomatic medicine*. Philadelphia: J. B. Lippincott Co., 1954.

72. SPERLING, M.   The role of the mother in psychosomatic disorders in children. *Psychosom. Med.*, 1948, 2:377.

73. SPITZ, R. A.   Hospitalism. *Psychoanalytic Study of the Child*, Vol. I. New York: International Universities Press, 1945.

74. SPITZ, R. A.   The psychogenic diseases in infancy. *Psychoanalytic Study of the Child*, Vol. VI. New York: International Universities Press, 1951.

75. SPITZ, R. A.   The derailment of dialogue. *J. Amer. Psychoanal. Assn.*, 1964, 12:752.

76. SWIFT, C. R. and SEIDMAN, FRANCES L.   Adjustment problems of juvenile diabetes. *J. Amer. Acad. Child Psychiat.*, 1964, 3:500.

77. SYMPOSIUM.   Colic in infants. *Pediatrics*, 1956, 18:828.

78. TITCHENER, J. F., *et al.*   The family in the psychosomatic process. *Psychosom. Med.*, 1960, 22:127.

79. WOLF, S. G. and WOLFF, H. G.   *Human gastric function*. Cambridge: Oxford University Press, 1947.

80. WOLFF, H. G.   Brain and diabetes. *Diabetes*, 1959, 8:358.

Irving Kaufman

Psychotherapy of Children with Conduct and Acting-Out Disorders

THE DIAGNOSIS of the acting-out or antisocial child poses some of the greatest difficulty in child psychiatry. Unless the child has committed some very gross crime, the decision as to whether acting-out has actually occurred seems to be an arbitrary one, depending on such factors as the neighborhood in which the child lives, parental values and standards, and attitudes of the law enforcement authority. In some settings the acting-out behavior, whether it be lying or stealing or destructive acts, is viewed as "boys will be boys." In other circumstances the same action will be viewed as a serious assault upon the lives and property of the citizens of the community.

DELINQUENCY TYPES

Dr. Jenkins(5) has discussed two types of delinquency. In one type, the acting-out behavior occurs within a community setting where this is the way of life and hence acceptable to the environment. He sees this type of delinquency as being very different from the delinquency arising within the context of a conflict between the child and the values of the important persons in his environment. In both types of delinquents there is conflict between the child and the forces of authority such as schools (which

185

require regular attendance), police, and courts. However, for those children whose delinquency is actively supported by the example and attitude of their environment, intervention—therapeutic or otherwise—is in conflict with their usual behavior, and hence strains against their habitual mode of operating and whatever security they may derive from those operations.

As Johnson and Szurek(6) pointed out, delinquency is also the expression of the unconscious wishes of the parents. Therefore, in those environments where the child's antisocial behavior is in apparent conflict with the standards and values of his environment, the child is caught in these ambivalent struggles. There may be no conscious evident support for his antisocial way of life, yet the parent, by subtle signs such as not inquiring where the new bicycle came from, or in other cases becoming upset when the daughter "answers fresh" but not being concerned when she comes in disheveled at 4 A.M., communicates an unconscious condoning of the antisocial behavior. However, this type of parent can turn on the child and become hostile and punitive when the child is caught by the law-enforcing authorities. All of these children demonstrate in various ways severe disturbances in the development of their superego, and have a confused value system which makes their antisocial behavior on the surface acceptable to themselves despite the conflict with external authority.

There is still another type of child who does not necessarily live in a delinquent environment, nor does he appear to have a parent figure who is unconsciously pushing him toward antisocial behavior. Instead, this type of child has had a traumatic background consisting of many losses and separations such as numerous foster homes, repeated placements, with no sustained relationships to any set of parents or any specific environmental model. It is often impossible to single out in the background of these children any particular set of parent figures who have had any more significant relationship to the child than any other. For these children an important factor in the development of antisocial behavior is their response to the trauma of object loss, where they repeatedly form a relationship and then are torn away from it. This trauma will be discussed in greater detail as we progress in our presentation of the concepts of the acting-out child. At this point I would like to add that it appears that this type of situation represents the core conflict in many of the children who show antisocial behavior, regardless of the type of environment they appear to come from.

DIFFICULTIES CONFRONTING THERAPIST

Because antisocial behavior involves legal, moral, religious, economic, and social issues, it has been difficult to sort out the psychodynamic factors necessary to develop a framework of theory for the application of mental health concepts. In addition, this divergently oriented approach to the child who commits an antisocial act can only be confusing to the child himself, and often interferes with his rehabilitation. For example, repeated brief incarceration repeats the very traumatic and disruptive pattern of separation, loss, and abandonment which appears in the background of so many of the children who commit antisocial acts.

Another problem confronting the therapist who tries to work with the child who commits an antisocial act is that this type of behavior can exist within a wide range of personality structures. This includes children who are schizophrenic, mentally retarded, organically damaged, and, to a large extent, children with an impulse-ridden character disorder. It is necessary to differentiate the underlying personality structure because this affects the treatment plan.

Another crucial consideration in the management and treatment of delinquents is the fact that the arena in which they enact their problems is the social environment. This is in contrast, for example, to the individual with a psychosomatic disorder who expresses his disturbances through the avenue of physical symptoms. He is using his own body as the arena for the expression of his problems. Because the delinquent child steals from or attacks the environment, or commits sexual acts which are prohibited by the community, there are two major results from this situation. Frequently there are attempts to cope with the problem by manipulating the environment. For example, the delinquent child is locked up, or the family is moved into a different housing setting. While in some senses this may be indicated, it is necessary to recognize that such procedures may have no bearing on the future of the delinquent child or his family, nor affect on any way their antisocial behavior. For example, prescribing heat and massage for an individual who has a paralyzed arm because of a conversion hysteria has no bearing on the future of the paralysis.

The second major implication of the arena being the community often results in retaliatory or punitive measures being the method utilized to cope with the juvenile delinquent. This often relieves the feelings of the members of the community who are dispensing this justice or punishment or whatever procedure may be in order, but may have little bearing on the future behavior of the delinquent child, and have no effect in either preventing or not preventing future delinquencies.

Freud(3), in his discussion of criminals from a sense of guilt, talks about acting-out and antisocial behavior as a type of defense mechanism occurring within primarily neurotic individuals who handle their guilt about the oedipal wish to kill the parent of the same sex and to have sexual relations with the parent of the opposite sex. Freud stated that parricide and incest are the two great human crimes. Committing some crime which seems to the individual to be of lesser consequence, and then getting punished for that, is a way of relieving the guilt for these more serious offenses. In this same discussion, Freud pointed out that his comment about the committing of crime from a sense of guilt did not apply to individuals who have not developed moral inhibitions, nor who feel justified in their acts against society. It is my impression that children who are acting-out antisocially fall primarily into this latter category, and that they are acting-out in ways that come developmentally before the acquisition of a superego. This makes for major differences in their management and treatment, because if punishment which implies guilt and remorse is utilized, it will be ineffective in individuals who have not developed to that stage.

Many observers have noted that the largest number of antisocial, acting-out or delinquent children come from broken homes. From my own experience, I concur with this observation that the largest number come from either overtly broken homes or from some form of traumatic background which includes some sense of loss of parenting. The broken home or loss of parenting can result from such obvious phenomenon as desertion or abandonment of the child, divorce, and separation, the child being placed in a series of foster homes. In upper- and middle-class families the child may be neglected by being cared for by a series of governesses. Whatever the form it takes, it is perceived by the child in the same way. The child finds himself forming a relationship where he begins to feel some involvement with the individual, and then repeatedly finds that the relationship is interrupted. The child perceives this action as a sadistic one, and apparently has no way of coping with it except to strike back against the representatives of the deserting figures in his life. The kind of loss these children experience occurs at a time beyond the critical age that Spitz talked about when he described the anaclitic depression, and it occurs at a point where the child has developed sufficiently to appreciate a meaningful object relationship, and also to appreciate the loss of that relationship. The normal reaction to object loss is to develop sadness, unhappiness, grief, and to work it out by means of a depression. This the children do not do. Instead, they seem to have a great intolerance for tension, sadness, anxiety, and unhappiness, and when confronted with situations which stimulate them to feel sad or anxious they use various methods to avoid it, such as literally running away, shutting out the stimulus if they can, or taking refuge in their antisocial behavior, which may range anywhere from stealing to sexual promiscuity, drinking, and so forth.

One of the ultimate objectives of therapy is to help the individual develop a sufficient ego and superego so that he can face the emotions and anxieties associated with these traumas of his life in ways other than antisocial behavior.

The following case vignette illustrates some of the characteristics found in many of these children.

Case: John Allen was a 16-year-old boy who was brought into the court because the police found in his possession a large amount of stolen goods. When asked about it, he said, "I don't know what you're talking about. Some guy came along and handed me this stuff. I never saw him before, and you cops are always picking on us kids." John was an illegitimate child, doesn't know who his own father is. Mother has married and now has four other children. She and her husband are constantly fighting. The husband is a severe alcoholic, and will come home at times and beat up the wife and children rather indiscriminately. The mother has been quite promiscuous, and at times will be entertaining men at home; if the man is coming and the children are around she will lock the children out, often leaving them unattended for hours. John had been a school problem since he started school. He was fresh, he would knock the books out of other children's hands, he would trip them. He began to truant and began to steal, and has been apprehended by the police numerous times. He showed no guilt or remorse over his crimes, and feels that he was never given a break so why should he give any sucker a break. He said if he could get away with anything he would. This information came much later in the treatment contact. Initially he was nonverbal, would only answer in mono-syllables, said that everything was fine. He denied any concern about anything. He projected all his problems onto the authorities, saying they just picked on him. He indicated no wish for therapy, and acted as though his main wish was that any therapist or "do gooder" would leave him alone. His affect ranged from indifference to sullen hostility when pressed about any issue.

Another way to look at his behavior would be to consider that his rejection and hostility toward the therapist or anyone who wished to intervene in his life was a reflection of the way he had been treated, and he was reacting in the only way he knew existed. He was using the ego mechanisms of isolation of affect from his conscious thought; he was denying any participation in crime; he was denying any feelings; he was projecting his problems onto the community and to the authorities; he was identifying with the aggressor, and felt that he had been mistreated and therefore he could do what he wanted to get what he wanted. In addition, he was utilizing the mechanism of the repetition compulsion by repeatedly stealing and doing other antisocial acts as a way to cope with the tensions and anxieties he had experienced, the emotions of which he could not allow himself to feel. There is no evidence of guilt, remorse, or other signs of the superego development. This boy appears to be fixated at pre-oedipal levels, of the type that Freud described as the criminal who acts without a sense of guilt, in contrast with the neurotic type Freud described. This boy appeared to be trying to fill up his emptiness by the acquisition of material things, and to cope with his feelings of hostility by striking out against members of the community. In this sense he had displaced and projected his conflicts from the original objects, the parents, onto the entire community, and was setting up a hostile, acquisitive interaction between himself and the community where he would take, strike out, smash, and commit acts of vandalism and stealing.

His level of psychosexual development is characteristic of the pre-oedipal child; he was exhibitionistic, sadistic, masochistic, and showed a wide range of pregenital behavior, with a major focus on the sadistic and masochistic components.

His object relations were particularly disturbed in that he trusted no one. He took a "hit them first" attitude.

TREATMENT OF ANTISOCIAL PERSONALITIES

The treatment of this type of individual is particularly difficult because the regular approach in psychotherapy assumes that a conversational interaction can be set up. These are individuals who do not trust words, who are not used to discussing their problems or their feelings. Instead, when they become tense or anxious they handle it by some kind of action. In practice, this means that unless the anxiety can in some way be contained or managed by the therapeutic situation, treatment in any sense is not possible. Actually, there are two components to the treatment process. One component could be called a process of restitution, and the other one could be called resolution, resolution of the unconscious conflicts. However, for this type of child, an hour or two of therapy a week will not be sufficient, unless his environment is stabilized to the extent that he knows where his next meal is coming from, and unless he is not being stimulated by delinquent parents (i.e., acting-out of alcoholic and promiscuous mothers and fathers).

The problem of this type of child has been diagnosed as antisocial character disorder by Kate Friedlander(4) and Sidney Berman (1), and as an impulse-ridden character disorder by Fenichel(2) and Kaufman(7), et al. Their personality includes difficulties in most areas of their lives involving a relationship to the established institutions of the community. A community facility such as a boys' club may be established, but they prefer to meet in the basement of some house with springs popping out of the "liberated" overstuffed chairs and a light hanging down without the benefit of a shade. They do not attend church or young people's groups. Their adaptation to school is characteristically a problem. The problems begin with restlessness, with fresh and disobedient behavior. Problems in social adaptation are generally complicated by problems in the learning process itself. Their inability to sit still, concentrate, and complete the class assignments all contribute to the negative, hostile interrelationship between these children and the school. This is a prototype of the aberrations between these children and their environment. School is frustrating and a source of disappointment to these children, and these children are frustrating and a source of disappointment to the school. Achievement in terms of class status is dependent on education and economic advancement. These children tend to fail in both these areas and they perpetuate a subculture characterized by lower socioeconomic achievement and lower educational attainment. Their tendency to deal with their environment in terms of the immediate reward involves an impulsive focusing on the pleasure principle instead of the reality principle.

Therapeutic intervention of any kind comes into conflict with this habitual mode of functioning. In effect, the environment says "sit still and concentrate on school work, postpone immediate gratification for some future illusory reward." These children do not "buy" these promises. Instead, they take what they can get when they can get it. There is frequently the question, "Should the environment impose its middle-class standards on individuals who cannot conform?" This is complicated by the fact that the middle-class institutions such as schools find these children to be their dropouts who take the most menial jobs, and come into conflict with the legal authorities. In other words, unless middle-class standards are communicated to these children, they are punished by this same society in one way or another for not conforming to these standards.

Therapeutic intervention with these children and their parents is a difficult and long-term process. Whether the treatment is done on an individual or group basis the child regularly tends to go through a predictable sequence of reactions.

At first, these children are negativistic, hostile, and deny any problems. The tendency is to run away from treatment. Part of the reaction is because they have not had a stable sustaining figure on whom they could count. In this sense they are recapitulating in therapy their own life experiences. Often the therapist tends to react to this rejection of himself by calling the patient hard to reach or unmotivated. The patient is frightened and threatened. Unless the therapist can be resourceful and overcome this resistance in the patient and in himself, the case is often lost at this time. In addition, there are patients who feel discouraged, rejected, and negatively disposed to their environment. It is very easy for the therapist to empathize with these feelings and feel that the situation is hopeless. The result is that these cases tend to go from crisis to crisis and setting to setting.

For example, in the same family the boy may be truant from school and later on get into difficulty because he is caught stealing. The parents may be seen by a protective agency because they neglect the children. The daughter may get pregnant out of wedlock. The community responds to these outcroppings of problems by taking them piecemeal and attempting to deal with these external manifestations of a central problem. The absence of a family diagnosis and collaborative effort to work with the core problems instead of symptoms results in a multiple-agency approach to these antisocial problems.

In some instances it is possible to get past this initial phase of isolation, denial, and resistance to treatment. This can often be accomplished through the work of a talented, intuitive individual who does not react negatively to the rejection of the patient. Instead, the therapist permits and utilizes the recurring crises as an opportunity to share the characteristic life pattern with the patient. In effect, it is necessary to sit them out and be present before, during, and after these recurring episodes. Some time during this second phase of treatment the patient may acknowledge that he is distressed, unhappy, or in physical pain. This stage means that instead of projecting his difficulties away from himself he is able to acknowledge that something troubles him. Frequently, the signs of distress are in the form of somatic symptoms. In effect, the patient is saying it hurts. It is necessary to help him see that the therapist recognizes the hurt as meaningful, and that he is offering support, help and nurture. This is different from the castration concerns of the neurotic patient and the fears of annihilation of the psychotic patient. The anti-social, acting-out patients of this type are reacting to their feelings of loss of a sustaining parent concerned over their welfare. In addition, this experience enables the patient to communicate his feelings about not having had a parent who cared, and to have the experience of someone who is aware of his distress at this level and who does care.

The patient at this point is far from being cured. He is just beginning to open up and let the therapist in on his fears and frustrations. It is also typical for these patients, at this point in treatment, to regress back to earlier patterns when stress builds up. The treatment pattern is one where the patient moves from denying that anything bothers him in any way to acknowledging that he hurts. Then he tends to become frightened, particularly around the issue of trust, and regresses back to his isolation and denial. This is discouraging for the therapist, who often wonders if the time and effort applied to the case is worth the trouble. However, if one is willing to ride out these regressions and not see them as reflections of one's skill as a therapist but a demonstration of the patient's feelings about himself, it is possible to use these crises in the therapeutic process. The patient communicates the idea that "it happened." By this he means that he got upset and stole, or took a car without authority, or got involved in drinking or a sexual episode. He tends to see himself as the victim of forces, the nature of which he does not comprehend.

One of the goals of therapy is to help the patient develop an observing ego where he can see the cause and effect sequence of events which lead him into his acting-out behavior. Ordinarily his defense system of isolation and denial is geared to ward off intervention. However, in some cases it is possible to help the patient see that there is a sequence of events. Frequently the precipitating event is some disappointment, frustration, or loss. If the patient can see that he reacts to these losses or other anxiety-provoking situations by antisocial behavior, then much has been accomplished to enable him to begin to work on the final stages of resolving his problems.

In practice, the above approach to this type of patient is in contrast to either the neurotic or psychotic patient. The above described technique is designed to help the patient develop an intellectual framework to encompass and manage his emotions. This type of individual isolates himself from his feelings. However, he needs to understand that he has feelings, and that they have a reason and cause and effect sequence. The neurotic patient tends to have many intellectual rationalizations for what happens, and the frequent therapeutic question posed to the neurotic is, "How do you feel about this?" The objective is to help him grasp the emotional significance of what has occurred. In contrast, the antisocial individual needs help to also synchronize thought with emotion and action, but the emphasis is on developing the secondary process phenomenon of containing and controlling the behavior and the affect. Both of these types of patients are in contrast with the schizophrenic individual who so frequently isolates his feelings and denies the reality of what is occurring. He does not deny affect or sequence of events primarily, but denies reality. As a consequence of this, the therapy then is designed to cope with these distortions and help the patient learn the reality configuration of his internal world and how it relates to external reality. In some ways there is a similarity to the work with the impulse-ridden character disorder in the sense that the psychotic patient is operating at pre-oedipal pregenital levels. He is often in a peculiar and intense relationship with his own unconscious. There is danger in focusing on affect which may be explosive. In this sense, these patients are in opposition to the neurotic who particularly needs help in having affect mobilized and liberated. The psychotic patients also have disturbances in their superego development, and guilt, remorse, and ego-ideal components are not available for therapeutic manipulation.

If the impulse-ridden character disorder patient is helped to recognize that he has something troubling him and that this is connected to his antisocial behavior, then he is beginning to get ready for the third phase of his treatment. In this stage he can begin to face his feelings about himself. It is quite remarkable to see a "tough guy" denying type of delinquent reach this stage and break down and cry over what has happened to him. In the beginning of therapy, reaching out sympathetically to this type of individual is generally greeted with scorn, irritation, and resentment. At this third stage the patient himself begins to have developed sufficient ego to face and tolerate the feelings associated with what has happened to him. To be able to face the feelings, he has to have sufficient ego to bind the anxiety he feels, postpone immediate gratification, and tolerate the underlying depression. This requires the sustaining support of the therapist, who is aware of the seriousness of the struggle confronting the patient at this time and gives him the additional support he needs to resolve this conflict. If the patient arrives at this point, he is not only confronted with the problems of resolving his internal conflict, but he has to face the consequences of such an action.

To give up his antisocial way of functioning may well include a break with his familiar way of life, his friends, and his reaction to the major institutions in his environment, and even his own family. There are many pressures on him, both internal and external, to persist in his familiar way of operating. It requires tremendous support and ego strength to break free from all of this.

The treatment is usually of long duration, and in some instances the individual therapist or social agency working with these individuals find themselves in a locus parentis type of role. That is, the individual, once he has stabilized himself and resolved his underlying depression, can generally manage to carry on his daily life on his own. However, there may be points of stress caused by circumstances of life where the individual may need a brief period of help and support to gain his strength. The ego defect which produced the antisocial character formation remains as a potential defect in the character structure, and may lead to a relapse or lead to difficulties in child rearing, so that there is an unusually large number of second and third or more generations with the same type of antisocial problems.

CHILDREN WHO COMMIT CRIMES OF VIOLENCE

Another major grouping of children who commit acting-out and antisocial behavior are those who commit crimes of violence primarily. These crimes are often such things as setting fires, committing murder, acts of vandalism, or acts of sadism against people or animals. The background and personality structures of these children show certain similarities to the children in the impulse-ridden character disorder group, but closer study reveals that they tend to primarily have a schizoid personality and defense system. Their core conflict seems to be that of a fear of annihilation or destruction. They tend to handle this fear by projecting and displacing it onto the environment, and then attacking the environment in one way or another. The fire setting, for example, seems to be for the purpose of destruction, and is viewed as an oral process rather than a sexual one. The acts of murder or vandalism are clearly destructive acts, and these children seem to handle their anxiety and inner conflicts by the intensive aggressive behavior they demonstrate.

The following case of Randolph Williams, a 14-year-old white boy, illustrates many of the features we find in this type of case.

> *Case:* This boy had been in difficulty with school and the authorities before. He had committed some petty thefts and was known as being difficult to manage in the class room, but he tended to keep by himself and was very irritable. At the time of the current arrest he was picked up for fire setting. He had also previously been known to have savagely beaten up some younger children. In his home background his parents had separated many times, but his father lived in the same neighborhood and would come home at regular intervals to beat up the wife and children, and also to have sex relations with the wife, often in a hostile, provocative way, calling attention to what he was doing at times and involving the children in this kind of perverse way.
>
> Randolph's early history is one of much hyperactivity almost since his birth. At two years old he had been known to pull all the drawers out of one of the bureaus, stamping on them and smashing them. He had had an early and excessive interest in peeping under women's skirts. He had gotten involved in sex play with little boys and girls under the age of five. When he started school the teacher saw him as impossible to cope with, although he was recognized as being a very bright and creative child; but it was very difficult to gain his attention and keep him focused on the school work. Randolph's family was also known to the protective agency because the parents had severely abused Randolph and some of the other children at times; attempts to bring them into court had been unsuccessful because at these times the parents would present a united front. The mother kept the home neat and clean, the father always worked, and they were supportive and protective of each other when they were confronted with this outside threat.
>
> In the interview sessions Randolph spoke quite easily and freely about the fire. When asked about other fires he talked about them at great length and boasted about them. He had a friendly, affable manner, and even though he attempted to pick the therapist's pocket, his whole approach was quite talkative and outgoing. This is in contrast to the impulse-ridden character disordered children who tend to be very sullen, silent, and relatively noncommunicative. Randolph had many explanations and rationalizations for what he did, and even though they were not logical he stuck to them and talked about them quite freely. For example, he had first said he

started the fire because he felt cold, and this was a way not only to keep warm but to get people to come and pay some attention to him.

In the therapy of these children and their families, it is often necessary to work with them in an inpatient setting because they are dangerous to themselves and to the community. This is not always required, but in many instances in the early phases of the therapy such a child is apt to repeat his crime of violence, and unless he can be controlled, both he and the community are in danger of great harm. For example, one young boy had burned down three public buildings, including two churches and a school, before he was placed in an institution where he could be controlled. These children tend to reveal a kind of dependent interaction early in their treatment relationship. However, this does not mean that treatment is easy or short, because they have severe ego problems. In working with them the ego patterns previously mentioned quickly emerge. They see themselves as the potential victims of attack. They fight against it by becoming the aggressor. They see such things as the fire setting as a way of handling their internal tensions. They show no guilt or remorse over what they have done, but instead see themselves as the victims of circumstances.

For this group of individuals and the impulse-ridden character disorder persons, the early treatment needs to consist of stabilizing their environment, attempting to help them also see a logical sequence of events in relation to their behavior. One differrence with these more schizoid children is that one has a greater amount of fantasy and distortion of reality to deal with. They deny affect less, but they deny reality more in their presentation of themselves and their life pattern. Treatment with these children is also very long-term, and requires a devotion to individuals who also, even though they appear initially as dependent, ultimately tend to reject therapy because it interferes with their defense system.

With all these acting-out and delinquent children, unless one can work with the family or with the environmental setting in which they will live, much of what is done in the therapy sessions gets undone. For example, if the child has to be placed in a foster home it is frequently necessary to give considerable support to the foster parents, who take in a child who has not had the opportunity to have a home where someone cared for him. They feed and clothe the child, try to show him love and attention, and in return the child may literally break up things in the home, steal, act hostile and provocative, and even want to run back to his neglecting, beating, and obviously ungiving parents. This is often a blow to the ego of the foster parents; they need considerable support to see that the child is acting in the only way he knows how, and that he can only learn to act differently by the experience of the kind of home which they can offer to him.

THE BRAIN-DAMAGED CHILD

Antisocial or acting-out behavior can occur within the context of various organic and neurological disturbances, which include encephalitis, epilepsy, brain damage, and mental retardation. It is always hard to evaluate the role of an organic brain lesion as it affects personality. In general, the personality reaction to a brain lesion, whether it is an infectious one such as encephalitis, or brain syphilis or brain tumor, is that the brain lesion tends to release the underlying personality traits. It has long been known that the reactions of individuals to brain damage have been to develop the personality traits that already were there. In this sense, then, the treatment of the brain-damaged child who shows antisocial behavior needs to include whatever can be done for the organic picture, such as treatment for the epilepsy or the encephalitis. In addition, the specific personality aberration, in my experience, needs to be dealt with in many ways as one treats the personality aberrations of the individual where the behavior is the result of environmental trauma, so that the acting-out child with brain damage not only needs medical care, but he needs stabilization of his environment, in a setting which can tolerate his irritability and his acting-out, which can give him the kind of emotional support and experience that will enable him to contain his drives and affects, and to develop an ego and superego where he can sublimate these energies into community syntonic behavior, such as learning and constructive activity.

REFERENCES

1. BERMAN, S. Antisocial character disorder; its etiology and relationship to delinquency. Amer. J. Orthopsychiat., 1959, 29:612–21.
2. FENICHEL, O. The psychoanalytic theory of neurosis. New York: W. W. Norton & Co., 1945.
3. FREUD, S. "Some character types met with in psychoanalytic work," III Criminals from a sense of guilt. The Standard Edition, Vol. XIV. London: Hogarth Press, 1916.

4. FRIEDLANDER, K. *The psychoanalytical approach to juvenile delinquency.*
   New York: International Universities Press, 1947.
5. JENKINS, R. Motivation and frustration in delinquency. *Amer. J. Orthopsychiat.*, 1957, **27**:528–36.
6. JOHNSON, A., and SZUREK, S. The genesis of antisocial acting out in children and adults. *Psychoanal. Quart.*, 1952, **21**:323–43.
7. KAUFMAN, I., *et al.* Delineation of two diagnostic groups among juvenile
   delinquents: the schizophrenic and the impulse ridden character disorder.
   J. Amer. Acad. Child Psychiat., 1963, **2**:292–316.

8

Austin Des Lauriers

Psychotherapy with the Schizophrenic Child

THERE IS A GREAT DEAL more optimism, in our days, in the treatment of the schizophrenic child than there existed even 10 years ago. Ekstein(4), in his survey of the literature of the past few decades dealing with childhood schizophrenia and allied conditions, has pointed to the specific effort of workers in this field to understand the intrinsic structure of this childhood personality disorganization and the relationship of this structure to its symptomatology. This is seen as necessary in order to develop a rationale for the treatment of this complex condition. Readers are referred to this comprehensive survey for a critical and perspicacious overview of the problems of etiology and diagnosis of the disordered forms of behavior which have been classified under childhood schizophrenia (Des Lauriers [3]).

THEORETICAL CONSIDERATIONS

By *structure* of the schizophrenic aspect of personality disorganization in childhood, we refer to the dynamic relationship of the various components of this disorganization, rather than to the external causes or circumstances which may have contributed to bring it about. In other words, a structural understanding of childhood schizophrenia focuses on what this condition is, intrinsically, without attempting directly to say what factors—hereditary, chemical, physiological, endocrine, social, or environmental—may have caused it to be so. In this regard, then, whatever may be said of the family history, prenatal or postnatal; of the schizophrenic child; whatever determination may be made of the child's neurophysiological functioning or of the equilibrium of his endocrine system; whatever judgment may be made of the quality of the parental, and more specifically the maternal, attitude towards him, remains much less important for diagnostic and therapeutic purposes than what the schizophrenic behavior represents and reflects. Stated in this context, the childhood schizophrenic mode of behavior represents and reflects the absence in the child of whatever is needed in his development to enable him to establish with other people relationships and communications that can produce the satisfaction of his needs and the maturation of his personality functioning.

The Child's Relationship to Others

A structural definition of childhood schizophrenia requires therefore that it be couched in the framework of a clear understanding of the developmental process through which a child goes in order to establish adequate and satisfying relationships to others. These relationships are referred to as object relationships or reality relationships. At birth, the behavior of the child demonstrates little capacity for such reality experiences or such meaningful relationships. The child at birth is so closely tied up to the maternal environment that we speak of his behavior as global and undifferentiated, and of his experiences as oceanic and narcissistically primitive(3, 7, 10). The development of the child toward reality and object relationships can thus be conceptualized as a process of separation and alienation from the mother, and of increasing differentiation in those functions necessary to the satisfaction of his needs and the integration and organization of his experiences. There can be no relationship to others until the child has experienced himself as separated from others. There can be no integrated reality experience until the child has experienced himself as real by defining the boundaries of his own reality and identity (6).

It is precisely this quality of experience that the schizophrenic child appears to lack. In psychoanalytic terms this deficiency is primarily structural, inasmuch as it affects the formation and integrated organization of the ego, but it is also dynamic and functional inasmuch as the instinctual strivings are left, because of the ego deficit, with no adequate and satisfactory instrument of expression or gratification. Viewed in this

light the erratic, unpredictable, and disordered behavior of the schizophrenic child can be understood as an expression of this central ego
deficiency. It becomes extremely important, therefore, to attempt, in the
light of our present understanding of early ego development, to define
the factors involved in the schizophrenic personality deficit.

The process of growth in the human individual, as we have noted
earlier, is a movement from a stage of relative undifferentiation at birth to
stages of greater and greater differentiation, separation, and definition of
the self so that relationships to others, as such, become possible. Through
such relationships and communications with others the essential human
personal needs can be gratified. This developmental process can thus be
conceptualized as a movement away from a primary narcissistic position
in which there is no experience by the child of any separation from the
mother(7, 10). It must, however, also be seen as a progressive definition,
by the child, of the limits and boundaries that set him apart from his
mother and enable him to experience her as *other* than himself and
alienated from himself. How does such an experience take place?

The human child is not a conceptual abstraction. He is a functioning
organism, biologically and physiologically organized, regulated, and integrated within a body which has physical and psychological attributes. His
development is from the beginning the development of an organism
which has separated itself from another, the mother's, and whose differentiation from her can come about only if the limits and boundaries of
this body are clearly defined in his psychological experience. Such a
definition comes about through the physical and sensory interchange of
stimulating and alerting qualities between the child and the mother, and
the environment. Thus it appears quite sound psychologically to concep-
tualize the early emergence of the ego in the child as paralleling closely
the development in the child of the experience of his bodily limits which
separate and differentiate him from the mother. Such an experience
depends on the constant, intense, and variously diversified, amount of
sensory stimulations which arouse and alert the child, draw his attention
and consciousness to the various parts of his body thus stimulated, and
progressively bring about in him the awareness that he stands apart from
the stimulating environment. Such an environment cannot reach him
until it transgresses the barrier which his body creates and by which he
defines himself with respect to this environment.

Let us make clear that if normal psychological relationships to others
require that the individual be clearly defined from others, we must then
assume that in the normal process of growth such a separation or definition from others, *must* take place and therefore it is, in the living human

organism, a *basic need*. In this sense, then, we can say that the child seeks to separate his mother from himself, that he needs to establish the environment apart from himself, and that it is in the very process of doing just that, that he manages to define his personal and individual boundaries, and thus have a basis for normal relationships to others. From a developmental point of view, it is suggested that these boundaries are, in the child, first of all the boundaries of his body, of which he becomes aware through the multitude and variety of sensory stimulations which he experiences in his contacts with his mother and his environment and in his movements and actions in reaction to this environment. Stated in psychoanalytic terms, it is suggested that the early emergence of the ego in the child can be equated to the emergence of a body ego and that this emergence constitutes both the experience in the child of his bodily limits and of the external reality in which he can find satisfying objects to his needs (2, 3, 5, 6, 8, 9).

In essence then, the child needs to establish distance between himself and his mother before he can have her as a real object of interest. This interest can be positive or negative. If the child found, in his mother, a constant degree of satisfaction of all his pleasure-seeking activities, he would obviously have no need to move toward separation and differentiation; on the other hand, if he were to find in his mother only responses causing pain, displeasure, frustration, and dissatisfaction, the child would likely not survive. In either case, no possibility would exist of ego development. Thus the early emergence of a functioning integrated ego in the child appears structurally to be the experience of a body ego and dynamically to be motivated both by a positive drive to get from the mother need-satisfying reactions, while at the same time, aggressively (or negatively) establishing and maintaining distance and alienation between himself and the mother (3). The responses of pleasure or pain in the child to the diversified and numerous sensory stimulations which the mother provides in her ministrations to him, constitute the basic conditions of his awareness of his bodily boundaries and of his experience of himself as a separated and differentiated individual capable of relating to his mother as a subject in relationship to an object.

Capacity for Relationship Lacking in Schizophrenic

This capacity is missing in the schizophrenic child. In making this statement, we need not concern ourselves immediately with assigning a reason why this happened to the schizophrenic child, or with placing on any special circumstance or person the responsibility and blame for the pathological situation. To say that in the schizophrenic child is missing the capacity to separate and differentiate himself from his environment or to establish stable relationships to a mother experienced as a separated and differentiated individual, is simply to point to a core defect in the personality development of the child. The variety of pathological modes of behavior which are included in the clinical description of childhood schizophrenia are all reflections and facets or consequences of this core defect in the developmental process. Perhaps Dr. James Anthony(1) has best summarized the sum total of behavioral observations made by clinicians over the years when he has characterized the schizophrenic pathology as involving three central features:

1. A condition of a-cathexis, that is, the inability to form affective attachments to others and invest in them stable interest and attention. It was to this condition that I was referring as underlying the normal child's drive to turn to the mother, as a separated individual, for the satisfaction of his needs.

2. A condition of a-dualism, that is, the incapacity to separate himself from others; the capacity to do so, as has been underscored, is an essential condition to the existence of object relationship and the experience of reality.

3. A condition of a-genesis, which is the consequence of the preceding two afore-mentioned features, in that it represents the atypical development of the various ego functions.

In trying then to define the schizophrenic pathology in the child, for the purpose of describing a rational therapeutic strategy geared to this pathology, one can deliberately ignore the usual questions referring to "why" has this happened (rejection by mother; adrenal deficiency; defective introjects; and so on) and focus fully on the question of "what" the condition is. In this light it can be said: childhood schizophrenia is a defect, that is, the absence of something which should be there; that this defect is developmental, that is, it is the absence of something necessary to normal development; and, finally, that this defect is reflected (as outcomes) in the variety of symptoms which serve to describe the pathology. If the schizophrenic child could invest sufficient attention, interest, and love in himself, as a separated and differentiated individual, he could then experience his own needs and seek in others—that is, in those who are separated and differentiated from him—the gratification and fulfillment of those needs.

But then this implies that he would no longer be schizophrenic. How does a child, any child, learn to define himself as a separated and differentiated individual? How does he learn to pay attention to himself, become interested in what and who he is, and experience himself as the subject of whatever happens to him? He learns all this in the interactional

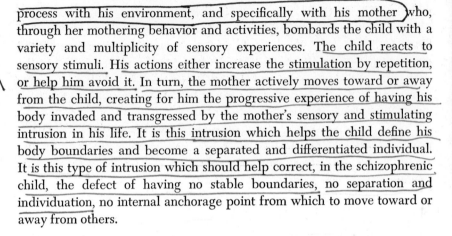

process with his environment, and specifically with his mother who, through her mothering behavior and activities, bombards the child with a variety and multiplicity of sensory experiences. The child reacts to sensory stimuli. His actions either increase the stimulation by repetition, or help him avoid it. In turn, the mother actively moves toward or away from the child, creating for him the progressive experience of having his body invaded and transgressed by the mother's sensory and stimulating intrusion in his life. It is this intrusion which helps the child define his body boundaries and become a separated and differentiated individual. It is this type of intrusion which should help correct, in the schizophrenic child, the defect of having no stable boundaries, no separation and individuation, no internal anchorage point from which to move toward or away from others.

PSYCHOTHERAPY

The therapeutic maneuvers which will be described in this section are predicated upon, and derived from, the clinical point of view described in the preceding discussion. This will give a rationale to the psychotherapy and a structure to the therapeutic process. It is important to emphasize here that the concern will be with describing a specific therapeutic attitude rather than giving a recipe for therapeutic techniques. Each child, schizophrenic or not, is different, as are therapists and mothers. The therapist needs to accept as a starting point that his is not the task to trace systematically the origin and causal factors of the disturbance (anymore than the orthopedic surgeon finds it necessary in reducing a leg fracture to wonder what sort of truck hit his patient). Rather he must recognize that the pathology he is confronted with amounts to an inability in the schizophrenic child to establish stable interpersonal relationships and experience those realities that can truly gratify his needs. The therapist's concern will then be directed relentlessly and without diversion to one simple goal to restore in the child the conditions of reality experience and of object relationships. This reflects the necessity to create for the child the basic conditions of ego development and ego functioning.

Establishing Contact

Where should the therapist start? First he must make some sort of contact with the child, and this contact (which he should not delude himself into thinking of as a relationship) should be impressive on the child. The child should be made very acutely aware that the therapist is there with him. In essence, the therapist must arouse the child's interest in the therapist by whatever means are at his disposal. The immediate goal is to mobilize some of the child's affective cathexis in such a way and at such a level of intensity that the child will give a response clearly directed at the therapist. Therefore the therapist must make himself forcefully present to the child. The word "forcefully" here is not meant to convey a bullying, aggressive stance; it means simply that the therapist should make sure, somehow, that the child knows he is there and responds to him. The therapist should not allow the child to escape that presence, even though he may be allowed, because of his sensitivity, his anxiety, or his general feeling of disorientation, to try to avoid it.

Example: Terry is lying in bed, her head buried in the pillow, her face to the wall. She has allowed no one to come near her. If the nursing staff approaches her, she hits out, scratches, tears the bedclothes, screams, and thrashes about frantically. Food in small quantity is placed nearby, some of which she may eat, but most of which she throws around the room. Her physical hygiene is limited and attendants have to carry her bodily to the washroom. The therapist, after locking himself in the room with her, approaches the bed, bends over, removes a strand of hair from her face, and says: "Hello, Terry!" Her immediate response is to fling her arm and turn her face away, her gesture making it clear, on the surface at least, that she wants nothing to do with him. "You haven't even looked at me, Terry, I'm Dr. D. and I want to be with you." In saying this, the therapist applies a slight pressure to her shoulder, as if to help her turn around to face him. Terry screams: "Get out! get out!," jumps up on the bed, throws her pillow, and starts kicking. "You don't have to be afraid, Terry, I'm Dr. D. and I'm going to stay with you. You're all excited and glad to see me, so stop your kicking, I am not going to go away right now!" Terry gets off the bed, and runs to the door as if she were going out; she finds the door locked, and as if this were reassuring to her, or this meant the end for her, she calms down completely, walks back to her bed very quietly, and when the therapist extends his hand, she takes it: "Now you can look at me, Terry; you see, I'm here and this is your hand holding mine." Terry gets in bed, smiles, then turns her head away, to indicate the end of her interest, or to make sure somehow that the therapist is really there. Quietly, the therapist sits on the bed beside her; he calls her name, and any movement she makes is taken to indicate that she is aware of his presence beside her. He talks to her, not so much to keep her entertained with information, as to keep her alert to his presence. . . .

The point, then, is for the therapist to make his presence known physically to the patient. The emphasis on the physical, rather than the symbolic, must be seen in the context both of the theoretical postulates discussed earlier and of the immediate therapeutic goal to be achieved. The patient's behavior must reflect an alert attention to and interest in, what is happening to him when the therapist is there. The therapist's moves are geared to alerting the attention and interest of the patient experiencing the presence of the therapist. Physical contacts in a proximate or relatively distant way create a sensory impact on the patient. Thus a sort of communication is established, which is physical, concretistic, immediate, and full of sensory stimulations.

A close comparison can be made here between this type of physical communication and the mutually stimulating interaction which takes place between a mother and her baby. The transactional process which defines what might be called the mothering activity is predicated upon the physical presence of the mother to the child, and upon the variety of stimulus-response patterns between mother and child which develop in this mutually wanted correspondence. The physical encounter between mother and child becomes the basis for a physical communication which takes place through immediate and varied sensory experiences involved in it, rather than through symbolic verbal imagery and representation. It matters little to the mother that her child has no verbal language, anymore than whatever she might choose to say matters to the baby. Their presence to each others takes place at a level which is immediate, concrete, physically sensed. Similarly, the therapist establishes a human contact with a schizophrenic child. He assumes in the child the need for such a contact, and he follows the developmental rules or conditions of the most basic communication between human beings. His presence is communicated through concrete, physical, stimulating, and impactful activity aimed at arousing attention and interest from the child. This attention and interest reflect a degree of affective cathexis in the patient, and the therapist must give direction, orientation, and focus to it.

For this purpose, any means can be used appropriate to the child's age and physical development, as well as genuinely fitting the temperament of the therapist. Tactile contacts are most useful, if they are not contrived, mechanical, or unwarranted. They must demonstrate the spontaneous and honest attentiveness of the therapist to the child, and be used, at times to control, restrain, and comfort him. At other times, they serve to stimulate pain or pleasure in various parts of his body. For instance, when her therapist finds Janet in her room, her hair disheveled and hanging over her face, her nails broken from biting at them or scratching the walls, what can be more natural and direct than to attend to the child's physical appearance: put a comb in her hand and help her fix her hair; sit close beside her and file down her nails evenly? No great amount of talk is needed; just enough to keep the child clearly oriented to herself and the therapist.

No far-fetched speculations as to the homosexual implications of the behavior need be allowed to cloud this moment of presence to each other, or create, in the therapist, qualms and fears which could destroy the security of the moment. A mother, in reaching for her little boy's hand, to comfort him or just for fun, does not stop to ask herself whether she's being seductive and will cause anxiety in her child. Only a sick mother would let such fantastic notions interfere with her attentive activity toward her boy. On the other hand, if her child had burnt his arm and was suffering in pain, she would not, except with great care and delicacy, touch his arm or try to move it. She would just try to make the child comfortable. A therapist, too, needs to exercise good sense, and sensitivity. Like a burnt child, the schizophrenic patient may be incapable of tolerating direct, immediate, tactile contacts. Such contacts may frighten him and he may try, in panic sometimes, to avoid them. Such behavior should not be understood to mean that the child does not want the *presence* of the therapist; only that he does not want to be touched. With Terry, the young girl mentioned earlier, physical contacts were not enjoyable unless she initiated them herself. Once the therapist realizes this, he learns to wait. He can make himself "touchable," but need not feel that he must now discuss with the patient the underlying motives, aggressive or libidinal, which make the child so fearful of tactile sensations.

Communication

In this last statement, a point is being made which can easily be misunderstood, but which, nevertheless, is central to the effective process of the therapeutic approach described here. The point emphasized bears on the idea of communication between people. Communication requires separation and differentiation between the people communicating. These are conditions of the communication. The intrinsic intentionality of the communication is to breach the distance, overcome the separation, bring the people together. From a developmental point of view, we have suggested that there exists a physical, sensory basis to human communication, that is, to the bringing together of two human beings. If one of the two individuals who meet does not possess a stable and clear experience of his own separation and differentiation from the other, how can he communicate, how can he receive a communication? Only if conditions are created that contribute to his experiencing himself as separated and differentiated. Only if he experiences his own boundaries and limits in reference to the other person. We say that this can be accomplished naturally by offering a multiplicity and variety of sensory stimulations which are intrusively and forcefully made part of the experience and response of the undifferentiated individual. This is what is meant by physical communication, and this is what gives a rationale to the therapeutic maneuvers of "contact" described above. But this does not mean that "verbal" communication is useless, though such verbal communication can become the greatest barrier and obstacle to personal communication between a therapist and a schizophrenic child.

To make this point clearer, let us return to Terry, for a moment. Terry is a young 16-year-old girl, of dull intellectual endowment. She comes from an upper middle-class family, where she is the oldest of three girls. Her developmental history leaves no doubt that, since childhood, her behavior has been psychotic. In recent months, however, she has become unmanageable, because of her rage outbursts and her destructive activities. This acute phase brought her to therapy. Excerpts from her first meeting follow:

> My sister has friends. I have a friend too. His name is Tom. Nobody else but me has Tom. We're going to be married when I'm 17. There are not many tomboys in this world. I think my cousin may be one too. I'm different. I'm a tomboy. Terry will marry Tom when she's 17. That's in July. We'll go away together. I might take my cousin with me. She might be a tomboy too. It takes a lot of science to do that. But I was born from a great family of scientists. John Seagrist in the 16th century was my father. . . . There now, you know all about it. Just you and me!

This verbal outpouring by Terry of her delusional reconstructive effort can hardly be said not to be meaningful. As a matter of fact, it is full of meanings! And yet, what does it mean? Is this the wishful fantasy of a lonely, adolescent girl desperately seeking friendship and love? Is this the angry attempt of a jealous girl to be different and possibly more interesting than her sister? Is this a regressive, autistic way of redefining for herself some kind of double identity in which she is both and at the same time a boy and a girl? Is she saying: "I have a great past and a great future, but I don't know who I am now"? What exactly is she saying? What is the meaning of her communication?

Terry, I submit, was not attempting to communicate anything verbally. Otherwise one would be faced with an irreducible contradiction: "I don't know who I am," she says: "I am Tom, I am Terry; I was born in the 16th century, and I'll be married when I'm 17. Who am I?" Assuming that "her language is her"(11), she is certainly a very diffused person, whose boundaries are so fluid as to encompass not only a double sexual identity, but the span of four centuries. And if she has no idea who she is, how can she possibly know who I am, how to communicate to me! Yet there she was, spouting her delusion to me. To say to her: "No, Terry, you're not Tom, you're just a girl, 16 years old," would be compounding her confusion. On the other hand, if I were to say: "I'll go to your wedding; I think Tom is lucky to have you," I would be pretending to play a part in a fantasy the conclusion of which I cannot envisage. Should I try to have her think and talk like I do, or should I try to think and talk like she does? But who is she?

Communication requires separation and differentiation. Terry may be Terry but she obviously does not experience herself as such. How can she communicate? Only if she is made to experience herself. Before she can communicate, she has to be in a condition to do so. Her physical separation and differentiation must be, in fact, not a fantasy. What the mother does to foster such an experience in her child must become the basic line of the therapeutic strategy. It is not therefore a question of saying to Terry: "No, you are not Tom!" or "All right, I'll go to your wedding," but rather: "You are here, you talk, I hear you, you hear me. What is said does not matter, just so you're here with me and feeling it."

Thus, by focusing on this immediate and direct form of communication, not only does the therapist avoid the pitfall of thinking that the patient is truly responding to him because patient and therapist "exchange words," but he also prevents the autistic and delusional qualities of the child's verbalizations from becoming the basis of an apparent communication with him. Language, through its extensive use of symbolic representations and its coded forms of reality references, erects such an intricate barrier between people that even the schizophrenic child uses it, in his anxiety or in his confusion, to avoid closeness and to establish distance. Again, the sensitive therapist may want and accept, for a time, this distance and "play along," so to say, in order not to unduly frighten his patient. But he should not confuse such a tactical maneuver with a strategic move aimed at bringing him in personal communication and contact with the disturbed child. When Sechehaye's patient, Renee, complained in her autobiography (12) that her therapist's questions and inquiries into her delusional statements gave these statements undue importance, made them sound like real things which had to be accounted for, and made her feel as if she were being indicted, she also was indicating how erroneous it is to think that one "communicates" because one talks. Words can be symbols or signs; when they are signs (regardless of their symbolic value) of the patient's need to be near, and are accepted as such by the therapist, they can keep patient and therapist together. As Renee says: "Only near her, I felt secure, especially from the time when she began to sit next to me on the couch and put her arm around my shoulders. Oh, what joy, what relief to feel the life, the warmth, the reality!" (12)

It is indeed this communication of life to the schizophrenic child, alone in his unbounded universe of confusion and fears, which is the strategic goal of the therapeutic approach described here. The basic needs of the child for a clear experience and definition of himself, as well as for objects outside of himself which can stimulate in him the feeling of being alive, cannot be met if the therapist allows himself to lose the child while searching for mysterious meanings in the primary process quality of the child's language. Unquestionably such search is always fruitful, because the schizophrenic language telescopes the most varied, and often contradictory, meanings in any one word or verbalization. Yet the reward at the end of the search very seldom leaves the patient any closer to reality, or the therapist any less distant from his patient. Should the therapist then ignore everything that is said? Should he avoid ever saying anything himself? The answer lies in common sense and in genuine interest in the patient. A greeting such as: "Good morning, doctor!" should not be responded to by saying: "What do you mean by that?" or by remarking: "You forgot to blow your nose this morning!" Similarly, if the child mentions in hilarious tones: "Guess what happened yesterday? My boyfriend drowned," the therapist should not immediately jump to the conclusion that the patient is wishing him dead, but he should simply recognize how alive and happy the patient appears to him at that moment. When a mother calls out to her youngster: "You'll have to come in now, Johnny!" and the boy retorts: "I'm not Johnny, I'm Davie Crockett," she does not start pondering or worrying over the possible aggressive or acting-out significance of this name in the life of her son;

she might say: "Well, it's time to come in anyway, Davie Crockett," or "Finish your game pretty soon, Davie, your soup is on the table!" She does not pretend to be anything else but what she is, unless the child specifically assigns her a role in the game. There is a difference between playing a game and acting-out a delusion. The therapist should always be prepared to allow his patient playfully to experiment with a close personal relationship with him; but he should never let himself be lost in a delusional parody of reality.

After over six years of intensive therapeutic communications, David, the disturbed adolescent about whom Beulah Parker reports in detail in her book *My Language is Me*(11), left her with this statement: "I'm still looking for meanings in life, but there can be meaning in just living." Just living, experienced and felt as being alive, separated and differentiated, defined and individualized as a human being, is the true foundation of reality relationships and interpersonal communications, because it is the basis of stable reality experience. This is the task of the therapy with schizophrenic children.

REFERENCES

1. ANTHONY, JAMES. An experimental approach to the psychopathology of childhood autism. *Brit. J. med. Psycho.*, 1958, **31.**

2. BRODY, S. *Patterns of mothering.* New York: International Universities Press, 1956.

3. DES LAURIERS, A. M. *The experience of reality in childhood schizophrenia.* New York: International Universities Press, 1962.

4. EKSTEIN, R.; BRYANT, K.; and FRIEDMAN, S. W. Childhood schizophrenia: A review of the literature, 1946–1956. *Psychoanalytic study of the child*, Vol. 13. New York: International Universities Press, 1958.

5. FEDERN, P. Narcissism in the structure of the ego. *Ego psychology and the psychoses.* New York: Basic Books, 1952.

6. FENICHEL, O. Early stages of ego development. *Collected papers*, Vol. II. New York: W. W. Norton & Co., 1954.

7. FREUD, S. *Civilization and its discontents.* London: Hogarth Press, 1930.

8. HARTMANN, H. Notes on the reality principle. *Psychoanalytic study of the child*, Vol. XI. New York: International Universities Press, 1956.

9. HOFFER, W. Development of the body ego. *Psychoanalytic study of the child*, Vol. V. New York: International Universities Press, 1950.

10. LOEWALD, H. W. Ego and reality. *Int. J. Psychoanal.*, 1951, **32.**

11. PARKER, B. *My language is me.* New York: Basic Books, 1962.

12. SECHEHAYE, M. *Autobiography of a schizophrenic girl.* New York: Grune & Stratton, 1951.

9

Peter Knowlton

Treatment and Management
of the Autistic Child

SINCE WORLD WAR II the field of child psychiatry has been confronted with growing numbers of children designated as psychotic. Such children do not present a new entity, as an excellent description of a psychotic child given by John Haslan(6) dates from 1809. In the early 20th century, with its growing interest in psychological matters, relatively little attention was paid to the psychotic child although a few isolated reports of cases appeared in the literature. Bender(1) was one of the first to describe a number of cases and to delineate their characteristics in a paper appearing in 1941. Since then the literature has become increasingly more extensive with significant contributions having been made by Kanner(7, 8), Eisenberg(3), Mahler(9), Putnam(10), Beata Rank(11), Goldfarb(4), as well as many others. In spite of the considerable literature now in existence on the subject, the exact cause of the disorder, its incidence, and the most effective methods of treatment remain obscure.

RECOGNIZING THE PSYCHOTIC CHILD

A great many symptoms have been attributed to the psychotic child but most characteristically they show a marked inability to socialize with their peers, mutism or bizarre noncommunicative speech, and an extreme resistance to change. The single salient feature shown by all of them is a severe distortion of their object relations which grossly distorts their ability to perceive people in their environment appropriately. This distortion may be in the direction of apparently seeing people as a kind of conglomeration of unrelated parts, to an almost total inability to see the other person, particularly the mother, as in any way separate from himself. These two extremes have been classified by Mahler as autistic and symbiotic respectively. Such a classification is not always easy, however, as many of these children can seemingly alternate from one extreme to the other and there are a number of shades of difference shown by the individual child under different conditions.

The age of onset of a psychotic disorder is often not clear. Typically a superficial history will indicate the onset at 18 months or two years when a sudden change of behavior is noted by the parents. A more careful study, however, will usually reveal gross deviations long before that time. The author knows of cases diagnosed at 4 months and has seen a case at 10 months. The incidence of psychosis in children is almost impossible to determine at present. The reason for this is that reported cases represent an unknown percentage of the true number. Often physicians are reluctant to make the diagnosis until the child reaches school age, and many cases of psychosis are misdiagnosed as retardation or brain damage. This is further complicated by the fact that retarded, brain-damaged and congenitally deformed children can also be, and not infrequently are, psychotic as well. It seems more than probable that the future will show a steady rise in the absolute and relative incidence of such children for a variety of reasons. Better diagnosis, the population explosion, improved medical techniques leading to greater survival of deviant children, and a wide variety of social changes would all appear to contribute to this probable trend.

DESCRIPTION OF AN AUTISTIC CHILD

It would appear axiomatic that the older the psychotic child the more difficult, if not impossible, will be his treatment. For this reason, this chapter will concentrate on the child three and under as offering the best chance of significant change. Even at this age, however, we have serious question as to how reversible the condition actually is. In order to illustrate the nature and origins of such children, the case of Mary has been chosen as an example. This case has not been chosen as a case in the usual sense but rather to serve the purpose of showing by description and example certain characteristics of these children, and the methods employed in attempting to elucidate the contributing factors in their development and present deviation. As a starting point, the mother's description of Mary's behavior during the course of a typical day can serve to illustrate certain features of the disorder and the extreme difficulty encountered in the daily care of such children.

Example: Mary was described by her mother as a two-year, eight-month-old child with blonde tousled hair and blue eyes. She was well nourished but on the thin side, and of average height for her age. On the whole, the mother described her as bird-like in her movements, swift, well-coordinated, and as she put it "fluttery." Her expression tended to be serious in general but at times she smiled seemingly without external stimulus. She had no speech but made incomprehensible and purposeless noises consisting of grunting sounds, and high-pitched screams unrelated to any apparent effort at communication. This description was later confirmed by clinical observation.

Typically, Mary's parents arose about 7 A.M. and tiptoed downstairs in their small row house hoping to be able to have breakfast together before Mary woke up. After her husband left for work at about 8 A.M., Mrs. S. would have a cup of coffee by herself, trying to collect herself for a predictably difficult day with Mary. Mary would wake up anywhere from about 7:15 to 8:30 and her mother could hear her rocking in her crib. The mother would usually go to her about 8:30 and the first task was to remove her diapers, which were invariably wet. Getting her dressed was not easy as she made no attempt at cooperating with the procedure. Brushing her hair was virtually impossible as she would resist it vigorously, pushing the brush away, turning her head, and screaming. Breakfast was a shambles as she would not sit at the table, but wandered aimlessly around the kitchen instead. She would eat dry cereal with her hands, dropping many bits, which she would then step on inadvertently. She would drink small amounts of milk from a cup, slopping much of it down her chin. Usually in the course of this procedure her eyes would light on the cookie jar, which was high up on the shelf. She would then take her mother's hand as a kind of tool and try to push it in the direction of the jar. Limiting her cookie intake was difficult for Mrs. S. as Mary would take as many as she could and stuff them in her mouth. After finishing these, she would again push the mother's hand towards the cookie jar and give a kind of whining grunt, a noise which the mother found particularly unpleasant. Sometimes the mother would give in to these demands and give her more cookies. Other times she would become infuriated and spank her with some violence, feeling guilty afterwards. At still other times, when she had steeled herself to some degree of patience, she would try to get Mary to say the word cookie but she never did.

After this she would put Mary in her room by herself while she went about her house work. Mary seemed quite content with this arrangement, but her room was a shambles, as she strewed her toys aimlessly around and had broken most of the plastic toys her parents had provided for her. The mother did not know exactly what Mary did when she was by herself, but often when she looked in on her she would see her twirling a block around and around without apparent purpose. Recently her parents had bought her a record player as they had noticed that she was responsive to music on the radio and became quite upset when it stopped for a commercial. The record player was put out of reach, which meant that Mrs. S. would have to restart the record when it stopped. Mary was insistent that the same record be played over and over and would cry, whine, and kick if her mother tried to put on a different one.

Shopping with Mary was extremely difficult and Mrs. S. kept this activity to the barest minimum. Unless watched every minute in the supermarket she would wander away, knock over cans of food, or send neatly stacked piles of oranges rolling on the floor.

Lunch was usually a repetition of breakfast, and she was returned to her room afterwards but took no nap. At this time the mother would attempt to have a few minutes to herself but found it difficult to relax. Later in the afternoon Mrs. S. would take her to the local park for a brief period. Mary seemed not to notice the other children and she would never approach them. Most of the other mothers in the park would watch Mary with curiosity, would glance at Mrs. S. sympathetically, but would seldom converse with her. As she felt embarrassed by her situation, Mrs. S. would tend not to encourage conversations. She did strike up an acquaintance with the mother of a five-year-old retarded child, but she also kept this relationship at a relatively superficial level. They would converse on general topics and although they apparently felt a mutual sympathy for each other, they never referred to their children. In summer weather she would place Mary in the small back yard with a basin of water. Mary would splash continually with this for as long as the mother would let her.

Mary's father usually arrived at 5:30 or 6 and frequently he would bring a small toy with the hope of interesting his daughter in it. If she noticed the toy at all, which was seldom, she would clutch it in her hand or turn it over and over, but she would never play with it in the way it was intended. Supper was again extremely difficult for all concerned as Mary would continue her wanderings. Her father would patiently try to induce her to eat or get her to sit down, without success. At 7:30 or so the mother would bathe her, an activity which Mary would seemingly enjoy as she splashed, laughed, and would try to grab the water with her hand. She was bathed at this time with the hope that she would be more relaxed in going to bed. This did not work too well as she continued awake in her crib, rocking and banging her head for two hours or more. The resulting noise was so great that the crib needed to be tied down and padding inserted to avoid injury to her head. Finally she would fall asleep and usually slept soundly through the night.

As a general point, Mrs. S. found Mary's lack of response to her almost unbearable. She found herself alternating between feeling intense sympathy for her daughter and violent rage which left her feeling extremely guilty. She poignantly described how sometimes she tried to hide in a closet hoping that Mary would give some sign of missing her, but this never happened.

DATA COLLECTION

Child's Development

Mary's behavior has all the earmarks of an autistic child—the extreme isolation, bizarre behavior, mutism, and so on—but why? This is no easy question to answer and we are faced with the problem of how to locate answers. Do we look for genetic or acquired defects in the child, do we look for abnormalities in the environment, or do we attempt to cover both possibilities in our investigations? This involves the issues of data collection and assessment which require discussion. Data collection in medicine consists of (1) history; (2) direct observation including physical examination; and (3) indirect observation such as chemical studies, X-ray, and electroencephalogram.

In Mary's case as an example, the history obviously needs to be obtained from the parents as they have had more experience with her than anyone else. Although the father can contribute his own observations to fill a picture, in a vast majority of situations the mother is in the best position to provide an appropriate history. This implies only that the mother usually has access to greater amounts of reliable information than anyone else and does not imply that she is the only contributing factor to the child's disturbance. There are certain considerations which need to be taken into account in data collection from the mother: (1) the circumstances of data collection; (2) the specific nature of the data requested; and (3) the sequences followed in developing the history.

1. Data collection of this kind can best be carried out with a mother in a service setting, in an atmosphere of warmth and interest in the mother as a person in her own right. It is her interest in help that provides the motivating power of the history, and it is only through her experiences that we are able to obtain any history at all.

2. The most usual history with which we are familiar focuses on certain more or less specific areas in the child's development and involves a combination of opinions and fact. Mary's history approached in this way might sound like this:

Pregnancy was described as normal, labor was about two hours, and no abnormalities were reported in the delivery except that the mother required a blood transfusion immediately afterwards. The mother knows of no period of anoxia and she was told that the infant was quite healthy in the immediate postnatal period. The infant was bottle fed and often regurgitated her feeding. This required several formula changes before she was able to hold her food down satisfactorily. She had colic off and on during the first nine months. There was some evidence that the mother was depressed during this period but she was vague about this. Weaning was rather abrupt at 10 months. Toilet training was started at about a year with the mother pressuring the child quite strongly. Training was never completed. As an informant the mother did not appear very reliable. She seemed rather cold, distant, and gave rather clipped answers to the questions asked.

Such a history does provide us with a degree of relevant information. From the maternal point of view we obtain a suggested picture of an overly rigid person incapable of gratifying the impulse requirements of her infant. Such a picture would not be incommensurate with Kanner's concept of the "ice box" mother or the schizophrenogenic mother described by others. We also get evidence of an infant who was apparently deprived at the oral level and who reacted to an overly strict toilet-training procedure which tended to emphasize her anal sadistic component. It is also suggested that the failure of oral gratification led to the failure of the establishment of a positive object relationship and gravely distorted the child's development. The concept of a shattered ego as postulated by the group working at the Putnam Center in Boston would seem quite appropriate in describing this child.

Mother-Infant Relationship

On the other hand, a history such as this leaves us with a number of unsettled questions. In many situations we have seen a single child in a family—often in a large family—who has suffered from such a serious disorder, whereas the others showed milder deviations or could easily be accepted as average. In fact, we have never seen a family with more than one psychotic child, although we have heard of such an occurrence. Does this mean that a genetic factor must be considered by way of explanation? Perhaps so, but it seems important to first recognize that a mother is not a fixed environmental quantity in the life of each of her infants but can vary greatly as the result of a number of factors significant to her. At what point in the life of the infant or child these differences become significant is a matter that is not easy to determine. Recent theoretical approaches suggested by Fairbairn, Bowlby, and others, as well as animal studies, notably by Harlow, indicate a new approach to the problem of the significance of the early mother-infant relationship. The fundamental point in this new approach is that the infant is essentially object seeking. This object-seeking force is considered to operate independently of the physiological need to achieve homeostatic balance. Admittedly such a concept is difficult, if not impossible, to prove one way or another at this stage of our knowledge. We can, however, allow the question of historical data collection to include such a possibility, with as little bias as feasible, and be in a better position, perhaps to see in time what theoretical approach applies most appropriately to the data at hand.

A further consideration in this matter is the conception which holds that the infant becomes a part object for the mother. The development of the infant as a part object in the mother's mind starts during her pregnancy and by the time the infant is actually born the mother may already have formed a more or less distinct image of her infant. This image formation is a complex matter, with many elements contributing to its development. Certainly her own past experiences are a major determinant, but in addition special circumstances occurring during the pregnancy itself appear to have a profound bearing on the mother's later perception of her infant. This is in keeping with the work of Bibring and her associates who studied the pregnancy period as a maturational crisis. They point out that in such a crisis period the mother is in a high state of flux in both her physiological and psychological state. This state of flux leaves her highly vulnerable to both positive and negative external influences. During this period, then, the mother's developing image of the fetus is particularly vulnerable to contingency factors occurring during the course of her pregnancy. Rose(12) and his associates were able to identify some 14 relatively commonly occurring contingency factors which apparently had strong negative effect on the mother's ability to develop an appropriate view of her infant as a part object. These factors can be listed as follows:

1. Multiple births.
2. Children born within 10 to 12 months of each other.
3. Dislocating geographical moves during early pregnancy.
4. Moving away from, or back to, a family group for economic reasons.
5. Unexpected loss of security, as the result of husband's sudden loss of job or business failure.
6. Marital infidelity on the part of the husband discovered during pregnancy.
7. Serious illness in the mother, husband, or significant relative.
8. Loss of husband.
9. Role reversal when a previously supportive person breaks down and becomes dependent.
10. Loss of a person with whom there was a significant object tie.
11. Previous spontaneous or criminal abortions, periods of sterility.
12. Health complications in the mother as a result of the pregnancy.
13. Experiences with close friends or relatives who have had defective or injured children.
14. The juxtaposition of conception with a series of devaluing experiences.

It can also be seen that certain factors connected with the birth or immediate postnatal period can impinge profoundly on the mother's view of the child as part object: prematurity which leaves the viability of the child in doubt; birth injury of a greater or lesser degree; congenital defect; or unexpected multiple births. Any of these events may put a severe strain on a mother's developed positive image or strongly reinforce an already developed negative one. It should be emphasized here that none of the matters discussed so far should be considered as *causative* in the development of the autistic child by themselves but do appear to have a strong contributing influence when the child develops in a psychotic direction.

To illustrate such a history, we continue the case of Mary as an example.[1] When asked to recount the circumstances of her pregnancy the following story was developed with the mother.

---

[1] The information summarized in this article was obtained through the use of a specially designed semistructured flow interview now being used as a research instru-

She had been married about two months when she became pregnant and was 21 years old at the time. She and her husband were living in a small apartment in a midwestern town of moderate size. Her 23-year-old husband had recently started out in the sales force of the local industry, having worked for this company since his graduation from high school five years earlier. His shift to the sales force represented a move forward for him as an aspect of the company's policy related to the regular advancement of its employees. At the same time, the shift meant that he needed to move to Philadelphia after two or three months as the main headquarters of the industry were located in that city. This move actually took place when the mother was about three months pregnant.

This move had a significant bearing on the mother in that she had lived in the same town all her life and was a rather natural part of the social network, including her rather closely knit family, and friends that she had grown up with. She anticipated the move with a combination of anxiety and interest. The good-bye parties given by her friends tended to make the departure more poignant; she recalls feeling acutely lonely on the drive east and cried quite a bit on the way.

They moved into a small apartment in the middle of the city. She had little to occupy her time in her new surroundings and missed her former social contacts. She spent her time on walks in the city, window shopping and in the home reading magazines or watching television. The only person with whom she established any significant relationship was her landlady, an older woman with a daughter her age who lived out of town. She would have a cup of coffee in the morning fairly frequently with this woman, and they would

---

ment in the Philadelphia area. The late John A. Rose was the principal architect of this interview outlined. It is of interest in that this interview can and has been used by representatives of any agency responsible for children with relatively little training in its use. This would include such agencies as a child guidance clinic, a children's hospital, a foster-care agency, a nursery school, a day-care center, as well as others. The history, development, and theoretical implications of this interview are of interest but cannot be described here. As a general matter the areas covered in sequence are as follows: (1) Parent-child-community interaction leading to the request for service. (2) Description of child's behavior and mother's reaction to that behavior during a typical day. (3) History of mother-child interactions starting from conception to present. Pregnancy covers circumstances, events, health, and behavior of mother. Description of delivery. Descriptions of child's behavior and mother's reactions at four month intervals in first year, six month intervals to three years, and as relevant after that. (4) Mother's background, including preschool memories, descriptions of parents, first day of school, school experience, onset of menstrual periods, high school academic and social experience, work record if any, meeting with husband, courtship and marital course. (5) Return to present with further delineation of relevant information. The information gathered has proved to be of great value in matching service to need and planning effective service whenever applicable.

spend their time telling about their lives and backgrounds. Her husband needed to travel about three days a week as part of his training as a salesman. She remembers feeling quite relieved when he came home from these trips and would complain mildly about his absences but felt guilty about doing so. She got established with an obstetrician and visited him for regular prenatal check ups. The pregnancy itself progressed without complications. She looked forward to the arrival of her child, feeling that this would satisfy some of the feelings of loneliness by giving her something to do, and although she had some discomfort in the latter parts of her pregnancy, this was not great and appeared not to be of pathological significance. In general, she recalls a vague sense of foreboding throughout her pregnancy but could not put her finger on its nature.

The delivery was expected to take place towards the latter part of October and plans were developed with that date in mind. Her mother was to come east for a few days to help her out when she got home from the hospital, and her husband had worked it out with the company that he would have no traveling to do for a couple of weeks after the arrival of the baby. In late September, the mother got the disturbing news that her father had had a heart attack, and although it was not considered serious it did require his hospitalization. It also placed her mother's plans in doubt. Early in October on a Wednesday morning at about 5 A.M. her labor pains began. This was about three weeks earlier than expected. Her husband was away at the time and after waiting a couple of hours she finally called her landlady, but it turned out that she was away visiting her daughter and was not available. She then called her obstetrician and was informed that he was attending a convention in Detroit. She was referred to his assistant and was told that he was involved in a delivery and was unable to talk to her directly. He did, however, relay the message for her to come to the hospital. At this point she was close to panic, as the labor pains were increasing in frequency. Finally, with a good deal of effort, she was able to get out the front door and hail a cab. She was rushed to the emergency entrance of the hospital, and the delivery took place in a treatment room where she was attended by an assistant resident and a nurse who did not have time to scrub up. She apparently lost a sufficient amount of blood during the delivery to require a transfusion, but aside from this there were no serious complications. (The hospital record indicated no anoxia or birth injury, the mother required one pint of blood because of blood loss. The rest of the hospital stay was noted as uneventful.)

Mary weighed 5 pounds, 6 ounces at birth and was described to the mother as quite healthy. She saw Mary shortly after birth and recalled her first impression quite vividly. She stated that she seemed shriveled and old to her and recalls having a weird association with a little old lady who sold apples on the corner in her home town. She was a familiar sight, and her parents often bought apples from her. This woman always responded very warmly to her, and she remembered feeling acutely sad when she heard of her death during her childhood.

Later in the day she was transferred to a semiprivate room in the hospital. One of the other women in the room with her had recently given birth to a child with considerable congenital malformations and talked about it at length with the third occupant of the room. She recalled that during the five days of her stay in this room she conversed with the other women very little, although it was difficult for her to avoid hearing the conversations. She had discussed the matter of breast feeding with her obstetrician, who was strongly in favor of her undertaking it. She tried it for two days in the hospital, but as her milk did not flow freely and Mary seemed unsatisfied after each feeding, she gave it up with some relief and shifted to the bottle. She met her pediatrician briefly on the third day of her hospital stay. He supplied her with some routine information about the baby and reassured her that she was quite healthy. She had reports from the nurses who worked in the nursery that Mary cried more than the other babies, but they said this almost humorously as they also talked about how she seemed alert and very alive to them. Her husband arrived the day after the delivery. He would have been back sooner, but as he was traveling and was quite far away, he couldn't be located immediately and it took him some time to get back. Mrs. S. remembers feeling quite an intense burst of anger when she saw him but covered this carefully, as she felt that he could hardly have done other than he did. Mary was quite fussy when she was brought to Mrs. S. at feedings at regular intervals, and Mrs. S. was quite distressed at the fact that after a feeding she didn't seem to settle down and would return to the nursery still crying. She remembers that she experienced some relief when Mary was taken from her. During her hospital stay she did very little and felt quite blue. Her husband visited her daily in the evening during visiting hours, but she spoke very little to him. He brought her small gifts to improve her spirits, but she was not very interested in them. Neither the pediatrician nor the obstetrician expressed concern about her depressed feelings, apparently feeling that it was a natural aftermath of her pregnancy, and they would visit briefly checking on her physical welfare. She was routinely discharged on the fifth day, which happened to be an exceedingly busy day on the obstetrical service. The mother remembered that she and her husband needed to wait around for quite a while so that the discharge could be worked out, as the nurses were extremely involved in their many tasks. Finally, a harried nurse was able to give her final instructions and work out the details of her discharge. The father had tried rather desparately to get someone in to help out in the early days at home. He could find no one but was finally able to arrange to take a few days off from his work so that he could help out with his wife and daughter.

If we examine this portion of the history in the light of the previous discussion, it is possible to identify several factors which would have a negative bearing on the mother's perception of her infant. It would appear that the central issue was the geographical move of substantial proportions which took place early in the pregnancy. We are struck by the drastic nature of this move from the mother's point of view, and her need to adapt to an entirely new set of circumstances, which was difficult for her to do. We have certain evidence that she began to see her unborn infant as a solution to her loneliness, which, although there are positive aspects to this image, suggests a difficult role for the infant to play in the mother's life. Part of her anticipated solution to her uncertainty in her new role also seemed to involve the idea that her mother would be there to help her in the early days of her own experience as a mother. Hearing of the fact that her mother might not be available must have been a serious blow to her, and her reaction to the news of her father's illness may have had a bearing on the timing of her labor. Admittedly, this is strictly in the realm of speculation. Subsequent events surrounding the delivery clearly led to further decompensation of her capacity as a mother, as they could scarcely have been better designed to do so. Her recollection of her first view of her infant seems bizarre but could conceivably be a projection of her own need for a maternal figure at a moment of extremely intense disturbance. In any event, it becomes a matter of concern, as it would appear to reflect some measure of her distorted image of her infant at that particular point in time.

Having established certain tentative ideas regarding the mother's view of her child as part object, and certain outlines regarding her position as a potential object for the child to relate to, we can now turn to the features of the development of the infant within this framework. In developing this section of the history the intent is to collect raw data for later interpretation. Ideally, this raw data should consist of at least enough information to allow for a comprehensive view of the trends involved in the child's development, and sufficient accuracy to enable us to be reasonably secure in the conclusions we tentatively reach. Regarding the amount of data, it has been found useful to plan to establish cross-sectional views of the infant's typical behavior at intervals of four months during the first year, and six month intervals after that up to the age of three. These time slices do not need to be precise in their spacing but do allow useful points of departure to be established. A useful approach to obtaining the data is to have the mother describe a typical day in the infant's life at such nodal points. The principle of description is a helpful one to follow here as opposed to opinion on the part of the mother.

It is often of interest to see the divergence between the two when this method is followed. A mother might say, for example, that her baby was a good baby. In describing the baby's day, however, she might reveal that the baby spent long hours playing quietly in his crib, drank out of a propped bottle, and never cried. We then have a rather significant view of what a good baby is in the mother's estimate. Certainly a mother may be hard put to give an accurate description of her baby at the suggested intervals, as one period of time obviously merges into another. Here, asking the mother to select an important event in her life can often fix the time in her mind quite effectively, and there is every reason to suspect that the accuracy is increased in this way. Such a reference point may be a moving date; an important event in her family such as a marriage, birth, or death; a significant event in the child's life such as a hospitalization; the day he first took a step; or the day she came back from the hospital with his baby brother. Around such times, descriptions of the infant's and child's behavior can usually be quite adequately developed. It is also important at the same time to obtain a description of the mother's behavior in relation to the child as well.

Turning again to the case of Mary we can see how this works in practice.

> After their arrival home the mother fed Mary using the formula and bottles provided by the hospital. She regurgitated some of this bottle and continued to cry after the feeding period. She was placed in her crib, cried for about three quarters of an hour, and then seemed to fall into an exhausted sleep. She woke up again crying and because of the mother's seeming exhaustion, the father picked her up and she quieted down. As soon as he put her down however she would return to her crying. The mother fed her again in about three hours with much the same results as the first time with the

regurgitation and the restlessness continuing. The four days that the father was home were similar in this respect, although the mother feels that she seemed to gradually settle down some during this period. The mother described how she went about her duties mechanically without enthusiasm and continued to feel blue. The mother found it quite difficult to recall in any detail the first five months of Mary's life. She remembers, however, that her own list-lessness and lack of enthusiasm continued and Mary did not seem to thrive. She continued to regurgitate in spite of a number of formula changes instituted by the pediatrician. At around two months she developed colic, described by Mrs. S. as characterized by intense crying and pulling her legs up and seeming to be in great distress. The feedings continued to be at irregular intervals as was her sleeping; her weight gain, although rather slow, was quite steady. Her bath time was usually one of the more pleasant times that mother and child had together as the mother described Mary as relaxing when she was in the bath. Baths were less frequent, however, than would be the case with many infants, as the mother could not find the energy to give her a bath every day. I have described her care of Mary as varying considerably. She had no schedule that she could recall; some days she would spend a good deal of time with Mary, but the next day she would leave her alone, going to her only when she cried excessively, and then only briefly.

When Mary was about five months old the mother got word that an uncle had died. Although she had no close connection with this uncle, as she had little to do with him and had only met him on one or two occasions, the event did help to focus her thoughts in time. She could recall that at that point Mary's day had changed very little in general outlines; her feedings remained irregular, and the mother had resorted increasingly to propping the bottle, which Mary accepted with very little protest and seeming relief. She would lie in her crib sucking on her bottle, and the mother felt that Mary seemed to prefer this method of feeding rather than being held, as at such time she became tense and quite squirmy when she tried to feed her. It was around this time too that she started to introduce solid foods into Mary's diet, using pablum and strained vegetables on the advice of the pediatrician. Mary, when offered a spoonful of such material would spit it out, cry loudly, and become rigid. The mother would repeat the process of introducing the food several times during the course of the day with the same response. After two or three days she would give it up but return to it a week or two later, and only very gradually did Mary come to accept the solid food and then not with relish. She does not recall her smiling at all. The father continued to take care of her to some degree on the days that he was home but his ministrations were less effective than they had been earlier, although the mother felt that the father was more effective in caring for Mary than she was. She was unable, however, to document this difference very clearly. Her colic had diminished considerably at this time, but she was still subject to periods when it would recur. Physically she developed to some degree and although her weight gain was satisfactory according to the pediatrician, the mother felt that her gain was rather slow. Although a restless, active baby in her crib, she held her head up in a wobbling kind of way, and as far as the mother could remember made no attempts at rolling over.

When Mary was nine months of age, another event of some significance occurred. This involved a visit from a friend from her home town who was passing through. This marked her first actual contact with anyone from her old neighborhood since Mary's birth. She had lunch with this friend and they spent the afternoon together. They discussed in detail the various events in her home town and Mrs. S. felt more stimulated than she had been in several months. She was rather startled to recall that, although her friend discussed her own child at great length and in considerable detail, she herself had said very little about Mary. Finally, near the end of the visit, her friend did ask about Mary and her recollection was that she was almost casual in her response. This event seemed to mark the beginning of the lifting of Mrs. S.'s depression, and she saw it herself as a turning point. Again this served as a focusing point in her memory, and her description of Mary indicated significant changes in her behavior. The colic had virtually disappeared by this time and physically she was progressing reasonably well; although the mother thought of her as rather thin, she also described her as being wiry and well muscled. The fussiness had greatly diminished, but she remained tense and full of restless energy. She seldom cried but had an expression that was serious and bewildered. In the morning she was content to stay by herself in her crib, playing with a small rubber toy which her father had given to her a couple of months before. When her mother dressed her she would be stiff and tense. She was on a limited number of solid foods, which had been gradually introduced over the months, and she preferred to feed herself with her hands, a highly messy procedure which the mother found quite repulsive. The mother tried to wean her at this point, which Mary strongly resisted, and it was not until 18 months that Mrs. S. was finally able to take the bottle away. She did drink from a cup, which was also a very messy procedure. Her toileting habits showed no regularity at all at this point.

After breakfast she was placed in a playpen where she was quite content to stay by herself and became absorbed in some small toy, which she would turn over and over and occasionally grasp with a hard grip; at other times she would suck on it with a kind of dreamy expression on her face. If a stranger happened to walk in and approach Mary, she would react almost in panic, move to the extreme corner of the playpen, and attempt to hide by pulling herself into a kind of a ball. Her sleep pattern continued to be irregular; she would fall asleep in her playpen from time to time during the course of the day and at night would frequently wake up, get on her hands and knees, and rock, banging her head at the same time. The mother, for the most part, left her to her own devices as she seemed more comfortable when that was done. She was also beginning to show signs of attempting locomotion, as she hitched herself awkwardly around the playpen and seemed to be trying to pull herself up. She was doing some crawling but in a kind of crab-like fashion—she moved herself partially sideways. The mother also reported during this nine-month period that Mary had frequent upper-respiratory infections with high fever, which responded quite rapidly to penicillin without after effects.

At a little over a year of age Mary had taught herself how to walk. She tended to walk on her toes; the mother described it as a kind of bird-like, hurried walk from the beginning. By this time the mother's depression had cleared considerably, if not entirely, and she turned her attention more fully to Mary. She decided then to try toilet training, got a potty-chair for her, and went about this procedure with some vigor. Mary's reaction to being put on the potty-chair was to stiffen, shriek loudly, and get off as quickly as possible. The mother persisted in her efforts for some 20 minutes or so, but when Mary continued with her resistive behavior she gave it up after a few days. After she became fully mobile, Mary began to get into various things in the living room, often destroying favorite objects which the mother had displayed there. The mother attempted to control this behavior by scolding, hand slapping, and spanking, all of which was ineffective; Mary seemed hardly to notice her mother's punishment and would return almost at once to her destructive behavior. The father tried a different tack of attempting to divert her, which was equally ineffective, as she would respond momentarily to the father's attempts only to go back again to her previous preoccupation. The mother tried to bring her concerns to the pediatrician who, because of his busy practice, could spend only a brief time with her. He tried to reassure her and to say that Mary would grow out of it and ordered a sedative to try to decrease Mary's tension. This had no particular effect on Mary as far as the mother could see.

By subsequent descriptions of time slices in Mary's life at 18 months and two years of age, the mother indicated very little change in Mary's behavior. She remained resistant to toilet training and the remainder of her functions remained very much the same. She did grow physically, again not rapidly. A little after she was two years of age, the family decided to move to their own dwelling. The hope was that with somewhat more space Mary would be able to develop better than she had in the rather confined quarters existing in their apartment. They moved to a row house in a suburb of Philadelphia where they had a small yard and a park nearby. Both parents were greatly disturbed by Mary's reaction to this move, as she cried almost continuously for the first three days. The mother described this crying as not the usual cry of a child in pain or in need, but more of a kind of screaming cry without tears. She stayed close to her crib, often climbing into it and seeming more settled than she was anyplace else. She resisted very strongly being put in the back yard, which was enclosed, but the mother felt that this was not really a wish on Mary's part to stay in but much more of an avoidance of a new situation. Several days after they had moved in, the mother found that she was able to keep Mary occupied by putting her in the back yard with a basin of water in which Mary would splash with her hand, seemingly without purpose, for as long as the mother would allow her to do it. They also discovered that Mary was quite pleased with the record player which they had gotten her about the time of the move, and she began to be involved with music at that point. The move also occasioned a need for a change of pediatricians; because of the failure of the move to do anything substantial, the mother began to talk more fully about her concerns with her pediatrician, who recognised the serious nature of the situation and subsequently referred them for psychiatric help. The main symptom that the mother brought to the attention of the pediatrician was Mary's failure to develop speech.

Whatever the inaccuracies of the history, it would appear that we have sufficient information to demonstrate developmental trends. As a starting point, it is of interest to turn to the work of Chess and Birch(2) and their studies of infant behavior. Through some very careful research work they have established nine categories of behavior within which specific behaviors of infants can be placed. These categories are:

1. Active versus passive.
2. Regular versus irregular in biological function.
3. Positive versus negative prevailing mood.
4. High versus low intensity of response.
5. High versus low threshold of response.
6. Approach versus withdrawal.
7. Adaptable versus nonadaptable.
8. High versus low distractibility.
9. Long versus short persistence and attention span.

They have been able to demonstrate that when a large sample of descriptions of an infant's behavior are rated on a 3-point scale, clustering shows up by six months of age. Later observations indicate that such behavioral characteristics continue in time and apparently form a basic aspect of the temperament of the individual child. They offer no opinion regarding the inherent versus environmental contribution to the origins of these behaviors, although they do lean in the direction of feeling that these characteristics are related to innate aspects of the infant.

The history as outlined does not lend itself to a strictly scientific approach to the categorization of these behaviors, as insufficient information is available to be absolutely sure. It would appear, however, that Mary could be tentatively classified as at least moderately active, highly irregular in her biological functioning in terms of eating, sleeping and toileting. She shows a consistently negative mood with no evidence of any positive displays. Her vociferous protests suggest a high intensity of response. Certainly her response to certain stimuli—for example, new people—leads to a suspicion of an unusually sensitive child with a low threshold of response. Her withdrawal from people and new experience is strongly in evidence. Her adaptation to new experience—for example, new foods—is extremely slow. She is not easily distracted when moved to involve herself with something, as suggested by her father's inability to distract her. Her persistence is high when it comes to certain inanimate objects, but very low when it comes to paying attention to people.

Although we have no ready explanation for the origins of these behavioral reactions, we are struck with the possibility that the combination of conscious and unconscious components operating within the mother in the early days of her care of her infant could have contributed markedly to the infant's patterning of response. Her inconsistency of approach, her negative expectations of the infant, her periods of withdrawal from her, and her absorption in her own desperate concerns could explain, at least in part, the infant's organizational trend and patterning.

In any event, it would appear that by six months of age a very serious degree of alienation existed between mother and infant. The infant's behavior was of such difficulty as to be hard for any mother to respond to, and this mother had even greater difficulty than most. The father's apparently greater success with the infant served only to add to the problem, in view of his inability to sustain the relationship and the possibility that it might well have served to lead the mother to feel even worse about her capacity as a mother.

At nine months, as the result of further growth on the part of the infant and the mother beginning to find some restitution of her decompensated ego, we see a further stage of the disturbing trend. It would appear that at this point the withdrawal from each other became almost complete. They continued to have a degree of interaction with each other after that which was virtually entirely negative. Another point should be noted; namely, that frequent infections were described which responded readily to penicillin. It is interesting to speculate whether, prior to the days of antibiotics, children such as Mary were particularly vulnerable to uncontrollable infection, resulting in a high rate of infant deaths among such children.

Accumulation of raw data such as that described could add much to our knowledge of the origins of psychosis in children. Obviously one case cannot explain all cases, and the question of nature versus nurture remains basically unanswered. We get a glimpse, however, of the vast number of contributing factors which appear to have a bearing on the origins of such a child. The end product of the difficulty, whatever the origins would appear to be, is the inability of the infant to relate adaptively and effectively to new inner and outer events in its life. This incapacity seems also related to an inability to find a warm connection with the maternal object, which has a considerable bearing on the child's relation to new experience in his life. Perhaps in time it will be possible to elucidate these matters more precisely as a result of data collection such as that described and the longitudinal studies being conducted in many centers in the nation.

Mother's Developmental Background

Before leaving the subject we need to examine the question of why this mother was specifically vulnerable to the events which took place during her pregnancy and delivery. Here we can turn to the next section of the history which considers the mother's own developmental background. Here again we rely on description of events and certain cross-sectional nodal points in the mother's life. This will include a spontaneous description of her memories of her parents when she was a child, her first day of school, her performance and behavior in grade school, the day her periods started, subsequent dating in high school as well as performance and behavior, her graduation from high school, the day she had her first job (if any), subsequent work record, her meeting with her husband, courtship, and the course of her marriage. Significant events between specific nodal points usually show up rather naturally. Within this context Mary's mother produced the following story.

She was the oldest of four children, having two younger brothers, 2 and 4 years younger, between her and the youngest child, a girl, who was 13 years her junior. She described her mother as devoted but tense and talkative; her father as warm but rather dreamy, an adequate provider but never considered a great success in his hardware business. Her earliest recollection was of being sick around three or four, but she does not recall the nature of her illness. One night she began to have difficulty breathing. She tried to call her mother but couldn't and vaguely remembers a sense of panic. Her mother finally heard her breathing and came to her. She recalled her first day of school vividly and in detail. She started in kindergarten and her mother took her. She became frightened when they approached the school and began to cry when she got in the door. Her teacher seemed much larger than her mother, wore glasses, and her hair was slightly disheveled; this teacher took her by the hand and suggested that her mother leave, which she did very shortly. After her mother left she bit the teacher on the thumb, to which the teacher responded with a sharp slap. She doesn't know exactly what happened after this except that she remained frightened and remote from the teacher for the rest of the year. When her mother heard of this event she gave her a worried lecture about it, and she recalls promising her mother she wouldn't do it again. Many mornings she resisted going to school and her mother frequently took her to the door of the school but no further. She was never particularly good as a student in grammar school, describing herself as shy and seldom offering much in class; she was seldom asked to recite. Her menstrual periods started shortly after her 11th birthday. She discovered the effects of her menstrual flow at school while in the bathroom during recess. She was dreadfully concerned but said nothing about it during the rest of the school day. She ran home, broke down and cried, blurting out her story to her mother, fearing that she was seriously ill. Her mother, who had said nothing to her about the event prior to its onset, gave her a confused explanation which she remembers only vaguely. She was able to gain some comfort from what her mother said, however, in terms of an understanding that it was not an illness, that it would occur every month. She felt better when she was provided with the hygienic supplies. The significance of what was happening, however, she either did not take in or it was not adequately explained to her.

When she was 13 her younger sister was born. Her mother's pregnancy was not a topic of conversation, and although she was aware of her mother's condition she never dared ask about it, feeling that her mother was embarrassed by it. She also noted that her mother was more irritable during her pregnancy than usual, showing fits of temper which she would quickly cover up. This child had a congenital heart defect of a serious and uncorrectable nature, along with considerable retardation. Our mother became devoted to the child and would often rush home to care for her. Her own mother had apparently almost less to do with this child than Mrs. S. did. One day when the younger child was around three, she came home as usual to find her sister and mother absent. She learned from her brother that they had gone to the hospital and later learned that the child had died. She found it difficult to concentrate on her school work and took little interest in her life for some time after this event. Her mother appeared cold, distant, and preoccupied during this period and they talked not at all about the death which involved them both so intimately.

It was during this period of her adolescence that she gradually became aware of her future husband who lived next door. After her sister's death they began to date occasionally, going to the local high school dances together apparently as an aspect of convenience rather than attraction. As she emerged from her depression during her subsequent high school experience, she appreciated his attention as she had few other dates, being shy and, in her own estimate, not too attractive.

After graduation from high school she took a secretarial position in the local industrial firm, a branch factory of a large complex. She remembers her first day on the job as being very difficult; she felt lonely and bewildered, and as if all her skills had left her. She gradually became accustomed to her job and said it was one of the happiest times of her life. Her husband worked for the same company, first as a stock boy, and then gradually working himself up in the different capacities. After they had both worked for about a year and a half, their dating became more serious and after a brief engagement they were married. It was his anticipation of further advancement which allowed them to speak of marriage. She was hard put to identify any special qualities about him that she particularly liked except that he had been good to her, helped her to get over her depression, and it seemed somehow inevitable to her that they would get married. The marriage was approved by both of her parents as well as his. The wedding was small. She described him as an ordinary man, interested in his family but having few interests of his own other than his work. As mentioned before, shortly after this marriage they moved to Philadelphia as a result of the training program with which he was involved.

Their sexual life was not a source of great concern either to her or her husband, according to her. Although she had never reached orgasm, this did not appear to be a matter of great moment to her. In general, she described herself as quite passive in this role but never denied her husband's wishes except during her periods. He was not very aggressive in this area and his demands were not great.

Although the history of Mary's mother can be interpreted in many ways, according to a variety of theories, in terms of the question originally asked, concerning her specific vulnerability, certain themes appear to be recurrent. What seems apparent is that at each point of crisis—going to school, the onset of her periods, and the death of her sister—she reacted with a sense of abandonment, and we begin to get early signs of a depressive position, if not a depressive reaction, at each of these nodal points in her life.

It would appear, then, that the maternal contribution to Mary's difficulties was the result of a combination of her own past experience and the specificity of events which occurred during her pregnancy and delivery. It is a difficult matter to say whether, with a different background, Mary's mother could have weathered the experiences she encountered more successfully. Likewise, we cannot say with assurance that given more favorable circumstances during her pregnancy and delivery, her success as a mother would have been guaranteed. Nor can we say that if Mary had been a different kind of child things would have proceeded more satisfactorily. It would seem, however, that the combination of background, contingency, and innate factors in the child each contributed substantially but in unknown proportions to the disaster of Mary's development.

Father's Developmental Background

The contribution of the father to the development of children showing severe autistic features is more difficult to discern and therefore not easy to describe. This is reflected in the literature which, with the exception of Eisenberg's descriptions of fathers of such children, is notably lacking in this respect. The reason for this is not hard to understand in view of the fact that the father's role is not psychobiologically determined and socially developed as is the mother's, but rather emerges completely out of psychological and social factors. In other words, the role is much more what he chooses it to be as a result of his own development and his perceptions of his wife, infant, and himself, than the mother's role which is virtually forced upon her by biological circumstances. This means that the father's contribution needs to be examined in terms of the nature of the support he is capable of providing during the mother's critical pregnancy and postnatal periods. Eisenberg(3) has presented vivid examples of fathers who were incapable of giving emotional support to their wives as a result of their own emotionally barren beginnings. Characteristically they appear in his series as cold, aloof, and distant without substantial interest in their family life. Although this type of father is certainly not uncommon in the author's experience, this profile does not appear to be true in all cases of autistic children, by any means.

If we turn to the experiences of Mary's father we find his descriptions of Mary essentially similar to the mother's but less detailed, apparently as a result of his spending less time with her than her mother. In recounting his own recollections of Mary's beginnings, he remembered being vaguely apprehensive at the time his wife announced that she was pregnant. He was concerned about their financial situation which, although promising at the time, he regarded as precarious, realizing that if for any reason he lost his job, the special nature of his training would make it difficult for him to get another one of equal value. In addition to this, the fact that his wife stopped working when they moved to Philadelphia meant some loss of income to them. In his early days in Philadelphia he found the work difficult and thought of himself as something of an outsider in his department where he was the newcomer. He described how, when he met with new customers, he would speak too rapidly, his heart would pound, and he would often sweat profusely. He felt lonely on his road trips, would go to a movie or try to read at night, but found that neither occupation gave him any satisfaction. He looked forward to going home but discovered it difficult to talk to his wife. He would try to tell her about his work but she did not appear to be related to it, and he recalled feeling vaguely dissatisfied with her seeming lack of support. He recognized his wife's loneliness as being rather similar to his own but felt there was little he could do about it. He was not greatly concerned about his wife's pregnancy itself but asked about it from time to time, more as a topic of mild conversation than an expression of concern. At the point that word came that his mother-in-law would not be coming to help out with the new infant, he reported that he was sympathetic with his wife but at the same time secretly pleased, as he had not looked forward to her joining the household during that period. He made no attempt at working out other arrangements, as he worked out some vacation time with his company to coincide with the expected date of delivery. When his wife delivered he was on a business trip, as already mentioned. On this trip he suddenly began to feel much better. He was far less anxious, his business contacts led to several good sales, and he was invited to the home of one of his customers for the evening, which he reported enjoying. When word finally reached him that his wife had delivered, the news fitted his new mood of confidence, and passing out cigars to the people with whom he was in contact at the time seemed to him to deepen the sense of camaraderie that he felt.

On his return he was as eager to share his sense of well-being as he was to see his wife and daughter. He recalled being mildly distressed by his wife's seeming aloofness when he shared his good fortune, but attributed this to her having delivered a short time before. When she recounted what she had been through prior to and after her arrival at the hospital, he remembered forcing a sympathetic response but found it impossible to relate himself to what had happened. The fact that the doctor reassured him regarding the health of his wife and infant allowed him to continue his confident mood. The following day, after his return, this confident mood began to dissipate as he was faced with a new set of circumstances. This involved the fact that the time off which he had arranged did not now coincide with his wife's return from the hospital, and arranging a new time did not coincide with his company's plans. He tried desperately to get someone to help out by calling several agencies which were in charge of practical nurses, but none were available. Finally, he appealed to his superior who grudgingly allowed him two extra days which, added to the weekend, gave him a total of four days with his wife. He remembered being vaguely annoyed with his wife for putting him in this position but buried the feeling quickly.

The four days he was home were far from pleasurable for Mr. S. His wife's exhaustion and listlessness, and Mary's crying and restlessness, led him to undertake duties with which he was unfamiliar. The housework and formula making he did not like, but feeding and diapering Mary he enjoyed, and reported being secretly pleased by his ability to quiet her down when she was being fed a few times during the four-day period. He was relieved to return to work but remained concerned about his daughter's failure to thrive and his wife's difficulty in performing her duties. When he was home he often took over Mary's care, but not on any regular basis; his frequent business trips interrupted further any consistent pattern of care that he might have undertaken.

As time went on his wife's pleas that he be home more to help her out with Mary became more urgent, so that he requested a transfer within his company when Mary was about six months old. He did this with some reluctance as he knew that it would require starting over to some degree, and advancement would not be as rapid although his income would be about the same. The transfer was granted a month later, but in spite of his being home more in the evening he noted no startling change in his wife and child. In spite of his being home he found himself taking on less of the care of Mary, who by this time was fast becoming an even more difficult infant to care for. At the same time he found his new job duties far less satisfying than his old ones, as they involved the filling out of tax forms which were highly complicated and required considerable research to do correctly.

Following this series of events his life seemed to settle into a routinized affair. In his work he continued to do an adequate job. He had regular advances in salary but without substantial changes in duties. His relations with his wife improved somewhat after she recovered from her depression. He continued to be concerned by his daughter's seeming lack of progress but seldom thought about it consciously, feeling that she would "grow out of it soon." His concern began to be more urgent towards the end of her second year, particularly when she failed to develop speech. At this point he tried to do more with her, trying to get her to speak and to make her follow directions. When his efforts were to no avail he would often spank her at times harder than he expected, and he would feel guilty afterwards. As far as the father was concerned, it was essentially this situation that prevailed at the time they were referred for professional service.

The father's background was as follows. He was the youngest of three children having an older brother, six years older, and a sister, five years older. He described his mother as a tense person who demanded conformity from her children but did not seem to him to be vitally interested in their affairs. His father was a minor executive in the company Mr. S. worked for. He was described as not very ambitious, but a steady worker who made an adequate but not luxurious income. He did not recall his first day of school but described himself as an average student. In high school he played on the basketball team but was not a star. His marks continued in the average range and he had a small circle of friends. It was from these friends that he learned about sexual matters, which he found vaguely disturbing, but he did not dare discuss them with his father nor did the latter offer any information to him. He was shy in his relations with girls and did not date individually until his senior year when he began to take Mrs. S. out to the school dances. He was attracted by her shyness and undemanding nature, and the fact that she lived next door made it easier for him to date her. He started work after high school as already mentioned, and stated he was a steady worker. He was pleased with his progress and the fact that he was picked for training in the sales department. He felt he gained confidence in this experience and enjoyed the independence that his salary gave him. Along with this increased confidence he began to date his wife more frequently, and finally asked her to marry him shortly after he learned that he would be joining the sales department. His view of the marriage was somewhat different from what his wife described. Initially he had been quite pleased by her passivity, but as time went on he found her lack of responsiveness bothersome and her quiet demand irritating. Because of the difficulties she was having with Mary he considered her responses explainable and said little about the way he felt. In the sexual area he considered her as somehow nonparticipating and although vaguely dissatisfied with this aspect of his life, denied any infidelity.

In reviewing the father's contribution to Mary's difficulty, we are again struck with the number of facets involved both from his own background and the sequence of events which unfolded in relation to Mary's beginnings and early infancy. If he had been a stronger man with a more sure masculine identity, would he have been more capable of dealing with the situation at hand? If he had been more available as a substitute mother during Mary's early infancy, would this have been enough to help her through a period of her mother's unavailability? These and many other questions can be asked concerning his contribution but as yet we have no way of sorting out the tangled skein of events and personalities which lead to such developmental disasters as exhibited by Mary.

Physical and Neurological Studies

We need to recognize that the history alone cannot provide us with the definitive diagnostic answers but only provide us with some extremely useful hints as to the basic nature of the situation, to provide avenues for further exploration. Certainly thorough physical and neurological studies should be done with a child like Mary, but often the results are confusing and difficult to interpret. In Mary's case, for example, the general physical examination showed no significant findings, as was true of laboratory studies of a routine nature. A neurological exam, however, showed several equivocal signs—for example, possibly overactive deep tendon reflexes, a possibly positive Babinski on the left side, and a suggestion of weakness in the left arm. Skull X-rays were negative, and an EEG showed a diffuse dysrhythmia of a nonspecific nature. Formal psychological testing could not be done; the psychologist confirmed the autistic behavior that the child was showing but could not offer an estimate regarding the child's basic intellectual capacity. Such findings are typical for this group of children and unfortunately leave us unclear about these areas.

Psychiatric Examination of Child

A psychiatric interview revealed a rather small girl who was moderately well nourished. Her clothes were of good quality but had food stains on them, and her hair was rumpled, giving a general air of untidiness. She moved about the room freely and with quick darting motions. Her face was pretty but her eyes were expressionless and never seemed to take in the psychiatrist at all. Her vocalizations consisted of grunts, peculiar whining sounds, and occasionally a high-pitched kind of a cry. She seemed generally tense, as shown by the apparent hypertonicity of her musculature and her tendency to grind her teeth during the hour. For the most part she did nothing with the various play materials available except handle one or two of the blocks quite aimlessly. The nearest she came to recognizing the presence of the therapist was when he constructed a small tower of blocks with his back towards Mary. Observers who were watching the interview through a one-way-vision screen remarked that at this point Mary seemed to make a deliberate effort to see what the pist was doing, which required some degree of effort on her part to see around him. It was their feeling that Mary's subsequent act of knocking down the tower of blocks seemed quite deliberate. At the end of the hour she stopped at the top of the stairs and made her peculiar crying noise, making no move to go down. At this point the therapist picked her up and carried her. At first she was stiff in his arms and then seemed to relax to some degree.

TREATMENT ASPECTS

If we acknowledge that the development of children such as Mary, with severe autistic features, is the result of a great many different interacting factors, we need also to acknowledge that the end product, even at an early age, presents a formidable task of intervention. From the point of view of Mary's life span, we can see that the origins of her disorder date back to her earliest beginnings, and at the time of the evaluation her difficulties pervade every area of her life: her learning, her relationships with her parents and other children, as well as her self-care activities. In our experience, the treatment of such children has not been rewarding and it seemed pointless to offer the type of service which ordinarily exists in a child guidance clinic or private practice. As a result, what follows describes an idealized service which has never existed but hopefully may be tried some day. It is actually an extension of the author's experience with a small nursery-school program designed as an adjunct to the treatment of severely disturbed young children and operated within the framework of the Philadelphia Child Guidance Clinic. This program continued over a three-year period, terminating when a number of insurmountable problems involving transportation, financing, and staffing were encountered. During this period we felt that several valuable lessons were learned, and certain areas of expansion were suggested which could lead to more effective service being rendered. Even under the best possible service arrangements, the prognosis of a child such as Mary must remain extremely guarded and the chances seem exceedingly slim that her institutionalization at an early age can be avoided. At present we simply do not know at what age a child becomes no longer capable of forming affectional ties with people, particularly when we are not sure whether the capacity existed in the first place.

In designing an appropriate service we are confronted with three essential questions: (1) What should the service hope to accomplish? (2) What should it consist of in the way of staff and facilities? (3) What factors are involved in the timing and implementation of the service? If we consider the case of Mary as a prototype, it is possible to answer these questions with at least some degree of rationale. In general, the answers would not be exactly the same in other cases, but the differences would lie primarily in timing rather than in service design or staffing.

Objectives

As a first requirement the service would need to offer the opportunity to the child to develop emotional ties. If these can be developed by the child, the next step involves the use of these ties for the purpose of developing self-other differentiation and various ego skills.

For the mother, it would need to provide a sufficient relief from the overwhelming burden of being a mother to her child, but at the same time not allow her to abandon the role altogether. It should help in re-creating the elements involved in her previous crisis situations, but at the same time provide the supports which had been missing at the time these critical events in her life took place. This would hopefully lead to a more satisfactory crisis outcome with increased capacities to cope with the various aspects of her life, particularly as centered in her maternal role.

The father requires a service which is indirectly related to his parental role and primarily focused on his job difficulties. The reason for this focus is that in many of the fathers of disturbed children we have seen, we have noted that he has taken on a pseudomaternal role as a result of the mother's desperation, to his own detriment. As a general rule we feel that if the father is basically satisfied in his work, he can take on his family responsibilities much more adequately. We do not advocate that this be an exclusive focus but rather a matter which needs particular attention. In the case of Mary's father, for example, the question of his reapplying for a job in the sales department might be a matter of exploration, in itself as well as its implications for his family.

Staff and Facilities

In developing a service pattern to achieve these goals we need to consider several questions. Should it be an inpatient or an outpatient service? What personnel should be involved and in what ratio? What auxiliary services should be considered and under whose auspices? Many people would advocate an inpatient service as most suitable for this type of problem. Although such a service offers certain potential advantages, such as total control of the child's environment and complete separation of child and parents, there are disadvantages which need to be considered. Among these are that with a child of this age most parents find it extremely difficult to countenance such a total separation. In those instances where the mother was prepared to use such a service, we would be concerned about her readiness to abandon her child. This would in turn lead us to question whether such a mother would be capable of taking on the care of her child at a later date if improvements began to show up in the child. In such cases, it would seem more appropriate to consider the inclusion of foster parents to work with the inpatient service, or possibly an outpatient service if his eventual restoration to society is to be considered. This would avoid the child becoming a ward of the institution for all intents and purposes, which would greatly complicate his discharge if this were to become a practical matter. At a later age, six or seven, for example, institutional care becomes a more feasible plan if treatment is to be attempted, primarily because containment in the community becomes almost impossible and parents are far readier to consider such a plan realistically, rather than as an essentially magical solution to their difficulties.

The more common pattern of service for the three-year-old child involves a nursery-school program as an adjunct to the regular therapeutic services of a child guidance clinic. Ideally, such a program should operate on a five-day-a-week basis from 9:30 A.M. to midafternoon. This period of time would appear necessary to achieve the goal of adequate relief for the mother, and to offer the child a time span long enough for him to use the service if he can. There are certain practical questions which need to be considered in establishing such a program. Transportation is in many instances a serious matter, as the geographical distribution of referral is usually quite wide. Public transportation, particularly if the family lives at some distance from the facility, is all too often such a difficult matter that it does not lead to any degree of relief for the mother. If the father undertakes the transportation, as he may well do in certain instances, it may interfere with his job and thus undermine the goals set for him. Under the circumstances, a volunteer driver program can help greatly in getting the child and mother to the facility. In this respect, the 9:30 starting time is suggested to accommodate the driver, as well as to make the situation less harried for the mother. This is particularly important if there are other children in the family who need to go to regular schools. As to the size of the group, it is important to keep it relatively small. A group of six would appear to be the ideal number, with a staff ratio of one adult to two children. Their extreme isolation makes a larger group increasingly unmanageable; enlarging the staff makes staff integration more difficult.

The core therapeutic staff should consist of a child psychiatrist, social worker, and nursery-school teacher. This core group should be highly compatible, with clear and positive identifications with their own professional roles. The social worker and the psychiatrist should have considerable collaborative experience behind them so that communications between them are easy and flexible. The nursery-school teacher is usually the new member of the team and may require a year or so before she can become an integral part of the team. As adjunctive personnel, the nursery-school teacher should have two untrained aides with demonstrated interest in children. If possible, these aides should be different in character, one docile in temperament and the other more stimulating. The aides would be primarily responsible to the teacher. The social worker should have at her disposal a competent homemaker to be used at points of considerable stress in the family, such as illness requiring hospitalization, when the mother is feeling unusually anxious, or when other circumstances arise which indicate that additional support would be useful. An arrangement can at times be made with a local family agency to supply such a person, but there would appear to be advantages in having such a person directly under the control of the helping resource, to avoid administrative and supervisory complications when two agencies are involved.

Other adjunctive personnel who should be available would include the psychologist, pediatrician, and neurologist. The psychologist would not operate in the framework of his usual clinical testing role but rather in a research capacity. To do this he would have two essential responsibilities. First would be to explore methods of determing the contribution of various factors to the origin of the psychotic disorder, and which factors are involved in the changes in the child's behavior. To undertake this, he would need a sympathy with, and understanding of, the program and would need to be positively related to the personnel involved. At the same time, he would need a degree of objectivity in relation to the situation and adequate training in the various research tools now available, such as factor analysis and computer programming. His second area of responsibility would involve devising tests applicable to the unusual nature of these children, to allow at least some estimate of their basic intellectual capacity. This might involve tests which would not require interpersonal relationships for their administration but would rather be based on other aspects of motivation, such as the child's interest in material things.

A pediatrician associated with the facility and located nearby can be of considerable advantage. His availability for emergencies such as falls, the appearance of rashes, unexplained fevers, and so on can keep lines of responsibility clear and avoid the confusions which can arise if the psychiatrist undertakes such functions. He can also be useful in interpreting the complicated medical findings which may be involved in the child's history, or reports from other medical sources. It is important that this person be an integrated part of the program, as we have often noted that parents at the point of anxiety associated with internal change may look for a "medical out" by seeking an organic explanation for the child's behavior. Skillful and honest handling of such questions can be highly supportive of the parents at such times, whereas equivocal responses on the part of the pediatrician may halt the process of change and set back progress for a long period of time. This is equally true of the child neurologist, if not even more so. The not infrequent occurrence of "soft signs" and vaguely abnormal EEG tracings are difficult to interpret in their own right, and even more difficult to convey to parents in a way which is both honest and constructive in terms of the helping program.

The establishment and continuation of such a total therapeutic team is obviously not a simple matter. The cost is high and even at best its effectiveness uncertain. The shortages of personnel in general does not often allow for selection to be based on the appropriateness of a particular person to fill a position but rather on availability, if the position is to be filled at all. A weak link can disrupt the entire program. Even if the team can be adequately formed, there is the constant possibility of its becoming disrupted through illness or resignation, which again can disrupt its functioning.

In addition to these intramural considerations, the availability of certain extramural facilities with adequate liaison would be useful. A normal nursery school, particularly one using the initial contact interview as part of their regular procedure, could be helpful in early case-finding for the special nursery-school facility and serve as a basic training ground for teachers who might later join the therapeutic team. In addition to this, if a child showed some improvement, his inclusion in a "normal" nursery school could serve a useful purpose of "staging" by helping the child to meet more age-appropriate conditions. An inpatient facility which could house the child for brief periods of time without necessarily losing continuity or providing a formal therapeutic setting would permit further flexibility under certain conditions—for example, if the parents were suddenly called out of town on a family emergency and no homemaker was available. An adult hospital facility is sometimes necessary if one of the parents breaks down with a psychotic reaction, or hospitalization might be useful as a way of breaking up a particular kind of therapeutic impasse. In certain situations, for example, a mother will invest a psychotic part of herself in the child as part of her own means of maintaining organization. If the child improves, the mother may emerge with a psychotic reaction which may require the additional support of a hospital experience during the acute phase.

Implementation of the Service

Having described an idealized service model for the potential treatment of autistic children, it becomes possible to outline in broad principle, at least, how such a service model could potentially be used. Obviously this cannot be by prescription because of the complexities involved, but this does not mean that we need to approach the matter chaotically. As a starting point, it can be said that essentially we are introducing a family system into a service system. By system is meant the intricate combination of self-other perceptions which exist within an organized group, whether it is a family, a social organization of any type, or the service organization described. The behavioral reactions exhibited by each individual have their effect on the total system, and its various parts. In most social organizations there are stated rules which govern behavior to some extent, at least allowing for a functioning structure to be established. In a family there are rules as well, but with the possible exception of perhaps some highly unusual families, they do not operate under any stated "bylaws." As a result, the operational rules established by a family system are a product of an intricate process involving individual backgrounds of parents, mutual experiences in early marriage, contingency factors, critical periods, the individual temperaments of children born to the couple, as well as many other matters. Haley(5) has brought this matter out in interesting fashion. Since a family makes up its own rules as it goes along, so to speak, it is not surprising that many rules it makes are unworkable or detrimental to the development of the individual members. As a related matter, it can be said that it would appear that the more complex the society, the more difficult it becomes for a family to find precedents for the rules they establish. The reason for this is that in a primitive hunting society, for example, biological differences between men and women establish the basis for survival, and these differences form the basis for rule making. In a highly industrialized society, this becomes more complicated in that biological differences do not have as much to do with survival matters, so that a vast percentage of the jobs available can be done at least as well by women as by men. Sexual activity and child bearing (not necessarily child rearing), then become the fundamental differentiating points between men and women.

Likewise the clinic team needs to operate under a system of rules which are not easy to determine or to develop. For example, the concepts of case work and psychotherapy suggest a useful differentiation between the functions of social worker and psychiatrist, but in practice the designation often becomes arbitrary and the difference obscure. This can often lead to considerable collaborative complications. Likewise we are faced with the question of the contribution of the nursery-school teacher and how, with this age group, it is to be distinguished from a minor form of psychotherapy. This is particularly difficult with seriously disturbed children when the formalized concept implied in the word "school" is hardly applicable with such children. As an approach to these difficulties, the author has found that certain definitions of roles can be useful in this respect. For the social worker, the point of differentiation is not in terms of depth of relationship, unconscious material, or degree of pathology, but rests in the focus implicitly defined in the purpose for which the person is being seen. In this case it is the parent as parent. It is clear that the role of parent, being as involved as it is, actually includes every facet of the person's being either directly or indirectly. Although emphasizing such a focus may seem arbitrary and unnatural to many, it can actually resolve many a dilemma of collaboration. The nursery-school teacher's position is more difficult to define this way, as it involves a potentiality rather than an immediate actuality. Thus her approach needs to be in terms of defining in what way the child's attitude is not commensurate with learning, and watching for signs of change in this respect. The reason for adding two more professional aides to the nursery school is to center the care aspects of the child with them and to provide a range of personnel to which the child may relate.

In such a system, the psychiatrist has several responsibilities. As the leader of the team he needs to be constantly informed about the work of the various participants in the endeavor. In this position he can help in the clarification of communications and participate in the development of rule making. To accomplish these purposes he needs to conduct frequent meetings of the core members of the team with the research psychologist in attendance as observer. These meetings involve reports of behavior (communication) and timing of strategy (rule making). The psychiatrist as the child's therapist has an intricate role. When and where to see the child, for what purpose, and under what circumstances, seem like minor considerations but actually involve subtle matters involving the total system. No specific rules can be given for this but the number of choices available allow for great flexibility. For example, the child may be seen with the mother or without her, in the psychiatrist's office, or in the nursery-school room. He may be seen daily, weekly, or not at all. He can be seen for a clearly defined purpose or one which may be obscure. In any event, what is done or not done will have its effect on the family as well as the clinic system, an effect which may be infinitesimal or profound. The psychiatrist should also be in a position to see the parents together or separately under different conditions. For example, he might see the father alone to discuss his vocational difficulties or both parents together to discuss the purposes of psychotherapy with the child.

If we examine the case of Mary, some of these principles can be illustrated more effectively. Mrs. S., for example, grew up in an atmosphere in which she found it very difficult to establish the precedents for appropriate behavior involved in her role as mother. As a result of these conditions, when she met with circumstances which involved the need to establish appropriate behavior, her reaction was one of avoidance, with an implication that she was incapable of acting effectively by herself. Under earlier conditions, her avoidance became at least partially workable in that she could ignore circumstances which would require her to act responsibly. With the arrival of an infant, however, this was more difficult for her to do. The infant's behavior became a powerful pressure on her to change. Her emotional avoidance of her infant became a pressure on her husband to take over to which he responded to some extent, but not in a way which could be effective. At the point the family was actually seen, we can conceive of the situation as one in which each participant is influencing the behavior of the other negatively. The mother's behavior, for example, is dictating, to a considerable extent, the father's work. The child's behavior is, to a high degree, responsible for the mother's behavior such as determining mealtime and bedtime. The father's behavior has its effect on the mother's behavior by allowing her to avoid certain responsibilities involved in caring for her child. As a starting point then, the social worker's asking the mother what she would wish to convey to the child about going to school establishes a certain precedent. Obviously the mother could not convey anything meaningful to the child in words, but the question itself involves many implications. It establishes that the social worker expects her to be responsible in the area of parental role, but at the same time it does not set the rules for the mother's behavior. This mother would probably react with attempts to avoid the question or to get a prescription from the social worker. Immediately the stage is set for possible discussion of many issues which have a bearing on the matter—the mother's concept of school, her reaction to feeling an expectation placed upon her which she feels incapable of taking, her sense of abandonment under certain conditions, and so on. She has at her disposal in the face of such expectations two basic possibilities as a way of avoiding change in herself: (1) becoming depressed; (2) involving other people. The first is less likely but not out of the realm of possibility. The second possibility might involve inclusion of her husband or a request for psychotherapy. Either request can become a matter of discussion, the first with the social worker who could approach the question in terms of the usefulness for the mother, the effects on his schedule, and so forth. The request for psychotherapy would offer the opportunity for the psychiatrist to meet with the parents to discuss the matter. In the beginning phase of the experience, the request is more liable to be a defensive maneuver on the part of the parents than a valid question, as the psychiatrist is generally conceived of as having omnipotent powers at that point. His gentle refusal of psychotherapy then becomes a message that he is unwilling to take over as requested when he recognizes that the family attempt is to maintain a status quo by avoiding appropriate role differentiation within the system.

Again in the beginning, the possibility of transportation being provided by the clinic should not be brought in too quickly. It should first be determined how the family would consider solving it themselves. If the father indicates his intent to work this out, the possible effects on his job can become a topic of conversation. If his job is not in jeopardy or it makes no essential difference, then transportation does not need to be introduced. Out of this discussion could grow the basis for the father's participation in the program around his job. This matter, as stated above, would be worked out with the psychiatrist, as it represents a role different from his parental responsibility although not divorced from it.

Strategically, the nursery-school teacher is in a position to help in outlining the basis for treatment. To do this would involve careful collaborative planning before meeting formally with the mother. A highly selective process is involved, with the teacher having at her disposal a number of different situations which she might describe and discuss differently than the mother would be inclined to do. Thus, she might select a small bit of behavior illustrating the child's need to try to control the situation. Thus, a simple statement such as: "Every time we try to put on her coat she acts as if somehow we have nothing to do with it. It's really quite bothersome to us in the school not to be recognized as people in our own right. It's tough on her too, though, because it's pretty hard work when you have to make all the decisions on your own. We haven't pressed the point though, as we soon discovered that if you try to make her do something she just gets more resistive. What we do now is just get her coat on as quickly as possible, since it has to get done. We were wondering if the doctor might help so that she doesn't need to fight everyone." Such a statement establishes several points: (1) the school is not a coercive operation but still has definition; (2) the school personnel see the child in much the same way as the mother; (3) the child's task in treatment is suggested but left to the mother's decision; and (4) the child's strength is given some emphasis rather than her incapacity.

Therapy becomes, then, another factor in the total endeavor, with unfolding developments dictating how it is to be conducted. If the child shows some response, it can lead to frequent contact; if not, it can be cut down. The basic principle involved is to engage in a clarifying encounter with the child. Thus, if the child takes up any activity at all—for example, tearing up a piece of paper—the therapist has an opportunity to intervene in the activity. He may take it away or restrict the child's activity by holding her hand. There is a certain advantage in the case of Mary in that she characteristically is a persistent child. On the other hand, her wish to avoid people is also characteristic of her. Which will take precedence is not possible to predict at any one time. The therapist can, however, test this out by interposing himself to a greater or lesser extent. Thus, he may find that too much intrusion will lead her to give up the activity as a way of avoiding him, whereas too little will lead to her ignoring him and simply continuing the activity. If the right balance is reached, the child will possibly begin to recognize the existence of the therapist, as a first step towards new and hopefully more appropriate adaptive behavior. Even at best this is a painfully slow process, and many times the child will not permit such an encounter to develop. If it is successful, however, the stage is set for the child to permit others in his life to be positive rule setters, thus breaking through the autistic barrier.

Further developments in the total case can at times lead to the mother recapitulating her previous crisis events. The inclusion of the carefully supervised homemaker can counteract her sense of abandonment at such times and hopefully lead to a more successful outcome.

A service such as that outlined above needs to be constantly prepared for contingencies and ready to exploit them for the benefit of all concerned. Mary's grandfather had been ill as outlined in the history. His death is not out of the realm of possibility. If the mother needs to go to the funeral what would be involved as far as Mary is concerned? Should she go or stay behind? A homemaker would be useful under such circumstances, or perhaps a brief inpatient experience. Naturally the mother's decision would be paramount, but a number of different possibilities could broaden her decision-making potential.

The practical development of such a service would obviously be extremely expensive and fraught with great difficulties in developing and maintaining personnel. Without continuity the problems of collaborative enterprise become magnified. The cost and difficulties involved would need to be weighed, however, against the economic and emotional cost. These latter are difficult to estimate as they involve not only the economic factor of life-long maintenance of such children in psychiatric facilities, but also the terrible emotional drain on a family which can suffer untold hardship in attempting to cope with such problems. Perhaps these children are truly untreatable, but if this could be determined and the time could be estimated when the process involved in an autistic adaptation becomes irreversible, a considerable advance would have been made. At such a point it would be possible to come to terms with the impossible, and far cheaper services could be designed. Until such a time, it is difficult for those of us in the profession who have not lost our humanity to relegate a three year old to an essential human junkyard. If nothing else, experience with these children drives us to seek answers, but when our efforts fail, we come face to face with the humbling but hopefully not humiliating limitations of our human efforts.

REFERENCES

1. BENDER, LAURETTA. Childhood schizophrenia. *Nerv. Child,* 1941–42, 1:138–40.
2. CHESS, THOMAS, *et al. Behavioral individuality in early childhood.* New York: New York University Press, 1963.
3. EISENBERG, L. The fathers of autistic children. *Amer. J. Orthopsychiat.,* 1957, 27(4): 715–24.
4. GOLDFARB, WILLIAM. *Childhood schizophrenia.* Cambridge, Mass.: Harvard University Press, 1961.

5. HALEY, J. *Strategies of psychotherapy.* New York: Grune & Stratton, 1963.

6. HASLAN, JOHN. *Observations on madness and melancholy.* London: C. Hayden, 1809.

7. KANNER, L. A discussion of early infantile autism. *Dig. Neurol. and Psychiat.*, 1951, **19**:158.

8. KANNER, L. Autistic disturbances of affective contact. *Nerv. Child,* 1942–43, **2**:217–50.

9. MAHLER, MARGARET S. On child psychosis and schizophrenia. Autistic and symbiotic psychosis. *Psychoanalytic study of the child,* Vol. VII. New York: International Universities Press, 1952.

10. PUTNAM, MARIAN C.; RANK, BEATA; and KAPLAN, S. Notes on John I. A case of primal depression in an infant. *Psychoanalytic study of the child,* Vol. VI. New York: International Universities Press, 1951.

11. RANK, BEATA. Adaptation of the psychoanalytic technique for the treatment of young children with atypical development. *Amer. J. Orthopsychiat.*, 1949, **19**:130–39.

12. ROSE, JOHN A. The prevention of mothering breakdown associated with physical abnormalities of the infant. In CAPLAN, G. (ed), *Prevention of mental disorders in children.* New York: Basic Books, 1961. Pp. 265–83.

Alex H. Kaplan

Problems of Psychotherapy
with the Adolescent

THE QUESTION of direct psychotherapy with adolescents was very much an issue 25 years ago(40). When it became necessary to work with the individual adolescent because of persistent behavioral difficulties and symptoms, emphasis was placed on modification of the environment, group activity, the development of a positive emotional relationship, the giving of emotional support, and the use of catharsis as the main treatment techniques. Long before adolescents were actively seen in direct psychotherapy, younger children were being treated by psychotherapy and psychoanalysis. Gitelson suggested that in the treatment of adults and children the emotional positions of the therapist and patient are well demarcated; the adult patient accepts the therapist as a helper in a social relationship, and the child patient accepts the therapist as an understanding and benign parent.

UNDERSTANDING THE ADOLESCENT

The adult treating the adolescent has no such firm ground on which to base his own therapeutic efforts. The patient brings little that closely resembles the therapist's own adolescence. Since the adolescent adopts the social values of his peers, the result is decreasing knowledge and understanding of him by the adult and a lack of adequate empathy with the patient(21). To a considerable extent, this unease concerning direct psychotherapy with the adolescent also reflected a lack of adequate understanding of the psychology of the adolescent phase of development and of how the changes of adolescence affected the ego's capacity for further adaptive behavior.

Sigmund Freud(18), while emphasizing the sexual aspects of the transformation of puberty, pointed to the separation from parental authority as one of the most painful psychic accomplishments of puberty.

Simultaneously with the overcoming and rejection of these distinctly incestuous fantasies, there occurs one of the most important as well as one of the most painful psychic accomplishments of puberty; it is the breaking away from the parental authority through which alone is formed that opposition between the new and old generations, which is so important for cultural progress.

Anna Freud, in 1936(16), contributed two papers in which her

. . . interest in the adolescent problems were derived from her concern with the struggles of the ego to master the tensions and pressures arising from the drive derivatives, struggles which led in the normal case to character formation, in their pathological outcome to the formation of neurotic symptoms.

The study of the adolescent has always been difficult, since even in adult analyses the reconstruction of adolescence is relatively meager and there are few reported analyses of the adolescent. In addition, many analysts have an undue pessimism concerning the use of analytic therapy for the adolescent. Spiegel(36), reviewing the contributions to a psychoanalytic theory of adolescence, pointed to the need of adapting analytic techniques to the adolescent patient in particular situations, and expressed surprise at the absence of explicit discussions of an introductory phase analogous to the one used with children and delinquents.

Special difficulties are encountered in the treatment of adolescents since their emotional positions change so rapidly, leaving the therapist little time to modify his therapeutic techniques. One of the reasons why intensive therapy with the adolescent seems to be so difficult is that adolescence has been compared with states of mourning and unhappy love. While the individual is engaged in the adolescent struggle as he might be involved with the disturbed emotions of mourning and love, there is too little libido available to effect a relationship with the person of the therapist or to flow back regressively and reinvest former objects and positions(17, 33).

Adolescent crushes, happy or unhappy love affairs, are typical of the problems in this period. Often the therapist becomes the new love object of the adolescent, which heightens the young patient's interest in being treated but may not help therapy itself. Transference reactions in adolescents are not fully developed because the adolescent's libido is not as available for commitment to therapy(17).

The Adolescent Phase of Development

Adolescence can be viewed as the sum total of the individual psychological reactions to the state of puberty. It is a reaction to the inner tensions, to increased drive derivatives, as well as to outside social pressures. "The gradual advancement during adolescence toward the genital position and heterosexual orientation is only the continuation of the development which temporarily came to a standstill at the decline of the oedipal phase, a standstill which accentuates the biphasic sexual development"(7). Such reactions in adolescence almost always result in disharmony and turmoil and involve the experimentation with new and novel modes of behavior. Indeed, adolescents without such obvious disharmonious reactions are suspect of emotional difficulties. What has been more frequently emphasized during adolescence has been the breakdown of defenses and the regressive components of adolescence, without the emphasis on the beneficial aspects of the adolescent's so-called inconsistent and unpredictable behavior. The struggles between the forces of the ego, id, and superego can be seen as attempts to bring about a new psychic equilibrium.

It is normal for the adolescent to behave for a considerable length of time in an inconsistent and unpredictable manner, to fight his impulses and to accept them, to ward them off successfully and to be overrun by them, to love his parents and to hate them, to revolt against them, to be dependent upon them, to be deeply ashamed of . . . his mother . . . and desire heart to heart talks with her, to thrive on imitation of and identification with others while searching unceasingly for his own identity, to be more idealistic, generous, and unselfish than he will ever be again(17).

There are also the sublimatory creative and problem-solving aspects of adolescence. The very nature of its upheaval may counteract the effects of earlier emotional difficulties of childhood and offer the child new solutions to old conflicts. The regressive processes present in adolescence can be compared to other regressions in the service of the ego which encourage ego growth to counteract older and more pathological identifications(7). Geleerd describes this period "as a partial regression to the undifferentiated phase of object relationship which explains the increased

need for a love object and the need for union with this love object"(20).
However, there is the fear that the regression may go too far

. . . and result in dissolution of the self which explains much of the adolescent's
defiant and rebellious behavior, and his sudden, unpredictable changes of love
object. The partial regression results in an increase in perceptiveness which
may explain the enthusiasm, the capacity for being inspired and the creative
interests in adolescence(20).

Erickson(12) has referred to the adolescent phase of development as a
normative crisis with a high growth potential despite what seems to be a
marked fluctuation in ego strength. When such fluctuations are studied,
they are found to be aspects of a self-limited crisis which aids in the
process of adolescent identity.

The intensity of the reaction to the adolescent phase of development is
correlated with the character of emotional adjustment present in earlier
childhood and infancy and is influenced by hereditary, constitutional
factors and the individual's psychodynamic development. When the
adolescent's behavioral manifestations begin to look like the pathological
neurotic, psychotic, or antisocial states, further evaluation is indicated
with a penetrating study of the present ego strength as compared with a
longitudinal evaluation of the psychosocial development. The more
bizarrely and pathologically the adolescent reacts to the intensity of his
libidinal and aggressive drives and the loss of his infantile and incestuous
love objects, the more obviously sick he is. While everything seems to be
in disorder with outbursts of anger, love, and dependency feelings, and
when at times the super-ego seems to have shown marked change for the
worse, the healthy adolescent ego is able to establish a psychic equilibrium which keeeps his instincts under control and maintains a proper
reality orientation to his family and immediate environment.

Periods of Adolescent Development

There is now general agreement that the phase of adolescent development can be further differentiated into three more or less distinct periods.
The first begins with the onset of biological and physiological maturation
between 11 and 12 years of age, somewhat earlier in girls than in boys.
The middle period of adolescence is considered to extend between 14 and
16, when the phase of development reaches its peak. This is followed by
the late adolescence period, which varies between the ages of 17 to 20.
During adolescence the individual is expected to reach genital primacy
and to make a nonincestuous object choice. The early period of adoles-

cence is characterized by regressive behavior and the apparent loss of older mental mechanisms which have earlier been established, and by the reaction of the adolescent to the onrush of libidinal and aggressive drives. At the height of adolescence, the middle period, conflicts between homosexual and heterosexual strivings are in the foreground. These are expressed in the adolescent's displacement of libido onto his devoted friends and peer groups, and parent substitutes. Oedipal feelings at this time are repressed. "Asceticism, compulsion and unrealistic projection may be used"(8). During the late adolescent period, a period of consolidation takes place and the late adolescent becomes the young adult. Spiegel refers to adolescence as a reaction to disorder and an attempt at consolidation(38). "The definitive settling of conflicts at the end of adolescence means either that they lose their disturbing quality because they have been characterologically stabilized, or they solidify into permanent debilitating symptoms or character disorders"(7).

The end of adolescence is markedly affected by societal pressures which determine the length and duration of adolescence. The attitudes of the upper and middle classes in prolonging adolescence is much in contrast to that present in the lower socioeconomic classes.

PSYCHOTHERAPY OF THE YOUNGER ADOLESCENT

Since the period of adolescence extends from 12 to 13 years through 18 to 20 years, and since the problems during the early phases of adolescence (12–16 years) are different than those of the middle phase and the latter phase of adolescence, the psychotherapeutic approach must vary in accordance with the age of the child, the severity of the problem, the character of the problem (neurosis, psychosis, character disorder, and so on), and the ego's capacity for integration (ego strength). The early period of adolescence is very much like the latency period and the late period of adolescence is very much like that of the young adult. In addition, there are, of course, multiple cultural and social factors which need to be taken into consideration. The adolescent in one socioeconomic group and subculture is quite different from the adolescent in another. In addition, each adolescent approaches this phase of development with a personality whose growth and development has been modified by hereditary, constitutional, and other genetic factors in early childhood. The more seriously disturbed adolescent would obviously be a product of a more seriously disturbed family, and the severity of the adolescent adjustment is closely related to the character of the adjustment which the adolescent made as a young infant and child. Then again, the specific type of defense used will determine the nature of the therapeutic approach. The neurotic adolescent whose symptoms are ego alien tends to be more highly motivated for therapy than the acting-out, promiscuous, delinquent adolescent whose problems are ego syntonic. The latter children are usually involved with the police and courts and offer little opportunity for a therapeutic relationship. They frequently require a long period of preparation in a therapeutic environment before they are available for psychotherapy (see Patient "Frank," page 270). This is also true of the psychotic child who, although his symptoms are ego alien, frequently resists a referral to a therapist (see Patient "Edward," page 269). The same is true of a borderline of prepsychotic adolescent whose extreme anxiousness prevents him from voluntarily seeking help (see Patient "Owen," page 284). The sex pervert is also ordinarily not an individual who is seen voluntarily, and frequently must be forced into therapy, especially in his early and middle adolescent years (see Patient "Roy," page 286).

There has been much discussion as to the capability of the younger adolescent to undergo intensive psychotherapy and psychoanalysis, and only a few cases have been described in the literature(33, 34). It is clear that psychotherapy for the early and middle adolescent is more frequently supportive, to strengthen his ego-adaptive capacity, much as is required in more seriously disturbed patients prior to intensive psychotherapy. Actually, all psychotherapy must be modified to meet the needs of the adolescent child whose moods and attitudes are reminiscent of a more severely disturbed individual. Flexibility of technical approaches and treatment modifications must always be employed in order to achieve therapeutic success. However, therapeutic goals in the treatment of adolescents are not very clearly defined. Gitelson has discussed therapy during this period as "character synthesis" rather than as a way of providing the adolescent with a more benign reexperience of his past.

. . . treatment may fail, not because it is dynamically inaccurate, but because it is emotionally inadequate. . . . The therapeutic situation needs to be dependable rather than dependent. . . . Character synthesis with the therapist as catalyst, synergist and model is the immediate goal in treatment with problems of the adolescent (21).

With a better understanding of the psychodynamics of the adolescent phase of development, an increasing number of younger adolescents are being seen in more intensive psychotherapy and psychoanalysis with the use of specific techniques applicable to the adolescent. The typical, orthodox, classical techniques are rarely usable in their pure form since the analyst fulfills the role of a parent substitute even though in a more neutral fashion. There is more activity in helping the adolescent learn to test reality and to increase the tolerance of the ego to pathogenic conflicts. The transference is never as strong as in adult analysis, the working through is only possible to a limited degree, and a systematic analysis of all defense mechanisms is not possible and is even contra-indicated(19). It is my impression that more younger adolescents can be treated intensively if enough technical changes in psychoanalytic therapy are used in accordance with the needs of the specific adolescent.

The younger adolescent is mainly involved with the here and now— with the struggles at home, with his peers, in the school, and with the therapist. He is rarely available for the analysis of past conflicts. At times such therapeutic activity may weaken his adaptive capacities. The educative process in treatment is significant as it is with younger children. In fact, the therapy of adolescents draws heavily on the psychotherapy employed both with children and adults; the length of therapy is shorter than that of the adult and more like that with children. Involvement with the adolescent's parents is necessary within almost every therapeutic problem as in the therapy with children(42).

The Therapist

Ideally, the therapist treating the adolescent should have a background of training both in child and adult psychiatry. The therapist without training in child psychiatry is limited in his ability to handle the younger adolescent whose problems and the manner in which they are handled are so similar to those of the latency-period child. It is axiomatic that the therapist should be a person who has more or less successfully worked out his own adolescent and other emotional problems, so he can handle the intense anxiety which is often developed in the interaction with the adolescent without developing counter-transference reactions. A personal psychoanalysis is indicated for those individuals doing intensive psycho-therapy, whether with children, adolescents, or adults. In addition, they should be particularly cognizant of the cultural backgrounds of the adolescents, their language, idioms, dress, and mores. Without such knowledge, marked resistance develops in the therapy proper and the empathy necessary for a proper understanding of the adolescent's problems and collaboration in therapy is not possible. While this is particularly true for the adolescent, it is also true for children and adults as well.

The treatment of minority and lower socioeconomic groups is fraught with the danger of failure unless the cultural subgroups' mores are fully understood. Hollingshead and Redlich have demonstrated the fact that, basically, therapists tend to treat patients within their own socioeconomic groupings(25). Since the adolescent is a product of a new generation, in many ways he tends to fit into a new subcultural group whose mores need to be understood before a psychotherapeutic interaction can be developed.

Despite all that has been said of the therapist's background training and his recognition of the adolescent's role in his society, the therapist must be able to be flexible in his approach, be ingenuous, consistent, have infinite patience, change roles when necessary, and have sufficient intuitive ability to empathize with his patient, often assuming changing roles as an understanding parent, a benign educator, a protector, and a good friend. The adolescent is particularly sensitive to the feeling and attitudes of the therapist, the therapist's unconscious counter-transference reactions as well as to the conscious presentation of himself. While most adolescents are eager for help, even though they will not voluntarily come in for treatment, they have specific needs with which the therapist must ally himself and be quite willing to go along for a long period of time until the adolescent is ready to change his needs and interests. This requires infinite patience and a trusting attitude which recognizes that treatment cannot be furthered by forcing adult demands on the adolescent when the latter is psychologically unready to accept them. This is true of the adolescent's sexual interest and his need for independence despite his intense dependency urges. In this connection the therapist must be ready to be authoritative when necessary to protect the adolescent from excessive states of anxiety developing from the adolescent's over-craving for freedom when such needs are neurotic or self-destructive(23). Steele emphasizes

. . . the importance for successful therapy of a dynamic understanding of the specific conflicts and needs of the adolescent, willingness on the part of the therapist to ally himself with these needs as the adolescent presents them, and help for the adolescent which enables him to correct the blunders of the past through a consistent and patient cooperation(39).

Beginning of Treatment

Young people between the ages of 12 and 16 rarely volunteer to come for therapy despite serious emotional problems of a neurotic, psychotic, borderline, sexual perversion, or acting-out variety. Such treatment is generally instituted by parents, school authorities, or the police. The original contact of the psychiatrist is generally with the school, the police, or the parents, at which time a complete psychosocial history should be taken which not only includes the reason for referral to a psychiatrist but a study of the parents themselves and their interaction with the child and family from birth onward. The hereditary, constitutional, early genetic, and psychodynamic factors(31) need to be evaluated in terms of the adolescent's presenting complaints in order to make the necessary diagnostic evaluation between what would be considered an adolescent turmoil in a normal child and those behavioral characteristics considered to be pathological.

The next contact, which should be arranged as soon as possible after the parents are seen, will be with the child who comes with greater or lesser reluctance to see the therapist. The period of adolescence is a period of considerable secrecy, when children turn away from confiding in their parents to maintaining secrets with their peers, within their gangs, or other groups such as clubs, sororities, or fraternities. To have to talk openly and respond to penetrating questions by the therapist is productive of much anxiety. With this recognition and with the previous historical information at hand, the therapist must choose those aspects of what he has learned in an attempt to further evaluate the problems of the child and to establish rapid rapport with the patient. It is most crucial that the therapist ally himself with the patient in those ways which would lead to a fruitful relationship, otherwise therapy itself is doomed to failure. As indicated previously, it is essential for the therapist to be aware of and conversant with the adolescent aspects of behavior, language, and customs, for there is nothing more disturbing to an adolescent than to have to speak to an older person with whom he cannot communicate because of the differences in generations. This does not mean a protrusion by the therapist in an intrusive way upon the patient, but the maintenance of a neutral attitude and the ability to interpret and enter into those areas about which at first the patient is willing to communicate to the therapist.

Obviously the neurotic and suffering young adolescent is anxious to be helped and is more spontaneous in his remarks and associations. Generally speaking, however, the young adolescent is reluctant to talk and must be questioned in ways which would bring out the type of information which would further the therapeutic process through first, relationships with the therapist; and second, the opening of those areas of conflict within the patient himself so that he may become more consciously aware of his problems. More active interpretations are necessary in order to carry out the aforementioned therapeutic goal of the beginning of therapy.

Care must be taken not to fall into the trap of identifying with the parents of the child with whom most adolescents have considerable conflict and much ambivalence. To be a parent figure too much like the patient's own parents is to doom therapy to immediate failure. Various techniques may be used to encourage the growth of a more positive development with the therapist and each therapist himself has his own specific techniques. Often the therapist must be firm, authoritative, sometimes cajoling, other times sarcastic, responsive to the patient's own sarcasm, and at times "out acting-out the acting-outer," or at least making it clear to the acting-out adolescent that the therapist is fully aware of the patient's capability to act-out. Certainly in the beginning of therapy the therapist must not be judgmental, and it must be clearly established with the patient that his parents also have problems. At all times it is necessary to clarify the question of confidentiality in terms of the patient, his parents, the police, and so forth. The important problem in the beginning of therapy with the young adolescent is to bring him into an awareness of his conflicts and the fact that he may be helped by means of psychotherapy.

Parental Involvement with the Younger Adolescent

There are few references in the psychoanalytic literature which specifically discuss the question of parental involvement in the treatment of the adolescent, and yet it seems obvious that therapy with the younger adolescent cannot succeed unless the parents are involved. Perhaps this is not as significant in the therapy of the late adolescent (17–20 years) where therapy might be adversely affected by a too close relationship of the therapist with the parents. However, for the younger adolescent (12–16 years) involvement with the parents seems to be mandatory if therapy is to show any degree of success. Parents insist on participating and their interest and needs must also be met. On the other hand, their involvement needs to be carefully evaluated so that it does not create too much resistance in the therapist-patient relationship and destroy the collaborative efforts made by the therapist.

In the following illustration, an Adjustment Reaction in Middle Adolescence, the therapist's over-involvement with the parents' concern about the acting-out symptoms of their daughter and the possibility of her pregnancy, blocked the development of a therapeutic relationship with the patient.

Example: Anne, 15½ years of age, was referred by her parents following an episode of absenting herself from home overnight and refusing to talk about it. She was, according to her adoptive parents, a loving and conforming child until this episode. Parental handling has always been inconsistent and overindulgent. Anne has said she hates her mother but tolerates her father. Despite a high intellectual capacity and an earlier interest in school work, Anne has decided not to go to college, which distresses her parents. The impression was that of an adjustment reaction of an adolescent characterized by sexual acting-out. The acting-out, prominent in her games around pregnancy (letters and notes which the mother found), seemed to be a way of taking revenge on the mother by whom she feels rejected (complicated by the actual rejection by her own biological mother). The first contacts were the parents, who were greatly concerned that Anne might be pregnant. There were many phone calls and other communication from physicians. In this atmosphere, Anne was seen, and it was obvious she had already identified the therapist with her intrusive parents. Even after several hours, Anne had not been able to talk of her overnight episode nor her sexual proclivities. Continuing interviews with both parents was recommended to further evaluate the family picture and allow Anne to work through her anger with her parents, so she could be more accepting of the therapist. However, still being distrustful of the therapist and her parents, Anne refused conjoined interviews and further treatment. At this point her deviant behavior had subsided, she became more conforming and the parents could not oppose their daughter's decision. Subsequently she made an attempt at suicide, was depressed, and told another therapist that she never trusted the first therapist because he was too much like her father. There was some reality to her complaints that the first therapist had spent too much time with her parents because of their anxiety and Anne felt rejected.

Normally, the first contact is made with the parents or other authority figures and a complete psychosocial history should be taken. The secondary contact with the patient should follow as soon as possible and the significant details of the contact with parents should be reviewed with the patient in an effort to encourage the development of trust and confidence. As part of the diagnostic evaluation, I frequently have a psychological study of the adolescent made to corroborate the psychiatric evaluation and further check the severity of the pathology and the possible prognosis if psychotherapy is indicated. The patient may be seen several times if necessary for an appropriate study. With the younger adolescent, unless there is some contraindication, final recommendations are made in a joint conference with the parents and child. This has many advantages since it does not allow for the many distortions which commonly appear when patient and his parents are seen separately. The adolescent is not allowed the luxury of the denial of his problem, especially if the parents are available for rebuttal. This type of joint conference gives the child a reality picture of the therapist as opposed to that which he has of his parents, and usually results in further trust and confidence. The therapist demonstrates in such a conference that the child can be protected from his overanxious, punitive, or resistant parents and plans for future therapy can then be made for further individual or conjoint therapy(1).

For some younger adolescent children, the entire evaluation can be carried out in group interviews but attention must be paid to the adolescent's needs even though they may be unrealistic. This was true in the following illustration of a Conduct and Neurotic Disturbance in Early Adolescence.

> *Example:*   Bob was 13 years and 3 months old when referred for scholastic difficulties and emerging behavior problems, including constant talking in class, smoking, making small fires with paper, and setting off firecrackers in the college women's dormitory in his neighborhood. At home he had temper reactions, lied, and rationalized his acting-out. Hyperactive since birth, he used infantile language until 7, had episodic enuresis until 10, and was physically uncoordinated. Father, a physician, was passive-dependent and had isolated himself from his family, while mother was the more dominant family figure. The psychiatric evaluation was carried out in a group conference with the parents. Uneasy and tense, Bob sat stolidly on the couch, denying any problems. However, the mother quietly repeated the reason for his coming without indicting him and Bob quickly assented. Using me as his protector, he accused his parents openly of mistreating him as opposed to their reactions to his brother. Further study corroborated the diagnosis of an anxiety neurosis of childhood with erratic breakthrough of aggression which defended patient against his concern and conflict over his passive-feminine orientation. His defenses were so rigid that energies were not free for learning or masculine gratification. There were positive factors in his masculine ego ideals. When therapy was recom-

mended in the family group, patient sat slumped in his chair. His shoulders were hunched up, already involved in his passive stubborn resistance, expecting to be hurt and preparing to react in the only way he knew. When Bob still insisted he could get along without therapy, I went along with his wishes, indicating that we could wait and further evaluate the problem in the future. He was very happy, but his parents were obviously uneasy with my decision. The need to establish trust in the young adolescent, and to support him even though his rationalizations are without any basis in reality, is essential to involve the younger adolescent in a collaborative treatment rationship; and when treatment can be delayed because of lack of urgency, it may frequently be the best course of action.

There are other situations in therapy where individual psychotherapy has been stalemated by the extensive denial of the patient even though his difficulties at home continue unabated. The use of conjoint therapeutic conferences with the parents at such points helps to overcome the resistance, as indicated by a Personality Trait Disturbance of Early Adolescence.

Example: Charles, a 13-year-old early adolescent, small, concerned over his inability to compete physically with his peers, was referred because of educational difficulties, marked sibling rivalry, temper reactions at home, and inability to control his tears when only mildly frustrated. The oldest of three siblings, but smaller than his younger brother, patient had developed compulsive characteristics to defend himself against early intense oedipal feelings for his dominating, intellectual, and seductive mother. The father, isolated because of business and withdrawn passively as a response to his wife's aggressivity, was a good father only when he could rise above his own personal conflicts. Patient came dutifully for therapy, would answer laconically when questioned, and insisted on playing games to resist talking. While at first very uneasy with the suggestion of a family therapy unit, he gained confidence, especially when the initial sessions focused on the marital difficulties and the differing personalities of the parents, and how these modified the relationship of the parents to the children. Often the patient acted as judge, counselor, and critic of his parents, a new and aggressive role for him. With the parents' reactions as an example, he became more free to admit his own difficulties, frequently crying for 10 to 15 minutes at points of tension. On a number of occasions, his brothers were invited to participate when it seemed appropriate in the developing psychodynamic material. With increasing insight, the group finally reached the point where individual therapy for Charles was again embarked upon, with the parents now only being contacted by telephone.

Where the child is seen alone in individual psychotherapy, occasional contacts are maintained with the full knowledge of the patient and his acceptance. Frequently, when such contacts are necessary, patient and parents are seen together. In the early phases of therapy, this occurs much more frequently since both parents as well as their adolescent must be prepared for more intensive psychotherapy with the adolescent himself, as demonstrated in the following Neurotic Disturbance of Middle Adolescence.

Example: Donald, a 15-year-old boy, insisted on seeing a psychiatrist because of obsessive feelings that he might kill or maim individuals who upset him. Frequently they were directed against the family, mainly the father, sometimes against his peers. Of very superior intelligence, Donald was doing only average work because he practically never studied, was always late with his assignments, and annoyed teachers with his constant questions. Parents were highly motivated to force their son to live up to his intellectual capacity; father has a violent temper, is infantile in his attitudes, and without insight into his son's problems. Mother, intensely involved in mental health projects, while accepting therapy readily obviously resists the intrusion of psychotherapy into her own family domination through overprotection and overconcern. Patient, obese as a youngster, uneasy in competitive sports, is now a big, strapping, husky boy, but fearful of his aggressive impulses. Instead of studying, patient daydreams and compulsively masturbates with images of women. Psychoanalytically oriented therapy was instituted, but parents insisted on seeing the therapist alone to discuss therapy and find out "what they could do to help their son." I insisted on joint interviews with their son, which was accepted reluctantly by the parents. It soon became clear to the patient how he was perfectionistically trying to please his parents on the one hand without success, and reacting to his anger and sexual feelings with obsessive fears of violence. Father was markedly stubborn, attacking psychiatry and the therapist as well as his own son. Mother was placating but just as hostile in a covert fashion. After several such interviews, father refused to participate further, but he and mother agreed to allow therapy to continue. Patient uses the couch and, while he has difficulty free-associating, considerable progress has been made without further contact with parents.

Contact with the parents is of course essential when the question of hospitalization or institutionalization enters the picture. It is axiomatic that if the hospital plan is not the parents' plan, treatment of the adolescent will also fail. Frequently the parents need to be seen over and over again so they can arrive at a point where they are ready to go along with such a treatment plan for their child. An example is this case of a Psychosis of Middle Adolescence.

Example: Edward was a 15-year-old schizophrenic patient who insisted on a plastic operation on his nose (finally carried out by a plastic surgeon out of town), and then wanted his nose returned to its original character. He was concerned over his hair and other physical characteristics and had obvious paranoid characteristics. Patient was hospitalized three times and removed from the hospital a few days after each admission. Each time the parents had another rationalization for their actions. The parents had been poorly mated for years, and both were markedly guilty over the product of their obvious neglect and inconsistent behavior. Often the parents could not make a realistic distinction between what was sick or normal behavior in their son. Parents were seen by the writer for months before they could set limits for their son who had begun to regress at home and insist on therapy with another psychiatrist. However, they would not accept hospitalization. My contact with the parents has been a continuous one over many years, as their son has drifted with slow improvement from one psychiatrist to another.

Attempts at collaborative therapy(**26**), where parents are seen by one therapist and the patient by another, are fraught with considerable difficulties. Counterreactions are generally developed by each therapist towards the other's therapy, and few therapists are comfortable enough to be free to discuss their therapeutic activities with peers. My own experience with collaborative therapy in private practice or in hospitals with a therapeutic community concept of patient care has been disappointing. In child guidance clinics, where in the classical sense the psychiatrist may see the patient and a social worker the parents, what theoretically starts out as a collaborative therapeutic program on a practical level becomes two isolated therapeutic endeavors with little collaboration and much resistance developing between therapists. In my own experience, much depends upon the problem for which the adolescent has been referred. A period of conjoint family therapy in those situations when the family conflict or family neurosis is more pressing should be attempted. For those neurotic, depressed, or well-stabilized personality disorders, individual therapy with the adolescent is indicated with occasional conjoint family meetings as needed to maintain the course of the therapy. Such contacts with the parents are more frequent earlier in therapy and then usually drop out, especially at the point where the adolescent gives up trying to solve his own emotional conflicts by attempts to modify his parents' behavior or reactions to him either realistically or unrealistically.

Intensive Psychotherapy for the Younger Adolescent

What about more intensive psychotherapy or psychoanalysis for the younger adolescent? Almost everyone agrees that psychoanalysis in its orthodox adult form is not practicable because of the very nature of the adolescent phase of development. A variety of technical procedures described earlier have now been suggested to either prepare the younger adolescent for analysis(14, 32) or as actual "parameters"(10) in adolescent analyses.

Eissler emphasized that the techniques of treatment of the adolescent had to be correlated with the specific phase of the adolescent symptomatology and modified accordingly. When the therapist remained persistently tied to one technique of analysis, treatment frequently failed. He believed, however, that when an adolescent entered therapy with "a solidified form of psychopathology," the problems of psychoanalytic treatment are not different than that of the adult(11).

Even in child analysis, there is the ever-present problem of whether the specific analytic therapy with its changing techniques and parameters is actually psychoanalysis, psychoanalytically oriented therapy, or psychotherapy, and a discussion of these issues generally raises more problems than it solves(8, 29, 41). More controlled studies are needed to prove the validity and efficacy of one form of psychotherapy or another in the variety of emotional problems of adolescence. This same discussion is as fruitful for the psychoanalysis of the younger adolescent as it is for the analysis of the psychotic, borderline-state child, and even the late adolescent.

There are those disorders of the younger adolescent which preclude any form of individual therapy until the acting-out symptoms have been modified, the superego attitudes changed, and the essential conflict internalized(3). The following is an example of an Acting-Out Disorder of Middle Adolescence.

Example: Frank was first seen for diagnostic evaluation at eight and a half years of age. At that time the presenting complaints were enuresis, inability to sleep, poor school adjustment and achievement, disobedience, and regressive infantility combined with aggressive behavior to his sister and peers. Mother indicated patient was unwanted. She was deeply depressed for six weeks after her son was born. Hyperkinetic from birth onward, Frank was considered different from other children and always was hard to handle. At 15 he was the typical picture of a young toughie, in trouble with the police, markedly irritable, with no ability to postpone gratification. His behavior during his latency period was similar to that of early childhood. The picture was one of a person with very poor object relationships and distorted ego values. His motivation for therapy was only a pseudo response to the pressures of the police. No meaningful relationship could be established in outpatient therapy or even in a therapeutic community inpatient unit because of his extreme combativeness and marked testing of the employees. Unfortunately, adequate authoritative measures could not be instituted. Patient ran away several times. Only when urged to leave and when given all ward privileges was there the semblance of a beginning of therapy. However, countertransference reactions on the part of ward personnel, other patients whom he seduced, and relatives of other patients, led to a breakdown of therapy, and patient left the city to be picked up by the police shortly thereafter. Only a specialized therapeutic institution could help modify this patient. Milieu therapy, even without individual therapy, is necessary for a long period of time to help modify his superego attitudes. This boy's behavior was little changed from childhood on and his emerging pubertal change merely modified but did not change his behavior(**30**).

There are those behavioral and conduct disturbances whose etiology is unlike that of the antisocial or dyssocial type and is more closely related to a neurotic disturbance. These adolescents such as the following Neurotic and Acting-Out Disorder of Early Adolescence are more readily available for individual psychotherapy, often with some preparation using conjoint family therapy(**1**).

Example: Referral was prompted by the school who felt George, 13 years old, had personality characteristics like "Oswald who murdered President J. F. Kennedy." The school authorities saw George as a dangerous physical threat to our children and emphasized his acting-out characteristics. George's biological father had been separated from patient for many years with practically no personal contact. The stepfather, an ingratiating, talented artist, was evasive, a compulsive liar, and corrupt. There have been innumerable separations with frequent marital counseling. At home George is better behaved. Originally George was markedly reluctant to see the therapist, denying his conduct disturbance and projecting in a paranoid way the blame for his actions. "It is his friends, his teachers, the school, and so on, who are to blame." At the same time he appeared very tense, harried, and depressed, with frequent facial tics. We were soon stalemated in the interview until I recognized that George defended himself against the threat of further parental separation by creating guilt in others by temper outbursts and dramatization. When I indicated this to him and sympathized with his fears and depressive feelings, he was at first belligerent, but finally said "I'm happy on the outside of school, not inside." Then tears came to his eyes and he was more free to tell me about his family concerns, his sibling rivalry, and his wish to please his step-father, which did not seem possible. The essential problem was that of depression with marked separation anxiety. His impulsive actions at school seem to be breakthroughs enabling him to maintain balance. He needs to learn to share his feelings without fear that they will result in destruction to people he needs for support. The treatment plan was conjoint therapy with both parents. Patient needs to become more consciously aware of the family disharmony, what it means to him, and how he can master the conflict without pathological reactions of guilt and anxiety on his part, with reaction formations to the feelings of loneliness and depression. Perhaps at later date individual therapy with the patient will be attempted.

Therapeutic Goals for the Younger Adolescent

Goals in therapy will differ in accordance with the severity of the problems, the age of the child, and his motivation. Very often the goal in therapy is determined by the adolescent himself, who may be motivated and develop a positive relationship with the therapist, but may never develop the intensity of transference which is true of an older adolescent or an adult, or even a young child. This is in keeping with the changing phases of adolescent development where objects are continually being given up in the pursuit of other object relationships. The problems which are dealt with in the therapy of the adolescent are the here-and-now problems, rather than the past difficulties or the past experiences of the adolescent. It is rare that a young adolescent can be encouraged to free-associate and to relate his earlier conflicts with his family and environment. The adolescent's conflict is with his environment in the present, not only with his parents, but also with the therapist; when tension is relieved and the pressure of symptoms is diminished, very frequently the motivation for treatment disappears. The adolescent is ready to pursue other object relations and loses his enthusiasm for further contact with the therapist.

Frequently this occurs at a point where the young adolescent has developed a heterosexual object interest following the reduction of conflict and the diminution of anxiety for which he came for therapy(2), as illustrated in a Neurotic Disturbance of Middle Adolescence.

> *Example:*   Harold was 15 years of age when referred for compulsive hand washing related to the touching of his penis and anus, fear of germs, sleep rituals, and obsessive thoughts of hurting people. These symptoms developed prior to his going away to camp, which he feared. As a child he masturbated frequently, disliked being alone, and was naughty and mischievous. As he developed into puberty, he became conforming, fearful of aggressive actions, overly clean, concerned over details, with a strong need to be first in everything he did. Last year at camp he engaged in some sex play with two other boys. His symptoms are remarkably similar to his mother's who was in analysis while Harold was a young child. Psychotherapy was readily instituted on a three-times-a-week basis. Patient could not readily recall his past experiences, with which I was already familiar, but obsessively ruminated about his symptoms and his everyday experiences at school, less frequently than those at home. No major contact was necessary with the parents because of the ego-alien aspects of the symptoms, the patient's willingness for therapy, and the cooperativeness of the parents. However, when interpretations based on his concern in regard to his emerging sexual and aggressive feelings, with corresponding fears of castration and self-injury and reaction formation with compulsive symptoms, his fear of separation from his parents abated. Treatment was interrupted by camp but Harold did not return to therapy because of the lack of motivation. An interesting and dramatic aspect of treatment occurred when patient developed conscious recognition of his intense sexual feeling in regard to his mother, with the corresponding understanding of how much he acted like his mother. "You will sort of have to cut it out; I guess you'll have to cut off my leg" (passive submission to castration to solve his oedipal guilt). Patient returned four years later, following the marriage of two siblings, with similar symptoms but increased phobic anxiety at college which forced him to return home. At this point psychoanalytic therapy was started. After two years of intensive therapy and considerable working through of his problems with

diminution of symptoms, patient left home. He is continuing with his college career but has developed more gratifying heterosexual interests, and now is again unmotivated for further therapy.

Other Therapeutic Problems of the Younger Adolescent

There are a host of other pitfalls in the treatment of the younger adolescent which cry for individual techniques to encourage the development of a therapeutic climate such as is necessary for the angry mute adolescent who comes to therapy but will not talk. Frequently, play therapy techniques not used with the adolescents as a group must be tried in the hope of establishing some kind of a trusting therapeutic relationship. These individuals are seen more often in a hospital or institutional setting where the children are forced to stay. Often one must find areas of interest away from the sensitive areas, then hopefully return to the more emotionally laden areas. One must guard against the fact that frequently latent psychotic parents may send their adolescent child instead of themselves to therapy.

The school under-achiever is a chronic and difficult problem in therapy. The direct approach in psychotherapy meets the same passive wall of resistance leading to failure and self-punishment as the school work. Frequently therapy must await the period of late adolescence before any meaningful progress can be made.

Increasing numbers of younger adolescents are seen with problems of school phobia and anorexia. Often this may be the beginning of a psychotic break or a reaction to a psychotic parent. Whereas with the younger child, resolute parental or reconstituted outside parental authority may be used to force the child to go to school at the same time as therapy is started, this is not generally possible with the adolescent. Frequently a residential treatment source may be the only answer to the problem. Two illustrations of School Phobias in Early and Middle Adolescence follow.

Example: Ivan, a 15-year-old passive dependent boy, the youngest of six siblings, whose neurotic father had retired before the age of 50 because of a gastrointestinal neurosis, left high school in his first year because of intense phobic anxiety associated with the school. Patient's overprotective mother insisted on accompanying patient to his therapy hours and the first aspect of treatment was involved with the separation of the overly dependent patient from his orally incorporating mother. Without mother, patient had to walk six miles to the doctor, but real progress in therapy began at the point where patient could undertake this action. It took a full year of therapy for the patient to return to school.

Example: Jack, a 13½-year-old bright boy whose mother, a life-long compulsive neurotic, was dying of intestinal cancer, stopped going to school, but although he came to therapy, it was only as a result of intense threats by the family. Treatment bogged down and patient lay around the house irritating his dying mother in the only way he could try to make contact with her. Residential treatment was advised to help break the intense pathological bond with the mother which could not be modified on an outpatient basis.

Residential Therapy

When residential treatment is necessary, it has been my experience that the adolescent child reacts more quickly to the therapeutic aspects of the milieu if the ward is not highly populated by adolescents. The leavening effect of adult patients, who often are reacted to as parent surrogates, helps the adolescent patient with his own personal struggles. Adult patients, on the other hand, have a tolerance for only a small number of adolescents. When the ratio of adults to adolescents is too greatly modified, the adolescent struggles and acting-out with ward procedures and staff become overexaggerated, leading to marked resistance to any therapy(22).

While the therapeutic community concept of care for the hospitalized and institutionalized patient is now not an uncommon practice, such care serves the needs of the adolescent who requires residential treatment in a most effective way. At the Jewish Hospital of St. Louis such a unit includes a liberal proportion of adolescents to adults in their Therapeutic Community Ward. Every adolescent is a member of a subgroup that meet almost daily to take up matters of significance to the group and ward as a whole. In addition to patients, the subgroup may contain ward personnel (psychiatric aides, nurses, and such) and professional staff (psychiatrists, social workers, psychologist, sociologists, and so on). Requests for change of ward status, leaves from hospital, or modification of ward privileges are directed to the subgroup for their consideration and finally to a full community group which meets once a week. At the same time, each patient has an administrative psychiatrist who handles the everyday needs of the patient, leaving the psychotherapeutic relationship free of the administrative entanglements inherent in any inpatient unit. As a member of the subgroup, the adolescent may hold an administrative office of some executive quality. Such grouping affords wide freedom in communication between patients, ward personnel, and professional staff; it encourages catharsis, while acting-out is held in bounds by the democratic weight of the subgroup's decisions, or finally by administrative authority. Finally the adolescent is offered the best substitute for a family group within the confines of a residential and institutional setting(9, 15).

The interplay between members of the subgroup offers the therapist considerable material from the everyday life situation of the ward for discussion with the adolescent. Repetitive situations develop where the adolescent has the opportunity of exhibiting his pathological behavior as well as his capacity for adaptation, but with confrontation by other patients, which does not have the same intensity of meaning as if it had come from his psychotherapist. With proper communication between ward personnel, administrative psychiatrist, and psychotherapist, considerable understanding can be achieved of the adolescent's needs, his defenses, his creative capacities, and his pathological reaction to his emotional conflicts.

THE LATE ADOLESCENT PHASE OF DEVELOPMENT

Late adolescence (17–20 years) is more a period of consolidation than disorder and turmoil. It is a time of greater self-awareness and self-recognition by the adolescent of his purpose in life, his goals, his interests, and his sexuality even though he still is troubled by the residue of his problems of bisexuality. However, these conflicts are more in tune with the syntonic aspects of his personality and there is greater self-ease.

> Infantile conflicts are not removed at the close of adolescence, but they are rendered specific, they become ego-syntonic; i.e., they become integrated within the realm of the ego as life tasks. They become centered within the adult self-representation. Every attempt at ego-syntonic mastery of a residual trauma, often experienced as conflict, enhances self-esteem. The stabilization of self-esteem is one of the major achievements of adulthood. . . . But beyond the reorganization of drives which is characteristic for adolescence proper, there remain oedipal remnants that were not carried along the path of object love. Late adolescence involves the transformation of these oedipal residues into ego modalities. . . .(7)

However, this process is never really completed in late adolescence as it probably is never completed at any age.

Late adolescence is also the period when the sexual identity becomes fixed. The homosexual or other sex pervert begins to see himself as permanently different. "Indeed the formation of a stable and irreversible sexual identity is of foremost importance in terms of the phase-specific drive organization of late adolescence"(7).

Erickson describes the late adolescent period from a genetic point of view as follows:

The process of identity formation emerges as an evolving configuration—a configuration which is gradually established by successive ego synthesis and resynthesis throughout childhood; it is a configuration of gradually integrating constitutional givens, idiosyncratic libidinal needs, favored capacities, significant identification, effective defenses, successful sublimations, and consistent roles(7).

By this time the reactions to conflicts of earlier years (repression, fixations, other defense mechanisms) not necessarily resolved become precipitated into character traits, which brings about a consolidation out of the upheaval and violent movements of earlier adolescence, and with this consolidation comes greater capacity for sustained logical action for the carrying out of intellectual and creative tasks, and the ability to accept one's attributes in a positive way to face one's further tasks. The late adolescent still faces the resolution of his unsolved conflicts either in a healthy fashion, through further sublimatory efforts, or by breakdown, with the use of neurotic, psychotic, perverted, and acting-out defenses. This period of late adolescence when actual separation from the family must take place, as a result of schooling away from home, work, marriage, or military service, is also the period of the greatest incidence of mental disorders.

Psychotherapy of the Late Adolescent

In contrast to the younger adolescent, many of the late adolescents come more willingly for therapy. They are ordinarily the first contact made by the therapist, and this generally is acceptable to the patient's parents since the adolescent already has an independent status. I find it extremely important to avoid making the first appointment for the late adolescent with his parents, even though the latter may make the first contact. For most adolescents, this helps to set up more quickly a situation of trust and confidence and allows the adolescent to understand that the therapist is on his side of the dependency-independency struggle which ordinarily is going on in the family. Even for those very passive late adolescents, I actively resist the pressure of the adolescent to have his parents confirm an appointment with me.

Whenever possible, a complete psychosocial history is obtained from the late adolescent himself. This may be supplemented at a future date with information obtained from relatives with the patient's permission. With the significant background information plus the results of psychiatric interviews and psychological tests, a clinical, genetic, and psychodynamic diagnosis can be made and the appropriate form of therapy instituted. For those late adolescents with personality characteristics similar to that of the younger adolescent, psychotherapeutic techniques for the younger adolescent may be used as well as various forms of supportive therapy to encourage further ego growth and hasten the consolidation of the personality. Such adolescents may not have the capacity to develop the transference relationship necessary for more intensive therapy where regression is encouraged in the service of the ego, with the development of emotional insight and greater ego integration. There are those adolescent turmoil reactions where more intensive therapy is contraindicated, and often certain adolescent problems can be alleviated through contact with the parents alone.

The majority of late adolescents, because of the transformation of the residues of infantile conflicts into ego-syntonic character traits, may be treated in most instances very much like the young adult. The late adolescent is better organized psychologically for a trial at intensive psychotherapy and psychoanalysis. The criteria for psychoanalysis with such patients is very much the same as that for the adult patient: sufficient motivation for treatment and reasonable cooperation of patient; a favorable life situation; the lack of acuteness of the symptoms; normal intellectual capacity and introspective ability; and the presence of good ego strength or sufficient flexibility and capacity to modify existing pathological defenses, symptoms, and personality traits. The "determination of ego strength involves an evaluation of the client's present adaptation and social functioning, with his reaction to the current stresses in his life, as well as a historical evaluation of his physical and emotional growth, which includes a study of his antecedents and the constitutional and hereditary factors which may affect his ego strength"(28). There is of course a closer contact with the parents than with relatives of adult patients. With a more passive and neutral relationship to the late adolescent, there is much less need for the specialized techniques and parameters so necessary in the psychotherapy of the younger adolescent.

Treatment of the late adolescent is generally not as prolonged as that for the adult, not because the need is not present, but because the intensity of gratifications available to the late adolescent and early adult often does not leave sufficient libido for continued treatment. However, real therapeutic progress can be made and whenever possible intensive psychotherapy and psychoanalysis should be the treatment of choice. Conjoint family therapy is rarely as necessary or possible as with the younger adolescent, since the late adolescent has worked out many of the stormy conflicts with his family and the problems for which he comes to therapy are part of his own consolidated personality problems. Such organization of personality problems is not necessarily positive, as is evidenced by the lack of willingness to enter into any form of psychotherapy by a Neurotic Acting-Out Disorder in Late Adolescence.

> *Example:*   Karen was 18 years of age when first seen. Despite the character of her problem—"running away from home to get married since the age of 16½ (pregnant on one occasion with abortion or miscarriage)—it was the patient who suggested seeing a psychiatrist after an argument with her parents. However, despite her superficial compliance with the idea of getting help, Karen denied she had any problems, intrapsychic or otherwise, and continued to dramatize the idea of marriage, which to her meant deciding on china and silver service, and soon. She was an attractive, narcissistic, exhibitionistic girl, heavily made-up, with a quality of hardness and crudity to her face. However, she managed to project infantile vulnerability with her hardness at the same time. The impression was that of a moderate anxiety hysteria with breakthroughs in the form of acting-out in her need for a dual relationship. The acting-out had ego-syntonic aspects and was mediated somewhat by an undercurrent of guilt and despondency. She seemed fixated on an oral-narcissistic level. The running off to marriage with so many different boys reflected the infantile attempt to solve her unmet infantile and oedipal needs from her father. Father, a salesman, was away from home 75 percent of the time, obviously disinterested in his wife, and involved with the need to build up an estate. There was much evidence of corruption, evasion of parental responsibility, and lying to the patient which was condoned by the mother as well, who, though more insightful than her husband, was unable to free herself from the unhappy sadomasochistic relationship with him. Patient, like her father, was running away from home. Patient refused to allow any contacts with her parents either through conjoint interviews or alone. Her

blanket denial of her own problems, and her ego-syntonic comfort with her need to get married, precluded any attempt at therapy.

In contrast, treatment of a milder Acting-Out Disorder in the Younger Adolescent can be carried out on an outpatient basis with a better prognosis.

> *Example:* Lydia, a 14½-year-old girl, was referred because of exaggerated cyclothymic moods, disobedience, running off with boys on dates against her mother's wishes, and some physical violence in relationship with mother. This mother-daughter conflict followed the death of the father, less than two years prior to date of referral. There had been increasing problems relating to Lydia's sexual behavior and mother could no longer maintain control. Patient saw mother as a nagging, overprotective person, a snob, not interested in her friends who were from a lower socioeconomic group (probably true). Patient felt that mother had not accepted her as an adolescent with insight into her own needs. Examination revealed Lydia to have a neurotic disturbance with narcissistic and phobic features, cyclothymic mood alternation, and aggressive outbursts and acting-out to discharge anxiety tensions related to her mourning reactions to the death of the father and the recent behavior of the mother who started to go out with a man. Patient began to menstruate one month after father died. Conjoint therapy was instituted and the course of therapy was a stormy one, as the patient was capable of considerable outbursts of temper and uncontrolled behavior. After a time it became apparent that patient and her mother needed to be separated from one another. This was accomplished with some difficulty, mainly because of mother's guilt. Subsequently mother remarried despite patient's resentment, with an amelioration of Lydia's symptomatic behavior.

All adolescents are encouraged to accept the responsibility for the financial arrangements whenever possible. Such arrangements are made directly with the late adolescent or in joint interviews with the patient (younger or late adolescent) present. Thereafter the bill is given directly to the adolescent and resistances to payment even on the part of the parents are taken up directly with the adolescent for referral back to his parents. The adolescent is asked to accept all of the responsibilities for keeping his appointments, arranging for vacation time, and other responsibilities typical of the adult in psychotherapy or psychoanalysis. The struggle by the adolescent to avoid such responsibilities is an important phase of therapy. When the adolescent has income of his own, he is expected to pay for part or all of treatment. In the case of Quinn (page 285), treatment was greatly aided with the working through of the question of his own financial responsibility. Using some of his own money for therapy gave the patient greater freedom to continue the therapy without guilt not only for his sexual conduct, but also for his anger to the therapist and his resistance to treatment by not coming to certain hours.

Parental Involvement with the Late Adolescent

However, in continuing the diagnostic evaluation after the contact with the adolescent is established, the question may arise concerning a contact with the parents. This request should be evaluated in terms of the problems for which the adolescent came for treatment. Obviously the late adolescent is not a completely independent person. He is still an integral part of the family, who are at least financially responsible for him and for his therapy. Unless there is some contraindication to the request for a contact, and if the patient is willing and understands the pros and cons of such a meeting, I see the parents and the patient together one time. Such a conjoint meeting is not again solicited or advised unless it becomes necessary in terms of severe regression on the part of the patient, acting-out difficulties for which contact with the family must be made, or intense interaction between the patient and family for which another conjoint meeting may be held. Frequently, the request for such a meeting with the thrapist comes from the parents themselves. Such a request is always brought to the patient's attention for discussion and final decision. These requests from the parents often come under the ambivalent disguise of "how can we better behave to help John?" which can just as easily be destructive as constructive for the treatment. The patient is aware of the fact that he knows all of the information concerning therapy for discussion with his parents, but there are times when such parental contacts are necessary to support the patient or the family at points of considerable tension.

Frequently the suggestion is made that, because of the usual family turmoil that may develop while the adolescent is in therapy, an ongoing contact with another therapist be maintained by the parents. Another factor in the question of contact with the parents is whether the patient is involved in psychoanalytic therapy or more supportive psychotherapy. Contact with parents in the first case is avoided more stringently. I feel that much can be gained from an initial contact with the parents as part of the initial preparation for psychoanalysis and evaluation of patient's environment. I also have the impression that adhering too rigidly to the concept of no contact with relatives at any time may have a deleterious effect on the psychoanalytic process. The fact remains that parents are still very actively involved in their interaction with late adolescents; techniques of helping the parents with their own anxieties and needs should be carefully reviewed, and some solution arrived at that will not interfere with treatment, or, at least, not completely destroy it when parents' needs are not met or when the therapist views the late adolescent as a completely independent person, divorced from his parents.

In some situations, contacts with the family may have to be frequent and prolonged not only to protect the patient from the parent's wrath in regard to his behavior but also to encourage treatment, as illustrated in a case of Homosexuality in Late Adolescence.

> *Example:*   Mildred was 19½ years of age when she agreed to see me after a severe argument with her parents because she would not stop seeing a woman whom the parents felt was a mannish homosexual. When she was 11, and again at 14, I saw the patient because of inappropriate behavior, silly laughter, sudden mood changes, and crushes on older girl counselors at a summer camp. Examination at 11 and 14 revealed an immature, neurotic child with heightened heterosexual conflict and unsolved oedipal conflicts. Rape phantasies were prominent and consisted of feared but wished-for attacks by her father. There was marked conflict with a naïve, narcissistic, immature, overindulgent, and probably frigid mother. Father, mismated with his wife, was more available, warm and overaffectionate with patient. Patient claimed the reason she came to see me was related to her family difficulties. She denied any social or sexual problems. "She could get any man she wanted." Her mother, however, was so immature that patient had to be out of the house. I raised all of the questions the parents brought up with me and some of my own concerning her past and present circumstances, even the question of her being a homosexual, which she brushed off. However, she agreed to a joint meeting with the family and at that time held her ground well, denying any basic emotional difficulties. I supported her independent interests away from home and agreed with her that her need for psychotherapy should be her own choice. Four months later patient came in and confessed her homosexuality, for which she said she was not guilty or greatly concerned except for its effect on her family. What troubled her most was the possible dissolution of her homosexual love affair.

Contact was made again only on the basis of further discussion of her reactive depression. Subsequently patient found the courage to tell her father, then her mother, what the real problem was, insisted that she intended to stay that way, and refused treatment. There were a number of conjoint interviews and interviews with the family alone, with the therapist being protective of the patient. The parents had threatened their daughter with legal action, social exposure, exposure at school, all of which I actively opposed. Because of the parents' attitudes, a breakdown of all relationship between patient and family developed. It was months later that patient returned to see me, obviously still in great conflict, and finally agreed to enter psychoanalytic treatment away from home after I had actively interpreted her homosexuality as a defense against her fear of heterosexuality which had been present since her earlier years of pre-adolescence. Preparation for therapy took well over a year of contact with patient and her parents.

A more typical beginning of therapy and contact with the parents occurred in the case of a Neurotic Reaction in Late Adolescence.

Example: Nora, 18½ years of age, came home from college in her first year because of intense anxiety attacks and fearfulness because she suddenly became unsure of herself and the world around her. She has had separation anxieties since age 11, but in the last year of high school had a compulsive need to repeat names, think of them visually, break the names up in various components, and then put them back together again. When she saw her parents she had to reassure herself about their presence and think of them visually as well as in an auditory way. Mother apparently had completely infantilized her daughter since birth. Patient was not allowed any personal freedom until her senior year of high school. Patient still hugged her parents, sat in their laps, kissed them when she left home and returned. Her description of her symptoms confirms Erickson's concept of ego diffusion and her need to re-affirm her ego identity with repetitive and compulsive behavior(12). Patient was markedly dependent, asking for constant reassurance. Patient spoke negatively of her father (owns a small store in a lower socioeconomic old-fashioned market) and more positively of the upper socioeconomic status into which the family was propelled because of an unexpected inheritance. Father is passive-dependent, mother overprotective and dominating, with more conscious insight into her daughter's problems (much like her own as a child). Contact was made with parents and patient only once. Patient obviously was happy for such a contact, but because the parents were anxious and fearful of a psychotic break in their daughter, and because treatment procedures needed to be described and accepted by the parents, a conjoint meeting was held. There were no further contacts with the parents. Psychoanalytic therapy was the therapy of choice because of patient's ego strength and motivation and need for characterological changes. There was no evidence of latent psychotic trends. Treatment was uneventful but probably interrupted before all of the major problems were worked through. This occurred as Adatto(2) has indicated when patient developed a close physical relationship with the boy she felt she was going to marry, at which point she lost most of her motivation for therapy.

In the case of psychotic or latent psychotic late adolescents, contact with the parents is mandatory. At times, therapists do not enlist the help of the parents early enough at points where serious regression and breakdown of ego defenses are occurring and when such contacts might be used effectively to control patient's behavior, as described in the following two cases of Psychosis of Late Adolescence.

Example: Owen, 18 years of age, had become withdrawn and isolated. He remained in his room, didn't talk to his parents, and had all the furniture removed except his dresser and bed. Essays he had written over the past several months indicated that he had developed feelings of self-power and grandiosity and that delusional ideas were present. Other children in the family were also disturbed. Parents have been poorly mated since marriage and openly admit their marriage at present is only a matter of convenience for the children. Initial detailed efforts were made with the father who was simple and unsophisticated, passive-dependent in his attitudes towards authority. The parents had never been firm and authoritative with their children. However, patient called me several times in response to his father's insistence. Although he refused to come to see me at first, he promised he would when certain phantasied situations were to come to pass in several days. I accepted his delusional thinking and deferred more aggressive action to hospitalize patient. In response to my acceptance, his anxiety increased and his reactive dependency needs became more intense, at which time he called for an appointment and accepted hospitalization.

Example: Paul, 19 years of age, came to see me after I had a brief earlier contact with his father. Paul had seen another psychiatrist just prior to my contact. The presenting complaints were vague unhappiness, a marked urge to leave home, an urge to change his religion to Catholicism, homosexual feelings, and intense anxiety which seemed to be developing into a severe personality disorganization. The overall picture was that of a latent schizophrenic but Paul seemed able to reestablish control, which was an asset for therapy. Treatment was tempestuous and catch-as-catch-can from the very start. A strong homosexual transference developed with much regressive behavioral attitudes, acting-out, and an urge to run away from treatment. Since patient had made many unkind remarks about his father and mother, no contact was maintained with the parents, but retrospectively it was clear that Paul required and may have benefitted from more frequent family contacts, perhaps of a conjoint type, to offer him the kind of control from within the family which may have been of help to him.

Since sexual identity becomes fixed during late adolescence, homosexuality and other forms of sexual perversion become more prominent at this time. This does not mean that the perversion does not have its origins in earlier years (see case of Mildred, page 282) but the conscious acceptance of the sexual abnormality as a way of life occurs mainly during this time. Two contrasting examples of a Sexual Perversion of Late Adolescence and a case of Voyeurism of Middle Adolescence follow.

Example: Quinn was 20 years old when he was first seen. At the age of 19 he had seen another psychiatrist for similar problems but had not continued in therapy. Since the age of 13, patient says he felt he was leaning toward the same sex. There were minor physical contacts with boys in the past year. These occurred at a college away from home. Involved in his intense sexual interests and subsequent guilt and shame, patient failed in his sophomore year of college and returned home. Although he first indicated that his parents and he were one happy family, he soon recognized his mother as dominating, seductive, overprotective and infantilizing, and his father as passive-dependent. Normal sexual interests in the home were never encouraged. Mother seems completely devoid of heterosexual interests and father was too passive even for extramarital affairs. As a child Quinn was obese, with a strong inferiority complex. He shied away from athletics but also was not a good student. There were sporadic contacts with the opposite sex. At 18 there were several episodes of exhibiting himself in the nude in the park, and patient masturbated with visual phantasies of hugging men. At no time were there any typical homosexual episodes, but patient enjoys looking at men and where possible wants to be hugged by them while nude until he has an orgasm (usually he pays for such activities). No contact was made with patient's parents. Intensive therapy (psychoanalysis) was the treatment of choice, but because of patient's borderline psychotic characteristics, his educative needs, and his emotional resemblance to the younger adolescent, it was necessary to use some of the techniques which have been already described with the younger adolescent.

Example: At 13½, Roy was picked up by the police for voyeuristic as well as exhibitionistic behavior. More recently there had been several additional episodes with masturbation after voyeuristic behavior for which he was arrested. At one point the father was so disturbed about his son's behavior that he beat Roy severely. Later that night Roy attempted suicide. Despite Roy's behavior, father denied its pathology, and Roy himself, although under considerable tension with evidence of marked depression, extended the denial to all of his behavior. Roy's mother had died two years previously of a cerebral hemorrhage when she was seven months pregnant. Therapy was recommended but patient never became involved, completely isolating the extent of his changing sexual identity.

CONCLUSION

The primary basis for a meaningful psychotherapeutic interaction with the adolescent is a full knowledge of the normal adolescent phase of development with its emotional upheavals, attempts at experimentation, and later personality consolidation. Successful therapy will also depend on an adequate psychodynamic understanding of the emotional conflicts of the adolescent and his reality needs. Psychotherapy of the younger adolescent is more frequently ego supportive, educative, and experiential, with a greater involvement of the parents in the therapeutic process; the older adolescent is more frequently able to utilize a more intensive psychotherapeutic approach including psychoanalysis. Therapeutic goals and techniques should be flexibly chosen to give the adolescent, in his specific phase of development, that amount of insight necessary to help him with his inner conflicts and external reality problems and to bring about an increased ego integration with the capacity to face future normative and abnormal life crises without the need for pathological defenses and crippling symptoms.

REFERENCES

1. ACKERMAN, NATHAN W.   *The psychodynamics of family life.* New York: Basic Books, 1958.

2. ADATTO, CARL P.   Ego re-integration observed in analysis of late adolescents. *Int. J. Psychoanal.,* 1958, **39**:172–77.

3. AICHHORN, AUGUST.   *Wayward youth.* New York: Viking Press, Inc., 1935. (First published in German in 1925.)

4. BERNFELD, S.   Die heutige psychologie der pubertat (Present day psychology of puberty). *Imago,* 1927, **13**:1–26.

5. BERNFELD, S.   Types of adolescents. *Psychoanal. Quart.,* 1938, **7**:243–53.

6. BLOS, PETER.   Preadolescent drive organization. *J. Amer. psychoanal. Assn.,* 1958, **6**:47–56.

7. BLOS, PETER.   *On adolescence, a psychoanalytic interpretation.* New York: The Free Press, 1962.

8. BUXBAUM, EDITH.   Panel report, "The psychology of adolescence." *J. Amer. psychoanal. Assn.,* 1958, **6**:111–20.

9. CONE, WILLIAM.   The therapeutic community in action: A St. Louis experience. In WESSEN, ALBERT (Ed.), *The psychiatric hospital as a social system.* Springfield, Ill.: Charles C. Thomas, 1964. Pp. 147–65.

10. EISSLER, K. R.   The effect of the structure of the ego on psychoanalytic technique. *J. Amer. psychoanal. Assn.,* 1953, **1**:104–43.

11. EISSLER, K. R.   Notes on problems of technique in the psychoanalytic treatment of adolescents. *Psychoanalytic study of the child,* Vol. XIII. New York: International Universities Press, 1958.

12. ERICKSON, E. H.   *Identity and the life cycle.* New York: International Universities Press, 1959.

13. FOUNTAIN, GERHARD.   Adolescence into adult: an inquiry. *J. Amer. psychoanal. Assn.,* 1961, **9**:417–33.

14. FRAILBERG, S.   Some considerations in the introduction to therapy in puberty. *Psychoanalytic study of the child,* Vol. X. New York: International Universities Press, 1955.

15. FRANK, ALVIN R., and SENTURIA, AUDREY S.   The therapeutic community in a psychiatric general hospital. *Comprehen. Psychiat.,* 1962, **3**:181–90.

16. FREUD, ANNA.   The ego and id at puberty, and the Instinctual anxiety of puberty. *The ego and mechanisms of defense.* New York: International Universities Press, 1946. Pp. 149–89.

17. FREUD, ANNA.   Adolescence. *Psychoanalytic study of the child,* Vol. XIII. New York: International Universities Press, 1958.

18. FREUD, SIGMUND.   Three contributions to the theory of sex. *Basic writings of Sigmund Freud.* Modern Library ed. New York: Random House, 1938.

19. GELEERD, ELIZABETH R.   Some aspects of psychoanalytic technique in adolescence. *Psychoanalytic study of the child*, Vol. XII. New York: International Universities Press, 1957.

20. GELEERD, ELIZABETH R.   Some aspects of ego vicissitudes in adolescence. *J. Amer. psychoanal. Assn.*, 1961, 9:394–405.

21. GITELSON, MAXWELL.   Character synthesis, psychotherapeutic problems of adolescence. *Amer. J. Orthopsychiat.*, 1948, 18:422–31.

22. GREAVES, DONALD C., and REGAN, PETER F., III.   Psychotherapy at intensive hospital treatment level. In BALSER, B. H. (Ed.), *Psychotherapy of the adolescent*. New York: International Universities Press, 1957. Pp. 130–43.

23. HACKER, FREDERICK J., and GELEERD, ELIZABETH R.   Freedom and authority in adolescence. *Amer. J. Orthopsychiat.*, 1945, 15:621–30.

24. HARLEY, MARJORIE.   Some observations on the relationship between genitality and structural development at adolescence. *J. Amer. psychoanal. Assn.*, 1961, 9:434–61.

25. HOLLINGSHEAD, A. B., and REDLICH, F. C.   *Social class and mental illness.* New York: John Wiley & Sons, Inc., 1958.

26. JOHNSON, ADELAIDE M.   Collaborative psychotherapy: team setting. In HEIMAN, MARCEL (Ed.), *Psychoanalysis and social work.* New York: International Universities Press, 1953. Pp. 79–108.

27. JONES, ERNEST.   Some problems of adolescents. *Papers on psychoanalysis.* 5th ed. Baltimore: Williams and Workham Co., 1949.

28. KAPLAN, ALEX H.   Psychiatric syndromes and the practice of social work. *Soc. Casewk,* 1956, 38:107–12.

29. KAPLAN, ALEX H.   Social work therapy and psychiatric psychotherapy: an attempt at differentiation. *Arch. gen. Psychiat.*, 1963, 9:497–503.

30. LANDER, JOSEPH.   The puberty struggle against the instincts. *Amer. J. Orthopsychiat.*, 1942, 12:456–61.

31. LEVINE, MAURICE.   Principles of psychiatric treatment. In ALEXANDER, FRANZ, and ROSS, HELEN (Eds.), *Dynamic psychiatry.* Chicago: University of Chicago Press, 1952. Pp. 307–66.

32. NOSHPITZ, J. D.   Opening phase in the psychotherapy of adolescents with character disorders. *Bull. Menninger Clinic,* 1957, 21:153–64.

33. ROOT, NATHAN N.   A neurosis in adolescence. *Psychoanalytic study of the child,* Vol. XII. New York: International Universities Press, 1957.

34. ROSENBLATT, BERNARD.   A severe neurosis in an adolescent boy. *Psychoanalytic study of the child,* Vol. XVIII. New York: International Universities Press, 1963.

35. SOLNIT, ALBERT J.   Panel report, "The vicissitudes of ego development in adolescence." *J. Amer. psychoanal. Assn.*, 1959, 7:523–36.

36. SPIEGEL, LEO A.   A review of contributions to a psychoanalytic theory of adolescence. *Psychoanalytic study of the child,* Vol. VI. New York: International Universities Press, 1951.

37. SPIEGEL, LEO A.   Comments on the psychoanalytic psychology of adolescence. *Psychoanalytic study of the child*, Vol. XIII. New York: International Universities Press, 1958.

38. SPIEGEL, LEO A.   Disorder and consolidation in adolescence. *J. Amer. psychoanal. Assn.*, 1961, 9:406–16.

39. STEELE, ELEANOR A.   Discussion. In BALSER, B. H. (Ed.), *Psychotherapy of the adolescent*. New York: International Universities Press, 1957.

40. Symposium (1941), "Direct psychotherapy in adolescence" with case presentations by MAXWELL GITELSON and EUGENE I. FALSTEIN *et al.* *Amer. J. Orthopsychiat.*, 1942, 12:1–41.

41. WEISS, SAMUEL.   Parameters in child analysis. *J. Amer. psychoanal. Assn.*, 1964, 12:587–99.

42. WELSCH, E. E.   Discussion. In BALSER, B. H. (Ed.), *Psychotherapy of the adolescent*. New York: International Universities Press, 1957.

Index

Therapy
  adolescents in, 28
  with brain damaged children, 44
  early object relationship disturbances,
    44–47
  goals in, 1–8
  guidance v., 19–20
  individual v. group, 22–24
  institutionalized children in, 46–47
  limits setting in, 3–6
  parents in, 17–24, 82–83, 89–90, 104,
    132
  receptivity for, 37–38
  relationship, 16–17, 47, 107–8, 179,
    206–7
  where to take place, 8–9
Thumb sucking, 49

Tics, 130–31
Transference, 7, 90, 105–6, 107–8, 116,
  136, 161, 165, 169, 172

U

Ulcerative colitis, 166–69
Ulcers, 153
Urticaria; see Hives
Under-achiever, 274

V

Vagotonia, 163
Violence, 195–98
Vomiting, 142
Voyeurism, 285

*This book has been set in 10 point Caledonia,
leaded three points, and 9 point Caledonia,
leaded 2 points. Chapter numbers are in 48
point News Gothic Condensed, and chapter
titles in 24 point News Gothic Condensed.
The size of the type page is 27 x 45 picas.*